D1378293

MEASUREMENT AND ANALYSIS OF RANDOM DATA

Also by Julius S. Bendat
Principles and Applications
of Random Noise Theory (1958)

MEASUREMENT AND ANALYSIS OF RANDOM DATA

JULIUS S. BENDAT

President, Measurement Analysis Corporation

ALLAN G. PIERSOL

Vice President, Measurement Analysis Corporation

1966

JOHN WILEY & SONS, Inc.   *New York · London · Sydney*

PREFACE

For many years we have been concerned with both the theory and practical applications of random processes. Areas of application have included studies of communication signals, control systems, structural vibrations, acoustic noise, ocean waves, seismology, and biomedical data. During the course of such studies, it was clear that a severe gap existed between theoretical concepts and practical techniques for measuring and interpreting the random data involved. Little attention was given to the statistical aspects of experimental design and data evaluation, and wide discrepancies existed in the analog and digital techniques for analyzing and processing data. Theoretical requirements for analyzing stationary versus nonstationary data were not well defined. It was clear that a great need existed to bring together and clarify the various disciplines required to properly measure and analyze random physical data. This book is directed toward that goal.

This book was written to be a reference for practicing engineers and scientists, as well as a textbook for students. The reader is assumed to have a basic understanding of probability theory, statistics, and transform methods of applied mathematics, although many fundamentals are reviewed. Compromises are sometimes made on abstract theoretical principles to achieve results which can be applied to practical problems of interest. However, such compromises are introduced only when they are believed to be justified from past experience. This book is not devoted to specific applications. Instead, the main emphasis throughout is on problems of defining, measuring, analyzing, and interpreting random data regardless of the intended application.

Chapter 1 introduces the subject matter of this book and provides the basis for work in later chapters. The material discusses classifications for deterministic data as well as for random data. Basic concepts are described for probability density functions, correlation functions, and spectral density functions, and for joint properties of random data.

Chapter 2 reviews basic material on linear system dynamics which is required for developments in later chapters. Weighting functions, transfer functions, frequency response functions for constant parameter, and time-varying linear systems are discussed. Frequency response functions are illustrated for simple mechanical and electrical circuits.

Foundations of random process theory are covered in Chapter 3. Fundamental ideas of probability theory and random process theory are presented. Considerable attention is given to the proper definition and interpretation of stationary correlation and spectral relations, and their transformations by passage through linear systems. Equations are developed for describing both single-input linear systems and multiple-input linear systems. This chapter contains many theoretical and heuristic proofs to justify the stated results.

Chapter 4 presents general statistical ideas and techniques which are required for the evaluation of data regardless of its origin. The first part of the discussion covers statistical aspects of parameter estimation. This is followed by formulas, tables, and applications of the normal distribution, chi-square distribution, student t distribution, and the F distribution. Other portions of this chapter discuss confidence intervals and hypothesis testing. Important nonparametric techniques for evaluating data are outlined, and analysis of variance procedures are described.

These first four chapters constitute a review of background material which is needed to understand the proper techniques for analyzing and evaluating general random data. The remaining chapters present more specialized discussions of exactly how to perform various measurements and analyses of random data.

In Chapter 5 procedures are discussed for analyzing pertinent statistical properties of a single random data record, and for analyzing a collection of random data records. Theoretical derivations are given for the statistical errors of parameter estimates including probability density functions, correlation functions, and spectral density functions. This is followed by rules for determining required sample sizes and record lengths for performing these estimates and other estimates of frequency response functions and coherence functions. Practical statistical procedures are explained for testing basic assumptions such as randomness, stationarity, and normality, as well as equivalence of results from different data. Multiple-input linear system estimation errors are outlined.

Chapters 6 and 7 consider practical measurement methods for computing the desired descriptive properties of random data by analog instruments and by digital computers. Analog methods are reviewed for measuring spectral density functions, correlation functions, and probability density functions. This discussion includes consideration of the accuracy of the measurements as well as necessary engineering procedures for making the measurements. The digital computer material contains appropriate digital computer flow diagrams as well as calculation requirements for single and joint records. Special details are given for analyzing a multiple input-output problem.

Chapter 8 presents an example of an experimental program designed to verify the main theoretical error formula for power spectral density measurements of stationary data. In this way, basic statistical techniques of experimental design and data evaluation from previous chapters are illustrated for an actual problem.

Finally, Chapter 9 derives a number of important theoretical results for analyzing and interpreting nonstationary data. These results show how to estimate nonstationary mean values and mean square values by ensemble averaging, and how to describe nonstationary correlation functions and spectral density functions. Various input-output relations are developed for the passage of nonstationary data through linear systems.

We wish to acknowledge the many contributions to this book. The greatest help was provided by Loren D. Enochson, an associate of ours in the Measurement Analysis Corporation, who was initially responsible for writing much of the digital computer material, as well as some of the statistical material discussed in this book. Three other individuals who deserve special mention are G. Harold Klein, Librascope Inc., William T. Thomson, Professor of Engineering, University of California at Los Angeles, and George P. Thrall, Measurement Analysis Corporation.

Our secretaries, Betty Hooker and Gladys Schweder, handled all details of the transition from manuscript typing to publication with great skill and enthusiasm, and we gratefully thank them for their help. Finally, to the many government agencies, industrial companies, and individuals who supported and encouraged our work, we extend a further thanks for participating in the creation of this book.

JULIUS S. BENDAT
Los Angeles, California   ALLAN G. PIERSOL

CONTENTS

GLOSSARY OF SYMBOLS

A	number of reverse arrangements, arbitrary constant
$b[\ ]$	bias error of [ ]
B	cyclical frequency bandwidth
c	mechanical damping coefficient, arbitrary constant
C	electrical capacitance
$C_x(\tau)$	autocovariance function
$C_{xy}(\tau)$	cross-covariance function
$C(t_1, t_2)$	nonstationary covariance function
$C_{xy}(f)$	co-spectral density function (one-sided)
D	time displacement range
e	length of unexpected events
$E[\ ]$	expected value of [ ]
f	cyclical frequency
F	cyclical frequency range, statistical F variable
$F(t)$	mechanical forcing function
$G_x(f)$	power spectral density function defined for non-negative frequencies only (one-sided)
$G_{xy}(f)$	cross-spectral density function defined for non-negative frequencies only (one-sided)
h	sampling interval
$h(\tau)$	weighting function (unit impulse response function)
$H(f)$	frequency response function
$|H(f)|$	gain factor
$\mathrm{Im}[\ ]$	imaginary part of [ ]
j	$\sqrt{-1}$, index
k	mechanical spring constant, index
K	RC filter time constant, number of class intervals
l	time between sample records
L	electrical inductance

m	mechanical mass, maximum number of lag values
n	degrees-of-freedom
N	sample size
$p(x)$	probability density function
$p(x, y)$	joint probability density function
$P(x)$	probability distribution function
$P(x, y)$	joint probability distribution function
Prob[ ]	probability that [ ]
q	number of inputs
$Q_{xy}(f)$	quadrature spectral density function (one-sided)
r	number of runs, number of rows
R	electrical resistance
$R_x(\tau)$	autocorrelation function
$R_{xy}(\tau)$	cross-correlation function
$R(t_1, t_2)$	nonstationary correlation function
Re[ ]	real part of [ ]
s	sample standard deviation
s^2	sample variance
s.d.[ ]	standard deviation of [ ]
$S_x(f)$	power spectral density function defined for both positive and negative frequencies (two-sided)
$S_{xy}(f)$	cross-spectral density function defined for both positive and negative frequencies (two-sided)
$S(f_1, f_2)$	generalized (nonstationary) spectral density function
t	time variable, statistical t variable
T	observation time, averaging time
Var[ ]	variance of [ ]
W	amplitude window width
$x(t), y(t)$	time dependent variables
$\bar{x}$	sample mean value of $x(t)$
$\overline{|x|}$	mean absolute value (average rectified value) of $x(t)$
X	amplitude of sinusoidal $x(t)$
$X(f)$	Fourier transform of $x(t)$
$|[\ ]|$	absolute value of [ ]
$\widehat{[\ ]}$	estimate of [ ]
α	a small probability, level of significance
β	probability of a Type II error
$\gamma^2(f)$	coherence function
$\delta(\ )$	delta function
ϵ	normalized standard error
ϵ^2	normalized variance

ζ	mechanical damping ratio
θ	phase angle
$\theta_{xy}(f)$	argument of $G_{xy}(f)$
μ	mean value
ρ	correlation coefficient
$\rho(\tau)$	correlation function coefficient
σ	standard deviation
σ^2	variance
τ	time displacement
$\phi(f)$	phase factor
Φ	arbitrary statistical parameter
χ^2	statistical chi-square variable
Ψ	root mean square value
Ψ^2	mean square value

1

BASIC DESCRIPTIONS OF PHYSICAL DATA

Any observed data representing a physical phenomenon can be broadly classified as being either deterministic or nondeterministic. Deterministic data are those that can be described by an explicit mathematical relationship. For example, consider a rigid body which is suspended from a fixed foundation by a linear spring, as shown in Figure 1.1. Let m be the mass of the body (assumed to be inelastic) and k be the spring constant of the spring (assumed to be massless). Suppose the body is displaced from its position of equilibrium by a distance X, and released at time $t = 0$. From either basic laws of mechanics or repeated observations, it can be established that the following relationship will apply.

$$x(t) = X \cos \sqrt{\frac{k}{m}} t \qquad t \geq 0 \qquad (1.1)$$

Equation (1.1) defines the exact location of the body at any instant of time in the future. Hence the physical data representing the motion of the mass are deterministic.

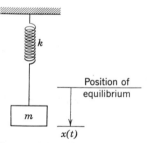

Figure 1.1 Simple spring mass system.

There are many physical phenomena in practice which produce data that can be represented with reasonable accuracy by explicit mathematical relationships. For example, the motion of a satellite in orbit about the earth, the potential across a condenser as it discharges through a resistor, the vibration response of an unbalanced rotating machine, or the temperature of water as heat is applied, are all basically deterministic. However, there are many other physical phenomena which produce data that are not deterministic. For example, the height of waves in a confused sea, the acoustic pressures generated by air rushing through a pipe, or the electrical output of a noise generator represent data which cannot be described by explicit mathematical relationships. There is no way to predict an exact value at a future instant of time. These data are random in character and must be described in terms of probability statements and statistical averages rather than by explicit equations.

The classification of various physical data as being either deterministic or random might be debated in many cases. For example, it might be argued that no physical data in actual practice can be truly deterministic since there is always a possibility that some unforeseen event in the future might influence the phenomenon producing the data in a manner that was not originally considered. On the other hand, it might be argued that no physical data in actual practice are truly random since exact mathematical descriptions might be possible if a sufficient knowledge of the basic mechanisms of the phenomenon producing the data were known. In practical terms, the decision as to whether or not physical data are deterministic or random is usually based upon the ability to reproduce the data by controlled experiments. If an experiment producing specific data of interest can be repeated many times with identical results (within the limits of experimental error), then the data can generally be considered deterministic. If an experiment cannot be designed which will produce identical results when the experiment is repeated, then the data must usually be considered random in nature.

Various special classifications of deterministic and random data will now be discussed. Note that physical data are usually thought of as being functions of time and will be discussed in such terms for convenience. However, any other variable can replace time as required.

1.1 Classifications for Deterministic Data

Data representing deterministic phenomena can be categorized as being either periodic or nonperiodic. Periodic data can be further categorized as being either sinusoidal or nonsinusoidal (complex periodic). Nonperiodic data can be further categorized as being either "almost-periodic" or transient. These various classifications for deterministic data are schematically illustrated in Figure 1.2. Of course, any combination of these forms may also occur. For purposes of review, each of these types of deterministic data along with physical examples will be briefly discussed.

1.1.1 Sinusoidal Periodic Data

Sinusoidal data are those types of periodic data which can be defined mathematically by a time-varying function of the form

$$x(t) = X \sin (2\pi f_0 t + \theta) \tag{1.2}$$

where X = amplitude

f_0 = cyclical frequency in cycles per unit time

θ = initial phase angle with respect to the time origin in radians

$x(t)$ = instantaneous value at time t

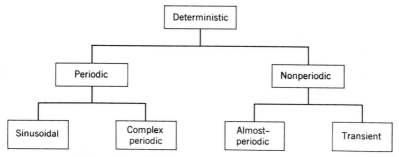

Figure 1.2   Classifications for deterministic data.

The sinusoidal time history described by Eq. (1.2) is usually referred to as a sine wave. When analyzing sinusoidal data in practice, the phase angle θ is often ignored. For this case

$$x(t) = X \sin 2\pi f_0 t \qquad (1.3)$$

Equation (1.3) can be pictured by a time history plot or by an amplitude-frequency plot (frequency spectrum), as illustrated in Figure 1.3.

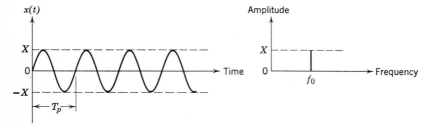

Figure 1.3   Time history and spectrum for sinusoidal data.

The time interval required for one full fluctuation or cycle of sinusoidal data is called the period T_p. The number of cycles per unit time is called the frequency f_0. The frequency and period are related by

$$T_p = \frac{1}{f_0} \qquad (1.4)$$

Note that the frequency spectrum in Figure 1.3 is composed of an amplitude component at a specific frequency, as opposed to a continuous plot of amplitude versus frequency. Such spectra are called *discrete spectra* or *line spectra*.

There are many examples of physical phenomena which produce approximately sinusoidal data in practice. The voltage output of an electrical alternator is one example; the vibratory motion of an unbalanced rotating weight is another. Sinusoidal data represent one of the simplest forms of time-varying data from the analysis viewpoint.

1.1.2 Complex Periodic Data

Complex data are those types of periodic data which can be defined mathematically by a time-varying function whose waveform exactly repeats itself at regular intervals such that

$$x(t) = x(t \pm nT_p) \qquad n = 1, 2, 3, \ldots \tag{1.5}$$

As for sinusoidal data, the time interval required for one full fluctuation is called the *period* T_p. The number of cycles per unit time is called the *fundamental frequency* f_1. A special case for complex periodic data is clearly sinusoidal data where $f_1 = f_0$.

With few exceptions in practice, complex periodic data may be expanded into a Fourier series according to the following formula.

$$x(t) = \frac{a_0}{2} + \sum_{n=1}^{\infty} (a_n \cos 2\pi n f_1 t + b_n \sin 2\pi n f_1 t) \tag{1.6}$$

where $f_1 = \dfrac{1}{T_p}$

$$a_n = \frac{2}{T_p} \int_0^{T_p} x(t) \cos 2\pi n f_1 t \, dt \qquad n = 0, 1, 2, \ldots$$

$$b_n = \frac{2}{T_p} \int_0^{T_p} x(t) \sin 2\pi n f_1 t \, dt \qquad n = 1, 2, 3, \ldots$$

An alternate way to express the Fourier series for complex periodic data is as follows.

$$x(t) = X_0 + \sum_{n=1}^{\infty} X_n \cos (2\pi n f_1 t - \theta_n) \tag{1.7}$$

where $X_0 = a_0/2$

$$X_n = \sqrt{a_n^2 + b_n^2} \qquad n = 1, 2, 3, \ldots$$
$$\theta_n = \tan^{-1}(b_n/a_n) \qquad n = 1, 2, 3, \ldots$$

In words, Eq. (1.7) says that complex periodic data consist of a static component, X_0, and an infinite number of sinusoidal components called harmonics, which have amplitudes X_n and phases θ_n. The frequencies of the harmonic components are all integral multiples of f_1.

When analyzing periodic data in practice, the phase angles θ_n are often ignored. For this case, Eq. (1.7) can be characterized by a discrete spectrum as illustrated in Figure 1.4. Sometimes complex periodic data will include only a few components. In other cases, the fundamental component may be absent. For example, suppose a periodic time history is formed by mixing three sine waves which have frequencies of 60, 75, and 100 cps. The highest common divisor is 5 cps, so the period for the resulting periodic data is $T_p = 0.2$ second. Hence when expanded into a Fourier series, all values of X_n are zero except for $n = 12$, $n = 15$, and $n = 20$.

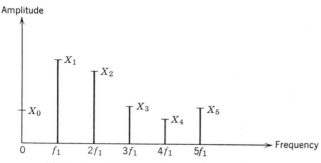

Figure 1.4   Spectrum for complex periodic data.

Physical phenomena which produce complex periodic data are far more common than those which produce simple sinusoidal data. In fact, the classification of data as being sinusoidal is often only an approximation for data which are actually complex. For example, the voltage output from an electrical alternator may actually display, under careful inspection, some small contributions at higher harmonic frequencies. In other cases, intense harmonic components may be present in periodic physical data. For example, the vibration response of a multicylinder reciprocating engine will usually display considerable harmonic content.

1.1.3   Almost-Periodic Data

In the previous section, it is noted that periodic data can generally be reduced to a series of sine waves with commensurately related frequencies. Conversely, the data formed by summing two or more commensurately related sine waves will be periodic. However, the data formed by summing two or more sine waves with arbitrary frequencies generally will not be periodic.

More specifically, the sum of two or more sine waves will be periodic only when the ratios of all possible pairs of frequencies form rational numbers. This indicates that a fundamental period exists which will satisfy the requirements of Eq. (1.5). Hence

$$x(t) = X_1 \sin(2t + \theta_1) + X_2 \sin(3t + \theta_2) + X_3 \sin(7t + \theta_3)$$

is periodic since $\frac{2}{3}$, $\frac{2}{7}$, and $\frac{3}{7}$ are rational numbers (the fundamental period is $T_p = 1$). On the other hand,

$$x(t) = X_1 \sin(2t + \theta_1) + X_2 \sin(3t + \theta_2) + X_3 \sin(\sqrt{50}t + \theta_3)$$

is not periodic since $2/\sqrt{50}$ and $3/\sqrt{50}$ are not rational numbers (the fundamental period is infinitely long). The resulting time history in this

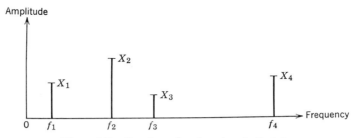

Figure 1.5   Spectrum for almost-periodic data.

case will have an "almost-periodic" character, but the requirements of Eq. (1.5) will not be satisfied for any finite value of T_p.

Based upon these discussions, almost-periodic data are those types of nonperiodic data which can be defined mathematically by a time-varying function of the form

$$x(t) = \sum_{n=1}^{\infty} X_n \sin(2\pi f_n t + \theta_n) \tag{1.8}$$

where $f_n/f_m \neq$ rational number in all cases.

Physical phenomena producing almost-periodic data frequently occur in practice when the effects of two or more unrelated periodic phenomena are mixed. A good example is the vibration response in a multiple engine propeller airplane when the engines are out of synchronization.

An important property of almost-periodic data is as follows. If the phase angles θ_n are ignored, Eq. (1.8) can be characterized by a discrete frequency spectrum similar to that for complex periodic data. The only difference is that the frequencies of the components are not related by rational numbers, as illustrated in Figure 1.5.

1.1.4   Transient Nonperiodic Data

Transient data are defined as all nonperiodic data other than the almost-periodic data discussed in Section 1.1.3. In other words, transient

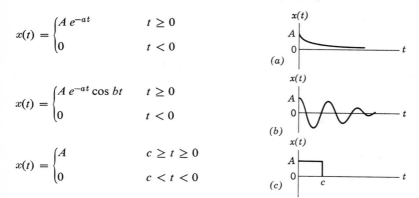

$$x(t) = \begin{cases} A e^{-at} & t \geq 0 \\ 0 & t < 0 \end{cases}$$

$$x(t) = \begin{cases} A e^{-at} \cos bt & t \geq 0 \\ 0 & t < 0 \end{cases}$$

$$x(t) = \begin{cases} A & c \geq t \geq 0 \\ 0 & c < t < 0 \end{cases}$$

Figure 1.6   Illustrations of transient data.

data include all data not previously discussed which can be described by some suitable time-varying function. Three simple examples of transient data are given in Figure 1.6.

Physical phenomena which produce transient data are numerous and diverse. For example, the data in Figure 1.6(a) could represent the temperatures of water in a kettle (relative to room temperature) after the flame is turned off. The data in Figure 1.6(b) might represent the free vibration of a damped mechanical system after an excitation force is removed. The

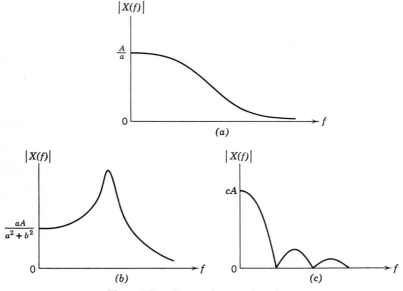

Figure 1.7   Spectra for transient data.

data in Figure 1.6(c) could represent the stress in an end-loaded cable which breaks at time c.

An important characteristic of transient data, as opposed to periodic and almost-periodic data, is that a discrete spectral representation is not possible. However, a continuous spectral representation for transient data can be obtained in most cases from a Fourier integral given by

$$X(f) = \int_{-\infty}^{\infty} x(t)\, e^{-j2\pi ft}\, dt \qquad (1.9)$$

The Fourier spectrum $X(f)$ is generally a complex number which can be expressed in complex polar notation as

$$X(f) = |X(f)|\, e^{-j\theta(f)}$$

Here, $|X(f)|$ is the magnitude of $X(f)$ and $\theta(f)$ is the argument. In terms of the magnitude $|X(f)|$, the Fourier spectra for the three transient time histories in Figure 1.6 are as presented in Figure 1.7.

1.2   Classifications for Random Data

As discussed earlier, data representing a random physical phenomenon cannot be described by an explicit mathematical relationship because each

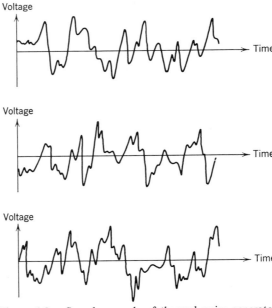

Figure 1.8   Sample records of thermal noise generator outputs.

observation of the phenomenon will be unique. In other words, any given observation will represent only one of many possible results which might have occurred. For example, assume the output voltage from a thermal noise generator is recorded as a function of time. A specific voltage time history record will be obtained, as shown in Figure 1.8. However, if a second thermal noise generator of identical construction and assembly is operated simultaneously, a different voltage time history record would result. In fact, every thermal noise generator which might be constructed would produce a different voltage time history record, as illustrated in Figure 1.8. Hence the voltage time history for any one generator is

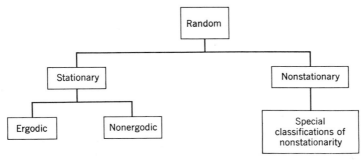

Figure 1.9   Classifications for random data.

merely one example of an infinitely large number of time histories which might have occurred.

A single time history representing a random phenomenon is called a *sample function* (or a *sample record* when observed over a finite time interval). The collection of all possible sample functions which the random phenomenon might have produced is called a *random process* or a *stochastic process*. Hence a sample record of data for a random physical phenomenon may be thought of as one physical realization of a random process.

Random processes may be categorized as being either stationary or nonstationary. Stationary random processes may be further categorized as being either ergodic or nonergodic. Nonstationary random processes may be further categorized in terms of specific types of nonstationary properties as discussed in Chapter 9. These various classifications for random processes are schematically illustrated in Figure 1.9. The meaning and physical significance of these various types of random processes will now be discussed in broad terms. More rigorous mathematical definitions and developments are presented in Chapters 3 and 9.

1.2.1   Stationary Random Processes

When a physical phenomenon is considered in terms of a random process, the properties of the phenomenon can hypothetically be described at any instant of time by computing average values over the collection of sample functions which describe the random process. For example, consider the collection of sample functions (also called the ensemble) which forms the random process illustrated in Figure 1.10. The mean value (first

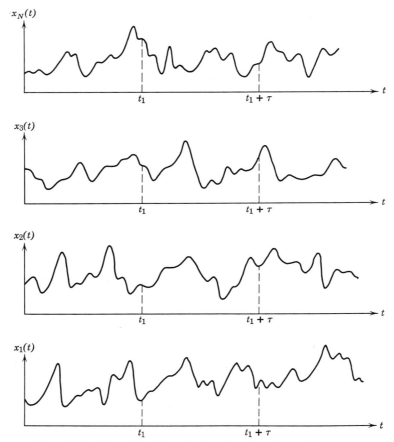

Figure 1.10 Ensemble of sample functions forming random process.

moment) of the random process at some time t_1 can be computed by taking the instantaneous value of each sample function of the ensemble at time t_1, summing the values, and dividing by the number of sample functions. In a similar manner, a correlation (joint moment) between the values of the random process at two different times (called the autocorrelation function) can be computed by taking the ensemble average of the product of instantaneous values at two times, t_1 and $t_1 + \tau$. That is, for the random process $\{x(t)\}$, where the symbol $\{\ \}$ is used to denote an ensemble of sample functions, the mean value $\mu_x(t_1)$ and the autocorrelation function $R_x(t_1, t_1 + \tau)$ are given by

$$\mu_x(t_1) = \lim_{N \to \infty} \frac{1}{N} \sum_{k=1}^{N} x_k(t_1) \tag{1.10a}$$

$$R_x(t_1, t_1 + \tau) = \lim_{N \to \infty} \frac{1}{N} \sum_{k=1}^{N} x_k(t_1) \, x_k(t_1 + \tau) \tag{1.10b}$$

where the final summation assumes each sample function is equally likely.

For the general case where $\mu_x(t_1)$ and $R_x(t_1, t_1 + \tau)$ defined in Eq. (1.10) vary as time t_1 varies, the random process $\{x(t)\}$ is said to be *nonstationary*. For the special case where $\mu_x(t_1)$ and $R_x(t_1, t_1 + \tau)$ do not vary as time t_1 varies, the random process $\{x(t)\}$ is said to be *weakly stationary* or stationary in the wide sense. For weakly stationary random processes, the mean value is a constant and the autocorrelation function is dependent only upon the time displacement τ. That is, $\mu_x(t_1) = \mu_x$ and $R_x(t_1, t_1 + \tau) = R_x(\tau)$.

An infinite collection of higher-order moments and joint moments for the random process $\{x(t)\}$ could also be computed to establish a complete family of probability distribution functions describing the process. For the special case where all possible moments and joint moments are time invariant, the random process $\{x(t)\}$ is said to be *strongly stationary* or stationary in the strict sense. For many practical applications verification of weak stationarity will justify an assumption of strong stationarity.

1.2.2 Ergodic Random Processes

The previous section discusses how the properties of a random process can be determined by computing ensemble averages at specific instances of time. In most cases, however, it is also possible to describe the properties of a stationary random process by computing time averages over specific sample functions in the ensemble. For example, consider the kth sample function for the random process illustrated in Figure 1.10. The mean value $\mu_x(k)$ and the autocorrelation function $R_x(\tau, k)$ for the kth sample function are given by

$$\mu_x(k) = \lim_{T \to \infty} \frac{1}{T} \int_0^T x_k(t) \, dt \tag{1.11a}$$

$$R_x(\tau, k) = \lim_{T \to \infty} \frac{1}{T} \int_0^T x_k(t) \, x_k(t + \tau) \, dt \tag{1.11b}$$

If the random process $\{x(t)\}$ is stationary, and $\mu_x(k)$ and $R_x(\tau, k)$ defined in Eq. (1.11) do not differ when computed over different sample functions, the random process is said to be *ergodic*. For ergodic random processes, the time-averaged mean value and autocorrelation function (as well as all other time-averaged properties) are equal to the corresponding ensemble averaged value. That is, $\mu_x(k) = \mu_x$ and $R_x(\tau, k) = R_x(\tau)$. Note that only stationary random processes can be ergodic.

Ergodic random processes are clearly an important class of random processes since all properties of ergodic random processes can be determined by performing time averages over a single sample function. Fortunately, in actual practice, random data representing stationary physical phenomena are generally ergodic. It is for this reason that the properties of stationary random phenomena can be measured properly, in most cases, from a single observed time history record.

1.2.3 Nonstationary Random Processes

Nonstationary random processes include all random processes which do not meet the requirements for stationarity defined in Section 1.2.1. Unless further restrictions are imposed, the properties of a nonstationary random process are generally time-varying functions which can be determined only by performing instantaneous averages over the ensemble of sample functions forming the process. In actual practice, it is often not feasible to obtain a sufficient number of sample records to permit the accurate measurement of properties by ensemble averaging. This fact has tended to impede the development of practical techniques for measuring and analyzing nonstationary random data.

In many cases, the nonstationary random data produced by actual physical phenomena can be classified into special categories of nonstationarity which simplify the measurement and analysis problem. For example, some types of random data might be described by a nonstationary random process $\{y(t)\}$ where each sample function is given by $y(t) = A(t)x(t)$. Here, $x(t)$ is a sample function from a stationary random process $\{x(t)\}$ and $A(t)$ is a deterministic multiplication factor. In other words, the data might be represented by a nonstationary random process consisting of sample functions with a common deterministic time trend. If nonstationary random data fit a specific model of this type, ensemble averaging is not needed to describe the data. The various desired properties can be estimated from a single sample record, as is true for ergodic stationary data. Because of the difficulty and importance of the nonstationary data analysis problem, Chapter 9 is totally devoted to this subject.

1.2.4 Self-Stationary Random Data

The concept of stationarity, as defined and discussed in Section 1.2.1, relates to the ensemble averaged properties of a random process. In actual practice, however, data in the form of individual time history records for a random phenomenon are frequently referred to as being stationary or nonstationary. A slightly different concept of stationarity is involved here. When a single time history record is referred to as being stationary, it is generally meant that the properties computed over short time intervals do not vary "significantly" from one interval to the next. The word significantly is used here to mean that observed variations are greater than would be expected, owing to normal statistical sampling variations. Hence the single sample record is stationary within itself. This concept of stationarity is sometimes called self-stationarity to avoid confusion with the more classical definition.

To clarify the idea of self-stationarity, consider a single sample record $x_k(t)$ obtained from the kth sample function of a random process $\{x(t)\}$. Assume a mean value and autocorrelation function are obtained by time averaging over a short interval T with a starting time of t_1 as follows.

$$\mu_x(t_1, k) = \frac{1}{T} \int_{t_1}^{t_1+T} x_k(t)\, dt \tag{1.12a}$$

$$R_x(t_1, t_1 + \tau, k) = \frac{1}{T} \int_{t_1}^{t_1+T} x_k(t)\, x_k(t + \tau)\, dt \tag{1.12b}$$

For the general case where the sample properties defined in Eq. (1.12) vary significantly as the starting time t_1 varies, the individual sample record is said to be *self-nonstationary*. For the special case where the sample properties defined in Eq. (1.12) do not vary significantly as the starting time t_1 varies, the sample record is said to be *weakly self-stationary*. If this requirement is met for all higher order moments and joint moments, the sample record is said to be *strongly self-stationary*.

An important point here is as follows. A sample record obtained from an ergodic random process will be self-stationary. Furthermore, sample records from most physically interesting nonstationary random processes will be self-nonstationary. Hence if an ergodic assumption is justified (as it is for most actual stationary physical phenomena), verification of self-stationarity for a single sample record will effectively justify an assumption of stationarity and ergodicity for the random process from which the sample record is obtained.

1.3   Basic Descriptive Properties of Random Data

Four main types of statistical functions are used to describe the basic properties of random data: (*a*) mean square values, (*b*) probability density functions, (*c*) autocorrelation functions, and (*d*) power spectral density functions. The mean square value furnishes a rudimentary description of the intensity of the data. The probability density function furnishes information concerning the properties of the data in the amplitude domain. The autocorrelation function and the power spectral density function furnish similar information in the time domain and frequency domain, respectively. It will be shown in Chapter 3 that, for stationary data, the power spectral density function technically supplies no new information over the autocorrelation function since the two are Fourier transform pairs. The two functions present the information in different formats, however, where one format is often more desirable than the other for specific applications.

These various descriptive properties for stationary random data will now be defined in broad terms. The discussions assume that the data in question are ergodic, so that the properties of the data can be determined from time averages of individual sample records.

1.3.1 Mean Square Values (Mean Values and Variances)

The general intensity of any random data may be described in rudimentary terms by a *mean square value*, which is simply the average of the squared values of the time history. In equation form, the mean square value Ψ_x^2 for a sample time history record $x(t)$ is given by

$$\Psi_x^2 = \lim_{T \to \infty} \frac{1}{T} \int_0^T x^2(t) \, dt \tag{1.13}$$

The positive square root of the mean square value is called the root mean square or *rms value*.

It is often desirable to think of physical data in terms of a combination of a *static* or time-invariant component and a *dynamic* or fluctuating component. The static component may be described by a *mean value* which is simply the average of all values. In equation form, the mean value μ_x is given by

$$\mu_x = \lim_{T \to \infty} \frac{1}{T} \int_0^T x(t) \, dt \tag{1.14}$$

The dynamic component may be described by a *variance* which is simply the mean square value about the mean. In equation form, the variance σ_x^2 is given by

$$\sigma_x^2 = \lim_{T \to \infty} \frac{1}{T} \int_0^T [x(t) - \mu_x]^2 \, dt \tag{1.15}$$

The positive square root of the variance is called the *standard deviation*. By expanding Eq. (1.15), it is seen that the variance is equal to the mean square value minus the square of the mean value. That is,

$$\sigma_x^2 = \Psi_x^2 - \mu_x^2 \tag{1.16}$$

1.3.2   Probability Density Functions

The probability density function for random data describes the probability that the data will assume a value within some defined range at any instant of time. Consider the sample time history record $x(t)$ illustrated in Figure 1.11. The probability that $x(t)$ assumes a value within the range between x and $(x + \Delta x)$ may be obtained by taking the ratio of T_x/T, where T_x is the total amount of time that $x(t)$ falls inside the range $(x, x + \Delta x)$ during an observation time T. This ratio will

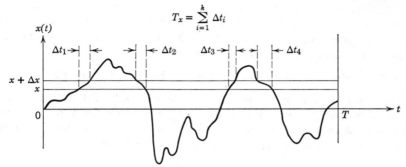

Figure 1.11   Probability measurement.

approach an exact probability description as T approaches infinity. In equation form,

$$\text{Prob }[x < x(t) \leq x + \Delta x] = \lim_{T \to \infty} \frac{T_x}{T} \qquad (1.17)$$

For small Δx, a first-order probability density function $p(x)$ can be defined as follows.

$$\text{Prob }[x < x(t) \leq x + \Delta x] \approx p(x)\,\Delta x \qquad (1.18)$$

More precisely,

$$p(x) = \lim_{\Delta x \to 0} \frac{\text{Prob }[x < x(t) < x + \Delta x]}{\Delta x} = \lim_{\Delta x \to 0} \lim_{T \to \infty} \frac{1}{T}\left(\frac{T_x}{\Delta x}\right) \qquad (1.19)$$

The probability density function $p(x)$ is always a real-valued, non-negative function.

The probability that the instantaneous value $x(t)$ is less than or equal to some value x is defined by $P(x)$, which is equal to the integral of the probability density function from minus infinity to x. This function $P(x)$ is known as the *probability distribution function,* or *cumulative probability distribution function,* and should not be confused with the probability density function $p(x)$. Specifically

$$P(x) = \text{Prob }[x(t) \leq x] = \int_{-\infty}^{x} p(\xi)\,d\xi \qquad (1.20)$$

The distribution function $P(x)$ is bounded by zero and one, since the probability of $x(t)$ being less than $-\infty$ is clearly zero while the probability of $x(t)$ being less than $+\infty$ is unity (a certainty). The probability that $x(t)$ falls inside any range (x_1, x_2) is given by

$$P(x_2) - P(x_1) = \text{Prob } [x_1 < x(t) \le x_2] = \int_{x_1}^{x_2} p(x)\, dx \qquad (1.21)$$

In terms of the probability density function $p(x)$, the mean value of $x(t)$ is given by

$$\mu_x = \int_{-\infty}^{\infty} x\, p(x)\, dx \qquad (1.22)$$

In words, the mean value is a weighted linear sum of $x(t)$ over all values of x, which gives a measure of the central tendency of $x(t)$.

Similarly, the mean square value is given by

$$\Psi_x^2 = \int_{-\infty}^{\infty} x^2 p(x)\, dx \qquad (1.23)$$

Hence the mean square value is a weighted linear sum of $x^2(t)$ over all values of x, which gives a measure of the dispersion of $x(t)$.

Illustrations. To help clarify the practical significance of probability density functions, consider four examples of sample time history records which might occur in practice: (a) sine wave, (b) sine wave plus random noise, (c) narrow-band random noise, and (d) wide-band random noise. Typical time history records for each of these examples are presented in Figure 1.12. In all cases, the mean value is assumed to equal zero ($\mu_x = 0$) for convenience.

Note that a sine wave is usually thought of as being deterministic since it can be described in detail by the equation $x(t) = X \sin (2\pi f_0 t + \theta)$. However, a sine wave may also be thought of as a sample function from a random process $\{x(t)\} = \{X \sin (2\pi f_0 t + \theta_k)\}$, where the initial phase angle θ_k for each sample function $x_k(t)$ is a random variable. Such an interpretation is made here to justify describing a sine wave in probabilistic terms.

A typical plot of probability density versus instantaneous value [$p(x)$ versus x] for each of the four examples is presented in Figure 1.13. The dish-shaped probability density plot for a sine wave, as illustrated in Figure 1.13(a), is defined by the following equation.

$$p(x) = \begin{cases} \left(\pi\sqrt{X^2 - x^2}\right)^{-1} & |x| < X \\ 0 & |x| \ge X \end{cases} \qquad (1.24)$$

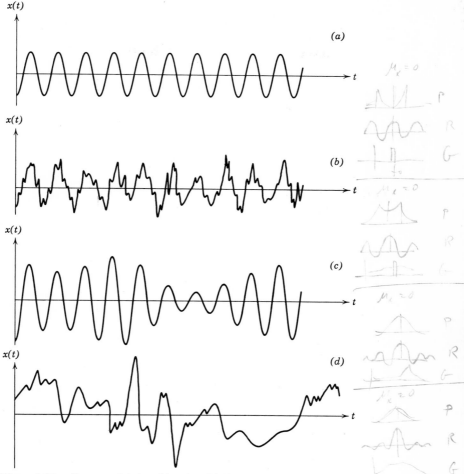

Figure 1.12   Four special time histories. (*a*) Sine wave. (*b*) Sine wave plus random noise. (*c*) Narrow-band random noise. (*d*) Wide-band random noise.

The bell-shaped probability density plots indicated in Figure 1.13(*c*) and (*d*) are typical of either narrow or wide-band random data. These probability density plots would ideally be of the classical Gaussian form as follows

$$p(x) = \left(\sigma_x \sqrt{2\pi}\right)^{-1} e^{-x^2/2\sigma_x^2} \qquad (1.25)$$

The probability density plot for a sine wave plus random noise takes on the predominant characteristics of both as illustrated in Figure 1.13(*b*). The four examples in Figure 1.13 illustrate a definite trend in the probability

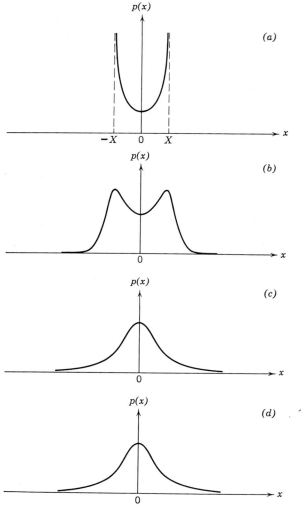

Figure 1.13 Probability density function plots. (*a*) Sine wave. (*b*) Sine wave plus random noise. (*c*) Narrow-band random noise. (*d*) Wide-band random noise.

density plot going from the sine wave case to the wide-band random noise case.

Applications. The principal application for a probability density function measurement of physical data is to establish a probabilistic description for the instantaneous values of the data. However, from

Figure 1.13, it is seen that the probability density function could also be used to distinguish between sinusoidal and random data. Furthermore, various nonlinear physical effects will often exhibit their presence in the probability density function to one who has sufficient experience in such interpretations.

1.3.3   Autocorrelation Functions

The autocorrelation function for random data describes the general dependence of the values of the data at one time on the values at another time. Consider the sample time history record $x(t)$ illustrated in Figure 1.14. An estimate for the autocorrelation between the values of $x(t)$ at times t and $t + \tau$ may be obtained by taking the product of the two values

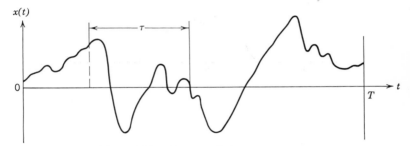

Figure 1.14   Autocorrelation measurement.

and averaging over the observation time T. The resulting average product will approach an exact autocorrelation function as T approaches infinity. In equation form,

$$R_x(\tau) = \lim_{T \to \infty} \frac{1}{T} \int_0^T x(t)\, x(t + \tau)\, dt \tag{1.26}$$

The quantity $R_x(\tau)$ is always a real-valued even function with a maximum at $\tau = 0$, and may be either positive or negative. In equation form,

$$R_x(-\tau) = R_x(\tau) \tag{1.27}$$

$$R_x(0) \geq |R_x(\tau)| \quad \text{for all } \tau \tag{1.28}$$

In terms of the autocorrelation function, the mean value of $x(t)$ is given (excluding such special cases as sine waves) by

$$\mu_x = \sqrt{R_x(\infty)} \tag{1.29}$$

In words, the mean value of $x(t)$ is equal to the positive square root of the autocorrelation as the time displacement becomes very long. Similarly,

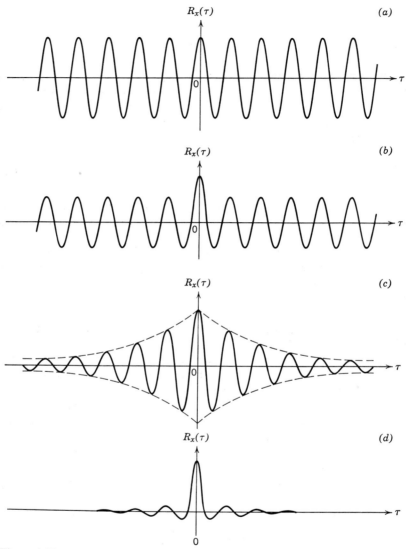

Figure 1.15 Autocorrelation function plots (autocorrelograms). (*a*) Sine wave. (*b*) Sine wave plus random noise. (*c*) Narrow-band random noise. (*d*) Wide-band random noise.

the mean square value of $x(t)$ is given by

$$\Psi_x^2 = R_x(0) \tag{1.30}$$

That is, the mean square value is equal to the autocorrelation at zero time displacement.

Illustrations. A typical plot of autocorrelation versus time displacement [$R_x(\tau)$ versus τ] for each of the four time histories in Figure 1.12 is presented in Figure 1.15. These plots are called *autocorrelograms*. The cosine-type autocorrelogram for a sine wave, as illustrated in Figure 1.15(a), is defined by the equation

$$R_x(\tau) = \frac{X^2}{2} \cos 2\pi f_0 \tau \tag{1.31}$$

The important feature of this autocorrelogram is that it persists periodically over all time displacements with the same period as the underlying sine wave, but phase angle information is lost.

The sharply peaked autocorrelogram which diminished rapidly to zero, as illustrated in Figure 1.15(d), is typical of wide-band random data with a zero mean value (if the mean value were not zero, the autocorrelogram would approach a value of μ_x^2). For the limiting case of hypothetical white noise (random data with energy distributed uniformly over all frequencies), the autocorrelogram is a Dirac delta function at zero time displacement ($\tau = 0$).

The autocorrelogram for the sine wave plus random noise is simply the sum of the autocorrelograms for the sine wave and random noise separately, as illustrated in Figure 1.15(b). On the other hand, the autocorrelogram for the narrow-band random noise in Figure 1.15(c) appears like a decaying version of a sine wave autocorrelogram. An important feature, however, is that this autocorrelogram will diminish to zero for large time displacements (assuming $\mu_x = 0$). The four examples in Figure 1.15 illustrate a definite trend in the autocorrelogram going from the sine wave case to the wide-band random noise case, just as was true for the probability density function.

Applications. The principal application for an autocorrelation function measurement of physical data is to establish the influence of values at any time over values at a future time. Because a sine wave, or any other deterministic data, will have an autocorrelation function which persists over all time displacements, as opposed to random data which diminishes to zero for large time displacements (assuming $\mu_x = 0$), an autocorrelation measurement clearly provides a powerful tool for detecting deterministic data which might be masked in a random background.

There are other less obvious applications for autocorrelation functions, but these are generally better interpreted from its Fourier transform, the power spectral density function, which is discussed next.

1.3.4 Power Spectral Density Functions

The power spectral density function for random data describes the general frequency composition of the data in terms of the spectral density of its mean square value. The mean square value of a sample time history record in a frequency range between f and $f + \Delta f$ may be obtained by filtering the sample record with a band-pass filter having sharp cutoff characteristics, and computing the average of the squared output from the filter. This average squared value will approach an exact mean square value as the observation time T approaches infinity. In equation form,

$$\Psi_x^2[f, f + \Delta f] = \lim_{T \to \infty} \frac{1}{T} \int_0^T x^2(t, f, \Delta f) \, dt \tag{1.32}$$

where $x(t, f, \Delta f)$ is that portion of $x(t)$ in the frequency range from f to $f + \Delta f$.

For small Δf, a power spectral density function $G_x(f)$ can be defined such that

$$\Psi_x^2(f, f + \Delta f) \approx G_x(f) \Delta f \tag{1.33}$$

More precisely,

$$G_x(f) = \lim_{\Delta f \to 0} \frac{\Psi_x^2[f, f + \Delta f]}{\Delta f} = \lim_{\Delta f \to 0} \lim_{T \to \infty} \frac{1}{(\Delta f)T} \int_0^T x^2(t, f, \Delta f) \, dt \tag{1.34}$$

The quantity $G_x(f)$ is always a real-valued, non-negative function.

An important property of the power spectral density function lies in its relationship to the autocorrelation function. Specifically, for stationary data, the two functions are related by a Fourier transform as follows.

$$G_x(f) = 2 \int_{-\infty}^{\infty} R_x(\tau) e^{-j2\pi f \tau} \, d\tau = 4 \int_0^{\infty} R_x(\tau) \cos 2\pi f \tau \, d\tau \tag{1.35}$$

The second equality exists because $R_x(\tau)$ is an even function of τ.

In terms of the power spectral density function, the mean value of $x(t)$ is given by

$$\mu_x = \left[\int_{0^-}^{0^+} G_x(f) \, df \right]^{1/2} \tag{1.36}$$

where 0^- means the lower limit of integration, zero, is approached from below, and 0^+ means the upper limit of integration, also zero, is approached from above. In words, the mean value of $x(t)$ will appear in $G_x(f)$ as a

Dirac delta function at zero frequency. The mean value is equal to the positive square root of the area under this delta function.

The mean square value of $x(t)$ is given by

$$\Psi_x^2 = \int_0^\infty G_x(f)\, df \tag{1.37}$$

where it is understood that the lower limit of integration is approached from below in order to include Eq. (1.36). Hence the mean square value is equal to the total area under a plot of the power spectral density function versus frequency.

Illustrations.   A typical plot of power spectral density versus frequency [$G_x(f)$ versus f] for each of the four time histories in Figure 1.12 is presented in Figure 1.16. These plots are called *power spectra*. The discrete power spectrum for a sine wave, as illustrated in Figure 1.16(*a*), is defined by

$$G_x(f) = \frac{X^2}{2}\, \delta(f - f_0) \tag{1.38}$$

where $\delta(f - f_0)$ denotes a delta function at $f = f_0$. In words, the power spectral density function for a sine wave is infinitely large at the frequency of the sine wave and zero at all other frequencies. However, the integral of the power spectrum over any frequency range that includes the sinusoidal frequency has a finite value equal to the mean square value ($X^2/2$) of the sine wave.

The relatively smooth and broad power spectrum illustrated in Figure 1.16(*d*) gives rise to the descriptive term "wide-band" for this type of random data. For the hypothetical case of white noise, this power spectrum is uniform over all frequencies by definition. The power spectrum for the sine wave plus random noise is simply the sum of the power spectra for the sine wave and random noise separately, as illustrated in Figure 1.16(*b*). On the other hand, the power spectrum for the narrow-band noise in Figure 1.16(*c*) is sharply peaked as for a sine wave (hence the term "narrow-band"), but still smoothly continuous as for random noise. Once again, the four examples in Figure 1.16 illustrate a definite trend in the power spectrum going from the sine wave case to the wide-band noise case.

Applications.   The principal application for a power spectral density function measurement of physical data is to establish the frequency composition of the data which, in turn, bears important relationships to the basic characteristics of the physical system involved. For example, consider an electrical circuit with a frequency response function of $H(f)$.

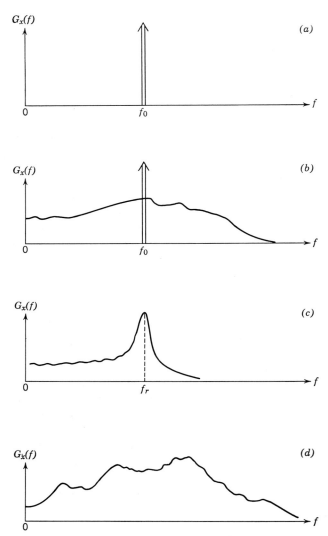

Figure 1.16 Power spectral density function plots (power spectra). (*a*) Sine wave. (*b*) Sine wave plus random noise. (*c*) Narrow-band random noise. (*d*) Wide-band random noise.

Assume a stationary random signal with a power spectral density function of $G_x(f)$ is applied to the input of the electrical circuit. The output from the electrical circuit will be a stationary random signal with a power spectral density function given by

$$G_y(f) = |H(f)|^2 G_x(f) \qquad (1.39)$$

It follows from Eq. (1.39) that measurement or knowledge of any two quantities enables one to estimate the third quantity. Note that only the magnitude of the frequency response function is involved in the relationship. Determination of phase information requires a cross-spectra analysis, which is discussed later.

1.4 Joint Properties of Random Data

The statistical functions discussed in Section 1.3 are useful to describe the properties of data from individual random processes. It is often desirable to describe certain common or joint properties of different data from two or more random processes. For example, assume one is interested in the height of waves at various points on the ocean's surface. The average properties of the wave height at each point could be described using the statistical functions discussed in Section 1.3. However, there may be additional important information in similar joint statistical functions which can be computed for the wave heights at two points on the ocean.

Three main types of statistical functions are used to describe the joint properties of sample records from two random processes: (*a*) joint probability density functions, (*b*) cross-correlation functions, and (*c*) cross-spectral density functions. These three functions are effectively extensions of the basic formulations used to describe the properties of individual sample records. They supply information concerning joint properties in the amplitude domain, time domain, and frequency domain, respectively.

These various joint descriptive properties for two sets of stationary random data will now be defined in broad terms. Once again, the discussions will assume ergodicity so that the joint time-averaged properties of single pairs of sample time history records can be considered.

1.4.1 Joint Probability Density Functions

The joint probability density function for two random sample records describes the probability that both sample records will simultaneously assume values within some defined pair of ranges at any instant of time.

Consider the pair of time history records $x(t)$ and $y(t)$ illustrated in Figure 1.17. The probability that $x(t)$ assumes a value within the range between x and $(x + \Delta x)$ while $y(t)$ *simultaneously* assumes a value within the range between y and $(y + \Delta y)$ may be obtained by taking the ratio $T_{x,y}/T$, where $T_{x,y}$ is the total amount of time that $x(t)$ and $y(t)$ simultaneously fall inside

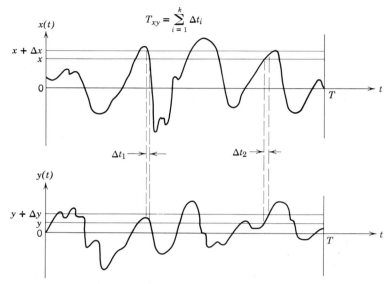

Figure 1.17 Joint probability measurement.

the ranges $(x, x + \Delta x)$ and $(y, y + \Delta y)$, respectively, during an observation time T. This ratio will approach an exact probability description as T approaches infinity. That is,

$$\text{Prob}\,[x < x(t) \le x + \Delta x,\, y < y(t) \le y + \Delta y] = \lim_{T \to \infty} \frac{T_{x,y}}{T} \quad (1.40)$$

For small Δx and Δy, a second-order (joint) probability density function $p(x, y)$ can be defined as

$$\text{Prob}\,[x < x(t) \le x + \Delta x,\, y < y(t) \le y + \Delta y] \approx p(x, y)\, \Delta x\, \Delta y \quad (1.41)$$

More precisely,

$$p(x, y) = \lim_{\substack{\Delta x \to 0 \\ \Delta y \to 0}} \frac{\text{Prob}\,[x < x(t) \le x + \Delta x,\, y < y(t) \le y + \Delta y]}{(\Delta x)(\Delta y)}$$

$$= \lim_{\substack{\Delta x \to 0 \\ \Delta y \to 0}} \lim_{T \to \infty} \frac{1}{T} \left[\frac{T_{x,y}}{(\Delta x)(\Delta y)} \right] \quad (1.42)$$

The probability density function $p(x, y)$ is always a real-valued, non-negative function.

The probability that the instantaneous values $x(t)$ and $y(t)$ are less than or equal to some values x and y is defined by the *joint probability distribution function* $P(x, y)$ as follows:

$$P(x, y) = \text{Prob } [x(t) \leq x, y(t) \leq y] = \int_{-\infty}^{x} \int_{-\infty}^{y} p(\xi, \eta) \, d\xi \, d\eta \quad (1.43)$$

As for first-order distribution functions, $P(x, y)$ is bounded by zero and one, where $P[-\infty, -\infty] = 0$ and $P[\infty, \infty] = 1$. The probability that $x(t)$ and $y(t)$ simultaneously fall inside the range $(x_1, x_2; y_1, y_2)$ is given by

$$P(x_2, y_2) - P(x_1, y_1) = \text{Prob } [x_1 < x(t) \leq x_2, y_1 < y(t) \leq y_2]$$

$$= \int_{x_1}^{x_2} \int_{y_1}^{y_2} p(x, y) \, dy \, dx \quad (1.44)$$

When the two phenomena in question are statistically independent, the joint probability density is given by

$$p(x, y) = p(x) \, p(y) \quad (1.45)$$

That is, the joint probability density function for such problems is given by a product of first-order probability density functions.

A typical plot of joint probability density versus instantaneous values $[p(x, y)$ versus x and $y]$ for a pair of random time history records is illustrated in Figure 1.18. Note that the plot has three dimensions. The volume under the joint probability density plot bounded by the values x_1, x_2, y_1, y_2 is equal to the probability that $x(t)$ and $y(t)$ will simultaneously have values within those ranges at any given time. Obviously, the total volume under the plot is equal to unity since the probability of the two sample records simultaneously having any value must be one.

Applications. The principal application for a joint probability density function measurement is to establish a probabilistic description for an event which is associated with two sets of correlated random data. For example, the prediction of collisions between two adjacent elastic structures which are vibrating randomly, but with some correlation, is a direct application for a joint probability density function. In some applications, it is desirable to relate the probability of occurrence of two events to the probability of occurrence of one of these events. These questions of "conditional" probabilities require knowledge of the joint probability density function. Special applications occur in establishing the expected number of zero crossings or threshold crossings of physical data, and in predicting peak value distributions or extreme value properties.

$$\text{Prob}[x_1 < x \le x_2; y_1 < y \le y_2] = \int_{y_1}^{y_2} \int_{x_1}^{x_2} p(x, y)\, dx\, dy = P_{1,2}$$

$$\text{Prob}[-\infty < x < \infty; -\infty < y < \infty] = \int_{-\infty}^{\infty} \int_{-\infty}^{\infty} p(x, y)\, dx\, dy = 1$$

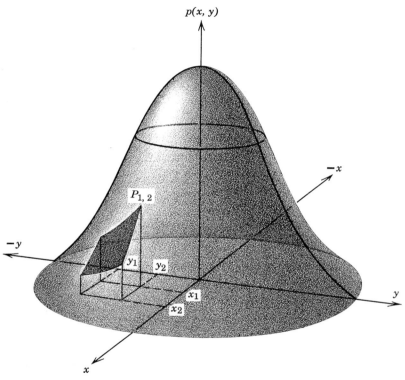

Figure 1.18   Typical joint probability density plot.

1.4.2   Cross-Correlation Functions

The cross-correlation function for two sets of random data describes the general dependence of the values of one set of data on the other. Consider the pair of time history records $x(t)$ and $y(t)$ illustrated in Figure 1.19. An estimate for the cross-correlation function of the values of $x(t)$ at time t and $y(t)$ at time $t + \tau$ may be obtained by taking the average product for the two values over the observation time T, exactly as is done for autocorrelation functions in Section 1.3.3. The resulting average product will approach an exact cross-correlation function as T approaches infinity. That is,

$$R_{xy}(\tau) = \lim_{T \to \infty} \frac{1}{T} \int_0^T x(t)\, y(t + \tau)\, dt \qquad (1.46)$$

The function $R_{xy}(\tau)$ is always a real-valued function which may be either positive or negative. Furthermore, $R_{xy}(\tau)$ does not necessarily have a maximum at $\tau = 0$ as was true for autocorrelation functions, or is

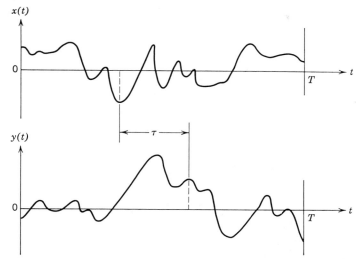

Figure 1.19   Cross-correlation measurement.

$R_{xy}(\tau)$ an even function as was true for autocorrelation functions. However, $R_{xy}(\tau)$ does display symmetry about the ordinate when x and y are interchanged. That is,

$$R_{xy}(-\tau) = R_{yx}(\tau) \qquad (1.47)$$

Two useful relationships which bound the absolute value of the cross-correlation function are

$$|R_{xy}(\tau)|^2 \le R_x(0)R_y(0) \qquad (1.48)$$

$$|R_{xy}(\tau)| \le \tfrac{1}{2}[R_x(0) + R_y(0)] \qquad (1.49)$$

When $R_{xy}(\tau) = 0$, $x(t)$ and $y(t)$ are said to be uncorrelated. If $x(t)$ and $y(t)$ are statistically independent, then $R_{xy}(\tau) = 0$ for all time displacements, assuming either $x(t)$ or $y(t)$ have a zero mean value. If the mean values for both $x(t)$ and $y(t)$ are not zero, the cross-correlation function would have a value of $\mu_x \mu_y$ for all time displacements in this case.

A typical plot of the cross-correlation versus time displacement [$R_{xy}(\tau)$ versus τ] for a pair of random time history records is illustrated in Figure 1.20. This plot is called a *cross-correlogram*. Note that the plot will sometimes display sharp peaks which indicate the existence of correlation between $x(t)$ and $y(t)$ for specific time displacements.

Applications. Cross-correlation function measurements have many important applications including the following.

Measurement of Time Delays. Suppose one is interested in determining the time required for a signal to pass through a given system. Assuming the system is linear, a cross-correlation measurement between the input

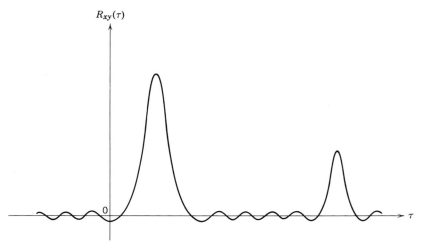

Figure 1.20 Typical cross-correlation plot (cross-correlogram).

and output may yield such time delay information directly. As the output from the system is displaced in time relative to the input, the cross-correlation function will peak at that time displacement equal to the time required for the signal to pass through the system. This is true because the average product of two linearly related signals will always be a maximum when the time displacement between the signals is zero. Hence a system time delay can sometimes be established directly by noting the time displacement associated with an observed peak in the cross-correlogram between input and output. It should be mentioned that this technique often fails in practice because the transmission velocity and/or path through the system may be frequency-sensitive. In such cases, the cross-correlogram may not display a distinct peak. This problem can be analyzed by using cross-spectra information, to be discussed later.

Determination of Transmission Paths. The use of cross-correlation function measurements to establish time delays leads directly to another important application, the determination of transmission paths. Consider the case of a linear system where an input may follow two or more different paths to produce an observed output. Assume the specific path followed through the system is of interest. For example, the operation of heavy factory machinery will often induce undesirable noise and vibration in neighboring office areas, where the energy might be transferred in several ways through the building structures or acoustically through the air. Before the noise and vibration can be effectively controlled, it is necessary to establish the exact transmission path. Such problems can often be solved by cross-correlating the input and output for the system in question. Since each transmission path through the system will generally be associated with a different delay time, a separate peak will occur in the cross-correlogram for each path which contributes significantly to the output. If the expected time delays associated with the various possible paths can be calculated, these expected delays can then be compared to the measured time displacements of peaks in the cross-correlogram to identify the paths contributing significantly to the output.

Detection and Recovery of Signals in Noise.   A third application of cross-correlation function measurements is the detection and recovery of a signal buried in extraneous noise, where the signal is not necessarily of a periodic form. It has been noted in Section 1.3.3 that an autocorrelation function is useful for this application. However, if the signal which one desires to detect and recover is known, a cross-correlation provides a more powerful tool. For this case, the input consisting of the desired signal plus noise is cross-correlated with a stored version of the signal. As for the autocorrelation case, the result will be the extraction of a correlation function for the signal from the noise. Because the stored version of the signal is free from noise, the cross-correlation function will produce a greater output signal-to-noise ratio than will the autocorrelation function for any given input signal-to-noise ratio.

1.4.3   Cross-Spectral Density Functions

The concept of a cross-spectral density function for two sets of random data evolves directly from the cross-correlation function. As the power spectral density function for a single time history record is the Fourier transform of the autocorrelation function, so the cross-spectral density function for a pair of time history records is the Fourier transform of the cross-correlation function. Because a cross-correlation function is not an even function, the cross-spectral density function is generally a complex number such that

$$G_{xy}(f) = C_{xy}(f) - j\,Q_{xy}(f) \qquad (1.50)$$

where the real part, $C_{xy}(f)$, is called the *co-spectral* density function and the imaginary part, $Q_{xy}(f)$, is called the *quadrature* spectral density function.

In direct frequency terms, the co-spectral density function can be thought of as the average product of $x(t)$ and $y(t)$ within a narrow frequency interval between f and $f + \Delta f$, divided by the frequency interval. The quadrature spectral density is the same except that either $x(t)$ or $y(t)$, not both, is shifted in time sufficiently to produce a 90-degree phase shift at frequency f. That is,

$$C_{xy}(f) = \lim_{\Delta f \to 0} \lim_{T \to \infty} \frac{1}{(\Delta f)T} \int_0^T x(t, f, \Delta f)\, y(t, f, \Delta f)\, dt \qquad (1.51)$$

$$Q_{xy}(f) = \lim_{\Delta f \to 0} \lim_{T \to \infty} \frac{1}{(\Delta f)T} \int_0^T x(t, f, \Delta f)\, y^\circ(t, f, \Delta f)\, dt \qquad (1.52)$$

where $x(t, f, \Delta f)$ and $y(t, f, \Delta f)$ are filtered portions of $x(t)$ and $y(t)$, respectively, and $y^\circ(t, f, \Delta f)$ denotes a 90-degree phase shift from $y(t, f, \Delta f)$.

It is convenient to express the cross-spectral density function in complex polar notation such that

$$G_{xy}(f) = |G_{xy}(f)|\, e^{-j\theta_{xy}(f)} \qquad (1.53)$$

where the magnitude $|G_{xy}(f)|$ and the angle $\theta_{xy}(f)$ are related to $C_{xy}(f)$ and $Q_{xy}(f)$ by

$$|G_{xy}(f)| = \sqrt{C_{xy}^{\,2}(f) + Q_{xy}^{\,2}(f)} \qquad (1.54)$$

$$\theta_{xy}(f) = \tan^{-1}\left[\frac{Q_{xy}(f)}{C_{xy}(f)}\right] \qquad (1.55)$$

By interchanging $x(t)$ and $y(t)$, one finds that $C_{yx}(f) = C_{xy}(f)$ while $Q_{yx}(f) = -Q_{xy}(f)$. Hence the following relationships apply.

$$G_{yx}(f) = G_{xy}{}^*(f) \qquad (1.56)$$

$$G_{yx}(f) = G_{xy}(-f) \qquad (1.57)$$

where $G_{xy}{}^*(f)$ denotes the complex conjugate of $G_{xy}(f)$. Another useful relationship similar to Eq. (1.48) is

$$|G_{xy}(f)|^2 \leq G_x(f)\, G_y(f) \qquad (1.58)$$

It is convenient when applying cross-spectral density information to use a real-valued quantity given by

$$\gamma_{xy}^{2}(f) = \frac{|G_{xy}(f)|^2}{G_x(f)\, G_y(f)} \leq 1 \qquad (1.59)$$

where $\gamma_{xy}^{2}(f)$ is called the *coherence function*. When $\gamma_{xy}^{2}(f) = 0$ at a particular frequency, $x(t)$ and $y(t)$ are said to be incoherent at that frequency, which is simply another word for uncorrelated. If $x(t)$ and $y(t)$ are statistically independent, then $\gamma_{xy}^{2}(f) = 0$ for all frequencies. When $\gamma_{xy}^{2}(f) = 1$ for all f, then $x(t)$ and $y(t)$ are said to be fully coherent.

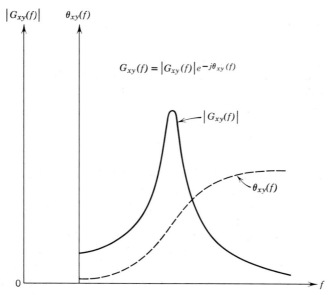

Figure 1.21   Typical cross-spectral density plot (cross-spectrum).

A typical plot of the cross-spectral density function versus frequency $[G_{xy}(f)$ versus $f]$ for a pair of random time history records is illustrated in Figure 1.21. This plot is called a *cross-spectrum*. Note that the plot consists of two parts which give a magnitude and phase.

Applications.   Cross-spectral density function measurements have many applications similar to cross-correlation function measurements. A few of these applications follow.

Measurement of Frequency Response Functions.   This fundamental application for a cross-spectral density function measurement evolves from an important relationship which it bears to the basic characteristics of the physical system involved. For example, consider an electrical circuit with a frequency response function of $H(f)$. Assume a stationary random signal with a power spectral density function of $G_x(f)$ is applied to the input of the electrical circuit. As noted in Section 1.3.4, the output from the electrical circuit will be a stationary random signal with a power spectrum given by Eq. (1.39). However, another important relationship exists. The cross-spectrum between input and output signals will be

$$G_{xy}(f) = H(f)\, G_x(f) \qquad (1.60)$$

The relationship in Eq. (1.60) permits the complete frequency response function for linear systems to be evaluated from cross-spectra measurements by the relationship $H(f) = G_{xy}(f)/G_x(f)$. Confidence statements about the accuracy of measuring $H(f)$ may be made by calculating the associated coherence function. These matters are developed in detail in Chapters 3 and 5.

Measurement of Time Delays. Another possible application for a cross-spectral density function measurement is the determination of time delays, considered in Section 1.4.2 as an application for cross-correlation function measurements. In this case, the phase angle $\theta_{xy}(f)$ of the cross-spectrum between the input and output for a system constitutes the phase shift through the system at frequency f. Hence the time delay through the system at any frequency f will be given by $\tau = \theta_{xy}(f)/2\pi f$. Note that the cross-spectral density function measurement permits the determination of time delays as a function of frequency, which is not available directly from a cross-correlation function measurement.￼

Linear Prediction and Filter Theory. Many applications for power spectral and cross-spectral density information occur in optimum linear prediction and filtering. It is necessary in these problems to determine an optimum linear filter according to some established criterion which will transmit and predict desired signal information while rejecting undesired noise information. The various power spectra and cross-spectra between input signals and noise, and output signals and noise, determine the optimum filter.

Consider the situation where one desires to obtain an estimate of the output $y(t)$ by a linear operation on the input $x(t)$. Suppose the measurement of $y(t)$ is distorted by extraneous noise $n(t)$ which is independent of $x(t)$. Then the optimum weighting function according to a mean square error criterion, if physical realizability is waived temporarily, has the form

$$H_{y|x}(f) = \frac{G_{xy}(f)}{G_x(f)} \qquad (1.61)$$

where the bar notation in $y \mid x$ indicates that $y(t)$ is determined, given $x(t)$. The minimum mean square error for the optimum system is

$$R_e(0) = \int_0^\infty G_y(f)[1 - \gamma_{xy}^2(f)] \, df \qquad (1.62)$$

where $\gamma_{xy}^2(f)$ is the coherence function between $x(t)$ and $y(t)$, as defined by Eq. (1.59). Observe that if the coherence function is unity for all frequencies, then $y(t)$ can be estimated by a linear operation on $x(t)$ with zero mean square error. The result in Eq. (1.62) indicates in practice how closely an actual system approximates the optimum system.

2

RESPONSE CHARACTERISTICS OF
PHYSICAL SYSTEMS

Before the measurement and analysis of random physical data is discussed in greater detail, it is desirable to clarify some pertinent concepts and fundamental definitions related to the dynamic behavior of physical systems. This chapter reviews the theoretical formulas for describing the response characteristics of ideal systems, and illustrates the basic ideas for simple physical examples.

An ideal system is one that has constant parameters and is linear between two clearly defined points of interest called the input or excitation point and the output or response point. A system has constant parameters if all fundamental properties of the system are invariant with respect to time. For example, a simple passive electrical circuit would be a constant parameter system if the values for the resistance, capacitance, and inductance of all elements did not change from one time to another. A system is linear if the response characteristics are additive and homogeneous. The term additive means that the output to a sum of inputs is equal to the sum of the outputs produced by each input individually. The term homogeneous means that the output produced by a constant times the input is equal to the constant times the output produced by the input alone.

The constant parameter assumption is reasonably valid for many physical systems of interest in practice. For example, the fundamental properties of an electrical circuit or a mechanical structure will usually not display significant changes over any time interval of practical interest. There are, of course, exceptions. The value of an electrical resistor may change owing to a high temperature exposure, or the stiffness of a structure may change due to fatigue damage caused by continual vibration. Furthermore, some physical systems are designed to have time-varying parameters which are fundamental to the desired purpose of the system. Electronic

36

communication systems are an obvious example. However, such conditions are generally special cases which can be clearly identified in actual practice.

A linearity assumption for real systems is somewhat more critical. All real physical systems will display nonlinear response characteristics under sufficiently extreme input conditions. For example, an electrical capacitor will ultimately arc as the applied voltage is increased and, hence, will no longer pass a current which is directly proportional to the applied voltage; or a metal cable will ultimately break as the applied load is increased and, hence, will no longer display a strain which is proportional to the applied load. To make the problem more difficult, common nonlinearities usually occur gradually rather than abruptly at one point. For example, the load-strain relationship for the metal cable would actually start deviating from a linear relationship long before the final abrupt break occurs. Nevertheless the response characteristics for many physical systems may be assumed to be linear, at least over some limited range of inputs without involving unreasonable errors.

The discussion in this chapter, except for Section 2.2, is limited to ideal constant parameter linear systems. Some interesting properties of time-varying systems as compared to constant parameter systems are discussed in Section 2.2. This basic material should form an adequate foundation for the developments in subsequent chapters.

2.1   Constant Parameter Linear Systems

The dynamic characteristics for a constant parameter linear system can be described by a *weighting function*, $h(\tau)$, which is defined as the output of the system at any time to a unit impulse input applied a time τ before. The usefulness of the weighting function as a description of the system is due to the following fact. For any arbitrary input $x(t)$, the system output $y(t)$ is given by the convolution integral

$$y(t) = \int_{-\infty}^{\infty} h(\tau)\, x(t - \tau)\, d\tau \qquad (2.1)$$

That is, the value of the output $y(t)$ is given as a weighted linear (infinite) sum over the entire history of the input $x(t)$.

In order for a constant parameter linear system to be *physically realizable*, it is necessary that the system respond only to past inputs. This implies that

$$h(\tau) = 0 \qquad \text{for } \tau < 0 \qquad (2.2)$$

Hence, for physical systems, the effective lower limit of integration in Eq. (2.1) is zero rather than minus infinity.

A constant parameter linear system is said to be *stable* if every possible bounded input function produces a bounded output function. From Eq. (2.1),

$$|y(t)| = \left| \int_{-\infty}^{\infty} h(\tau)\, x(t - \tau)\, d\tau \right| \leq \int_{-\infty}^{\infty} |h(\tau)|\, |x(t - \tau)|\, d\tau \qquad (2.3)$$

When the input $x(t)$ is bounded, there exists some finite constant A such that

$$|x(t)| \leq A \qquad \text{for all } t \qquad (2.4)$$

It follows from Eq. (2.3) that

$$|y(t)| \leq A \int_{-\infty}^{\infty} |h(\tau)|\, d\tau \qquad (2.5)$$

Hence if the constant parameter linear weighting function $h(\tau)$ is absolutely integrable, that is,

$$\int_{-\infty}^{\infty} |h(\tau)|\, d\tau < \infty \qquad (2.6)$$

then the output will be bounded and the system is stable. The condition in Eq. (2.6) is a sufficient condition for stability.

The condition in Eq. (2.6) is also a necessary condition for stability, as can be shown by the following contradiction. Suppose Eq. (2.6) is not satisfied. Let a particular bounded input $x(t)$ be of the following form.

$$x(t) = \begin{cases} 1 & \text{for those } t \text{ where } h(-t) \geq 0 \\ -1 & \text{for those } t \text{ where } h(-t) < 0 \end{cases}$$

Now, if the condition in Eq. (2.6) is violated, the output at $t = 0$ would be

$$y(0) = \int_{-\infty}^{\infty} h(\tau)\, x(-\tau)\, d\tau = \int_{-\infty}^{\infty} h(-\tau)\, x(\tau)\, d\tau$$

$$= \int_{-\infty}^{\infty} h(\tau)\, d\tau \to \infty$$

Hence a particular bounded input produces an unbounded output and the system is not stable.

A constant parameter linear system can also be characterized by a *transfer function* $H(p)$, which is defined as the Laplace transform of $h(\tau)$. That is,

$$H(p) = \int_{-\infty}^{\infty} h(\tau)\, e^{-p\tau}\, d\tau \qquad p = a + jb \qquad (2.7)$$

The criterion for stability of a constant parameter linear system (assumed to be physically realizable) takes on an interesting form when considered in terms of the transfer function $H(p)$. Specifically, if $H(p)$ has no poles in the right half of the complex p plane or on the imaginary axis (no poles where $a \geq 0$), then the system is stable. Conversely, if $H(p)$ has at least one pole in the right half of the complex p plane or on the imaginary axis, then the system is unstable.

2.2 Time-Varying Linear Systems

The dynamic properties of a time-varying linear system can be described by a *time-varying weighting function*, $h(\tau, t)$, which is defined as the output of the system at any time t to a unit impulse input at time $t - \tau$. As for constant parameter systems, for any arbitrary input $x(t)$, the time-varying system output $y(t)$ is given by the convolution integral

$$y(t) = \int_{-\infty}^{\infty} h(\tau, t) \, x(t - \tau) \, d\tau \qquad (2.8)$$

If the time-varying system is physically realizable and operates only for a finite time interval T where $0 \leq \tau \leq T$, then

$$y(t, T) = \int_{0}^{T} h(\tau, t) \, x(t - \tau) \, d\tau \qquad (2.9)$$

The conditions for physical realizability and stability for time-varying linear systems are the same as for constant parameter linear systems. That is, physical realizability requires that

$$h(\tau, t) = 0 \qquad \text{for } \tau < 0 \qquad (2.10)$$

and stability requires that

$$\int_{-\infty}^{\infty} |h(\tau, t)| \, d\tau < \infty \qquad (2.11)$$

Among the more interesting characteristics of time-varying linear systems are the bandwidth properties of such systems as compared to the bandwidth properties of constant parameter linear systems. To illustrate this point, consider a constant parameter linear system with a weighting function $h(\tau)$. From Eq. (2.1), for any arbitrary input $x(t)$, the nth derivative of the output $y(t)$ with respect to time is given by

$$\frac{d^n y(t)}{dt^n} = \int_{-\infty}^{\infty} h(\tau) \frac{d^n x(t - \tau)}{dt^n} \, d\tau \qquad (2.12)$$

Now, assume the input $x(t)$ is sinusoidal. That is,

$$x(t) = X \sin (2\pi ft + \phi) \qquad (2.13)$$

The second derivative of $x(t)$ is

$$\frac{d^2x(t)}{dt^2} = -4\pi^2 f^2 \, x(t) \tag{2.14}$$

It follows from Eq. (2.12) that the second derivative for the output $y(t)$ must be

$$\frac{d^2y(t)}{dt^2} = -4\pi^2 f^2 \, y(t) \tag{2.15}$$

Thus $y(t)$ must also be sinusoidal with the same frequency as $x(t)$. This result shows that a constant parameter linear system cannot cause any frequency translation but can only modify the amplitude and phase of an applied input.

Now consider a time-varying linear system with a weighting function $h(\tau, t)$. It no longer follows that a sinusoidal input will produce a sinusoidal output with the same frequency. The variable t in $h(\tau, t)$ causes frequency translation to occur in addition to amplitude and phase changes. For example, assume that $h(\tau, t)$ for a time-varying linear system is periodic in t with frequency f_1. Then, by expanding $h(\tau, t)$ into a Fourier series, one obtains

$$h(\tau, t) = h_0(\tau) + \sum_{n=1}^{\infty} h_n(\tau, t) \tag{2.16}$$

where $h_n(\tau, t)$ is sinusoidal in t with frequency nf_1. Now,

$$y(t) = y_0(t) + \sum_{n=1}^{\infty} y_n(t) \tag{2.17}$$

where

$$y_0(t) = \int_{-\infty}^{\infty} h_0(\tau) \, x(t - \tau) \, d\tau \tag{2.17a}$$

$$y_n(t) = \int_{-\infty}^{\infty} h_n(\tau, t) \, x(t - \tau) \, d\tau \tag{2.17b}$$

The quantity $h_0(\tau)$ represents a constant parameter weighting function, whereas $h_n(\tau, t)$ represents a time-varying weighting function of the form

$$h_n(\tau, t) = A_n(\tau) \cos \left[2\pi n f_1 t + \phi_n(\tau)\right] \tag{2.18}$$

Hence the output term in Eq. (2.17b) is given by

$$
\begin{aligned}
y_n(t) &= \int_{-\infty}^{\infty} A_n(\tau) \cos \left[2\pi n f_1 t + \phi_n(\tau)\right] x(t - \tau) \, d\tau \\
&= \cos 2\pi n f_1 t \int_{-\infty}^{\infty} A_n(\tau)[\cos \phi_n(\tau)] x(t - \tau) \, d\tau \\
&\quad - \sin 2\pi n f_1 t \int_{-\infty}^{\infty} A_n(\tau)[\sin \phi_n(\tau)] \, x(t - \tau) \, d\tau
\end{aligned}
\tag{2.19}
$$

Now suppose the input $x(t)$ in Eq. (2.19) is sinusoidal. For simplicity, let the amplitude be unity and the initial phase angle be zero such that

$$x(t) = \sin 2\pi f t \tag{2.20}$$

Substituting Eq. (2.20) into Eq. (2.19), and letting $B_n(\tau) = A_n(\tau) \cos \phi_n(\tau)$ and $C_n(\tau) = A_n(\tau) \sin \phi_n(\tau)$, the following result is obtained.

$$
\begin{aligned}
y_n(t) &= \cos 2\pi n f_1 t \int_{-\infty}^{\infty} B_n(\tau) \sin 2\pi f(t - \tau)\, d\tau \\
&\quad - \sin 2\pi n f_1 t \int_{-\infty}^{\infty} C_n(\tau) \sin 2\pi f(t - \tau)\, d\tau \\
&= [\sin 2\pi(nf_1 + f)t - \sin 2\pi(nf_1 - f)t] \int_{-\infty}^{\infty} \frac{B_n(\tau)}{2} \cos 2\pi f \tau\, d\tau \\
&\quad - [\cos 2\pi(nf_1 + f)t + \cos 2\pi(nf_1 - f)t] \int_{-\infty}^{\infty} \frac{B_n(\tau)}{2} \sin 2\pi f \tau\, d\tau \\
&\quad - [\cos 2\pi(nf_1 - f)t - \cos 2\pi(nf_1 + f)t] \int_{-\infty}^{\infty} \frac{C_n(\tau)}{2} \cos 2\pi f \tau\, d\tau \\
&\quad + [\sin 2\pi(nf_1 + f)t + \sin 2\pi(nf_1 - f)t] \int_{-\infty}^{\infty} \frac{C_n(\tau)}{2} \sin 2\pi f \tau\, d\tau
\end{aligned}
\tag{2.21}
$$

It is clear from Eq. (2.21) that the sinusoidal input will produce an output consisting of a collection of sinusoidal components with frequencies of $|nf_1 \pm f|$. This result illustrates the fact that a time-varying linear system will generally produce an output with a wider bandwidth than that of the input.

2.3 Frequency Response Functions

If a constant parameter linear system is physically realizable and stable, then the dynamic characteristics of the system can be described by a *frequency response function* $H(f)$, which is defined as the Fourier transform of $h(\tau)$. That is,

$$H(f) = \int_0^{\infty} h(\tau) e^{-j2\pi f \tau}\, d\tau \tag{2.22}$$

Note that the lower limit of integration is zero rather than minus infinity since $h(\tau) = 0$ for $\tau < 0$. The frequency response function is simply a special case of the transfer function where, in the exponent $p = a + jb$, $a = 0$ and $b = 2\pi f$. For physically realizable and stable systems, the frequency response function may replace the transfer function with no loss of useful information.

An important relationship for the frequency response function of constant parameter linear systems is obtained by taking the Fourier transform of both sides of Eq. (2.1). Letting $X(f)$ be the Fourier transform of an input $x(t)$ and $Y(f)$ be the Fourier transform of the resulting output $y(t)$, it follows from Eq. (2.1) that

$$Y(f) = H(f)\, X(f) \qquad (2.23)$$

Hence, in terms of the frequency response function for a system and the Fourier transforms for the input and output, the convolution integral in Eq. (2.1) reduces to the simple algebraic expression in Eq. (2.23).

The frequency response function is generally a complex valued quantity which may be conveniently thought of in terms of a magnitude and an associated phase angle. This can be done by writing $H(f)$ in complex polar notation as follows.

$$H(f) = |H(f)|\, e^{-j\phi(f)} \qquad (2.24)$$

The absolute value $|H(f)|$ is called the system *gain factor* and the associated phase angle $\phi(f)$ is called the system *phase factor*. In these terms, the frequency response function takes on a direct physical interpretation as follows. Assume a system is subjected to a sinusoidal input (hypothetically exciting over all time) with a frequency f producing an output which, as illustrated in Section 2.2, will also be sinusoidal with the same frequency. The ratio of the output amplitude to the input amplitude is equal to the gain factor $|H(f)|$ for the system, and the phase shift between the output and input is equal to the phase factor $\phi(f)$ for the system.

From physical realizability requirements, the frequency response function, the gain factor, and the phase factor for a constant parameter linear system satisfy the following symmetry properties.

$$H(-f) = H^*(f)$$
$$|H(-f)| = |H(f)| \qquad (2.25)$$
$$\phi(-f) = -\phi(f)$$

Furthermore, if one system described by $H_1(f)$ is followed by a second system described by $H_2(f)$, and there is no loading or feedback between the two systems, then the overall system may be described by $H(f)$ where

$$H(f) = H_1(f)\, H_2(f)$$
$$|H(f)| = |H_1(f)|\, |H_2(f)| \qquad (2.26)$$
$$\phi(f) = \phi_1(f) + \phi_2(f)$$

Thus, on cascading two systems where there is no loading or feedback, the gain factors multiply and the phase factors add.

It is important to note that the frequency response function $H(f)$ for a constant parameter linear system is a function of only frequency, and is not a function of either time or the system excitation. If the system were nonlinear, $H(f)$ would also be a function of the applied input. If the parameters of the system were not constant, $H(f)$ would also be a function of time. For time-varying linear systems described by $h(\tau, t)$, the corresponding frequency response function is denoted by $H(f, t)$ and is the Fourier transform of $h(\tau, t)$ with respect to τ, as in Eq. (2.22).

2.4 Illustrations of Frequency Response Functions

A clearer understanding of the frequency response function for common physical systems will be afforded by considering some simple examples. The examples chosen involve simple mechanical and electrical systems because these particular physical systems are generally easier to visualize. The analogous characteristics relating mechanical and electrical systems to other physical systems are noted.

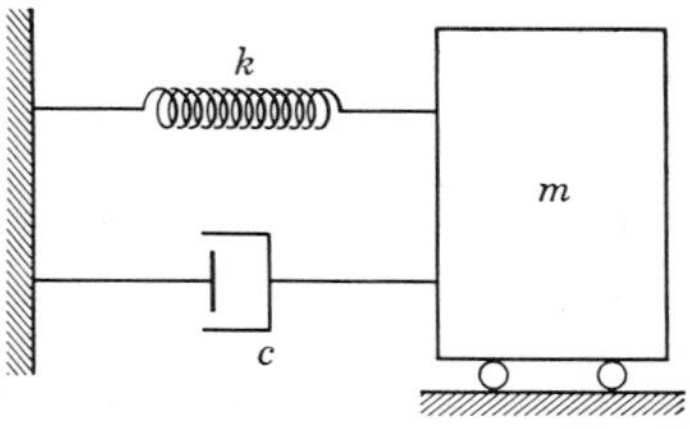

Figure 2.1 Simple mechanical system.

2.4.1 Mechanical Systems

Assume a simple mechanical structure can be represented by a lumped parameter system consisting of a mass, a spring, and a dashpot, where the motion of the mass is restricted to translation in only one direction as shown in Figure 2.1. In this figure, k is a spring constant in pounds/inch, c is a viscous damping coefficient in pound-seconds/inch, and m is a mass in pound-seconds^2/inch.

Before a frequency response function can be determined, it is necessary to define the input and output parameters of interest. There are a number of possibilities for the system in Figure 2.1, as will be illustrated now.

Force Input and Displacement Output. Assume the input of interest is a force applied to the mass, and the output of interest is the resulting displacement of the mass, as illustrated in Figure 2.2. Here, $F(t)$ is an applied force in pounds and $y(t)$ is the resulting output displacement of the mass in inches.

The first step toward establishing an appropriate frequency response function for this system is to determine the equation of motion. This is

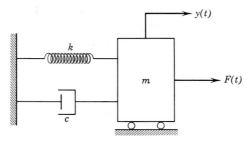

Figure 2.2   Mechanical system with force input.

accomplished by using the relationship from basic mechanics that the sum of all forces acting on the mass must equal zero, as follows.

$$F(t) + F_k(t) + F_c(t) + F_m(t) = 0 \tag{2.27}$$

where

$$F_k(t) = -k\,y(t) = \text{spring force} \tag{2.27a}$$

$$F_c(t) = -c\,\dot{y}(t) = \text{damping force} \tag{2.27b}$$

$$F_m(t) = -m\,\ddot{y}(t) = \text{inertial force} \tag{2.27c}$$

$$\dot{y}(t) = \frac{dy(t)}{dt} = \text{velocity}$$

$$\ddot{y}(t) = \frac{d^2 y(t)}{dt^2} = \text{acceleration}$$

Hence the equation of motion for this system is

$$m\,\ddot{y}(t) + c\,\dot{y}(t) + k\,y(t) = F(t) \tag{2.28}$$

In Section 2.3, the frequency response function is defined as the Fourier transform of the output of the system to a unit impulse. For this case, the output of the system is the displacement $y(t)$ whose Fourier transform is given by

$$Y(f) = \int_0^\infty y(t)e^{-j2\pi ft}\,dt = H(f) \tag{2.29}$$

It follows that

$$\dot{Y}(f) = j2\pi f\,H(f) \tag{2.29a}$$

$$\ddot{Y}(f) = -(2\pi f)^2\,H(f) \tag{2.29b}$$

Now, by taking the Fourier transform of both sides of Eq. (2.28), and noting that the Fourier transform for a unit impulse force $F(t) = \delta(t)$ is unity, the following result is obtained.

$$[-(2\pi f)^2 m + j2\pi fc + k]\,H(f) = 1 \tag{2.30}$$

Thus

$$H(f)_{f-d} = [k - (2\pi f)^2 m + j2\pi fc]^{-1} \tag{2.31}$$

where the subscript $f - d$ is added to indicate that this particular $H(f)$ relates a force input to a displacement output.

It is desirable to write Eq. (2.31) in a different form by introducing two definitions.

$$\zeta = \frac{c}{2\sqrt{km}} \tag{2.32a}$$

$$f_n = \frac{1}{2\pi} \sqrt{\frac{k}{m}} \tag{2.32b}$$

The term ζ in Eq. (2.32a) is a dimensionless quantity called the *damping ratio*. The term f_n in Eq. (2.32b) is called the *undamped natural frequency* and has the units of cycles per unit time. When these definitions are substituted into Eq. (2.31), the following result is obtained.

$$H(f)_{f-d} = \frac{1/k}{1 - (f/f_n)^2 + j2\zeta f/f_n} \tag{2.33}$$

Writing Eq. (2.33) in complex polar notation gives the frequency response function in terms of a gain factor $|H(f)|$ and a phase factor $\phi(f)$ as follows.

$$H(f) = |H(f)|\, e^{-j\phi(f)} \tag{2.34}$$

where
$$|H(f)|_{f-d} = \frac{1/k}{\sqrt{[1 - (f/f_n)^2]^2 + [2\zeta f/f_n]^2}} \tag{2.34a}$$

$$\phi(f)_{f-d} = \tan^{-1}\left[\frac{2\zeta f/f_n}{1 - (f/f_n)^2}\right] \tag{2.34b}$$

Note that $|H(f)|_{f-d}$ has units of $1/k$ or inches/pound. This particular function is sometimes called a *magnification function*.

Plots of $|H(f)|_{f-d}$ and $\phi(f)_{f-d}$ as defined in Eq. (2.34) are presented in Figure 2.3. Two characteristics of these plots are of particular interest. First, the gain factor has a peak at some frequency less than f_n for all cases where $\zeta \leq 1/\sqrt{2}$. The frequency at which this peak gain factor occurs is called the *resonant frequency* of the system. Specifically, it can be shown by minimizing the denominator of $|H(f)|_{f-d}$ in Eq. (2.34a) that the resonant frequency, denoted by f_r, is given by

$$f_r = f_n\sqrt{1 - 2\zeta^2} \qquad \zeta^2 \leq 0.5 \tag{2.35}$$

and that the peak value of the gain factor which occurs at the resonant frequency is given by

$$|H(f_r)|_{f-d} = \frac{1/k}{2\zeta\sqrt{1 - \zeta^2}} \qquad \zeta^2 < 0.5 \tag{2.36}$$

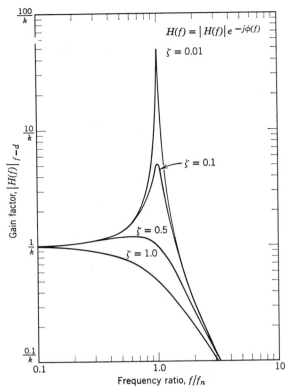

Figure 2.3 Frequency response function for mechanical system with force input.

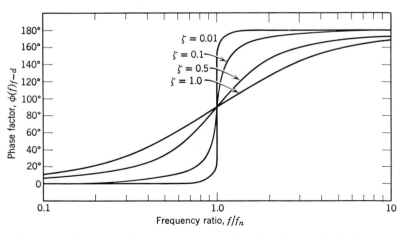

Figure 2.3 (*continued*) Frequency response function for mechanical system with force input.

Second, the phase factor varies from 0 degrees for frequencies much less than f_n to 180 degrees for frequencies much greater than f_n. The exact manner in which $\phi(f)$ varies between these phase angle limits depends upon the damping ratio ζ. However, for all values of ζ, the phase $\phi(f)_{f-d} = 90$ degrees for $f = f_n$.

Referring to Section 2.3, the frequency response function $H(f)_{f-d}$ may be interpreted as follows. Assume the applied force in Figure 2.2 is sinusoidal such that $F(t) = F_0 \sin 2\pi ft$. Then the output displacement would be given by

$$y(t) = F_0 \, |H(f)|_{f-d} \sin [2\pi ft - \phi(f)_{f-d}] \tag{2.37}$$

This particular interpretation actually provides another technique for determining the frequency response function. Specifically, one can solve for the output of a system to a sinusoidal input, and determine the frequency response function from the amplitude change and phase shift between the output and input. This will now be illustrated for the present problem.

The output of the system in Figure 2.2 to sinusoidal input will be given by the particular solution for Eq. (2.28) where $F(t)$ is sinusoidal, that is,

$$m \, \ddot{y}(t) + c \, \dot{y}(t) + k \, y(t) = F_0 \sin 2\pi ft = \text{Im} \, [F_0 \, e^{j2\pi ft}] \tag{2.38}$$

Im[ ] means the imaginary part of [ ]. Now, assume a solution to Eq. (2.38) in the general form of a sinusoidal output as follows.

$$y(t) = Y \sin (2\pi ft - \phi) = \text{Im} \, [Y \, e^{j(2\pi ft - \phi)}] \tag{2.39}$$

When Eq. (2.39) is substituted into Eq. (2.38), the following relationship is obtained.

$$\text{Im} \, [(-(2\pi f)^2 m + j2\pi fc + k)Y \, e^{j(2\pi ft - \phi)}] = \text{Im} \, [F_0 \, e^{j2\pi ft}] \tag{2.40}$$

The particular solution to Eq. (2.38) is given from Eqs. (2.39) and (2.40) as follows.

$$y(t) = \text{Im} \left[\frac{F_0 \, e^{j2\pi ft}}{k - (2\pi f)^2 m + j2\pi fc} \right] \tag{2.41}$$

Using the definitions from Eq. (2.32) and converting to a trigonometric form, the output $y(t)$ becomes

$$y(t) = \frac{F_0 \sin [2\pi ft - \phi(f)]}{k\sqrt{[1 - (f/f_n)^2]^2 + [2\zeta f/f_n]^2}} \tag{2.42}$$

where
$$\phi(f) = \tan^{-1} \left[\frac{2\zeta f/f_n}{1 - (f/f_n)^2} \right]$$

Hence the output is changed in amplitude by a factor equal to the gain factor defined in Eq. (2.34a), and shifted in phase by a factor equal to the phase factor defined in Eq. (2.34b).

Foundation Displacement Input and Displacement Output. Now consider a different case, where the input of interest is a motion of the foundation and the output of interest is the displacement of the mass, as illustrated in Figure 2.4. Here, $x(t)$ is an applied foundation displacement

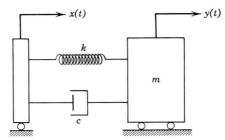

Figure 2.4   Mechanical system with foundation motion input.

in inches measured from a mean foundation position, and $y(t)$ is the resulting output displacement of the mass in inches measured from the position of equilibrium.

As before, the equation of motion for the system can be determined from basic principles as follows.

$$F_k(t) + F_c(t) + F_m(t) = 0 \qquad (2.43)$$

where

$$F_k(t) = -k[y(t) - x(t)] = \text{spring force} \qquad (2.43a)$$

$$F_c(t) = -c[\dot{y}(t) - \dot{x}(t)] = \text{damping force} \qquad (2.43b)$$

$$F_m(t) = -m\ddot{y}(t) \qquad = \text{inertial force} \qquad (2.43c)$$

Hence the equation of motion for this system is

$$m\,\ddot{y}(t) + c\,\dot{y}(t) + k\,y(t) = k\,x(t) + c\,\dot{x}(t) \qquad (2.44)$$

Once again the frequency response function for the system will be given by the Fourier transform of the response displacement $y(t)$ for a unit impulse foundation displacement $x(t) = \delta(t)$. By taking the Fourier transform of both sides of Eq. (2.44), and noting that $\dot{X}(f) = j2\pi f$, the following result is obtained.

$$[(-2\pi f)^2 m + j2\pi f c + k]\,Y(f) = [k + j2\pi f c] \qquad (2.45)$$

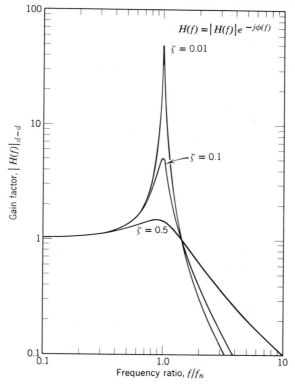

Figure 2.5 Frequency response function for mechanical system with foundation motion input.

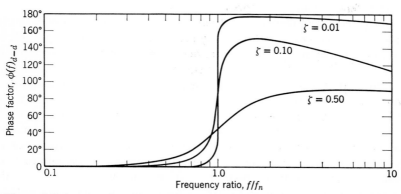

Figure 2.5 (*continued*) Frequency response function for mechanical system with foundation motion input.

Thus

$$Y(f) = H(f)_{d-d} = \frac{k + j2\pi fc}{k - (2\pi f)^2 m + j2\pi fc} \tag{2.46}$$

where the subscript $d - d$ means that this particular $H(f)$ relates a displacement input to a displacement output.

Using the definitions from Eq. (2.32), the result in Eq. (2.46) may be written as

$$H(f)_{d-d} = \frac{1 + j2\zeta f/f_n}{1 - (f/f_n)^2 + j2\zeta f/f_n} \tag{2.47}$$

In complex polar notation, Eq. (2.47) reduces to the following gain factor and phase factor

$$H(f) = |H(f)|\, e^{-j\phi(f)} \tag{2.48}$$

where

$$|H(f)|_{d-d} = \left(\frac{1 + [2\zeta f/f_n]^2}{[1 - (f/f_n)^2]^2 + [2\zeta f/f_n]^2} \right)^{1/2} \tag{2.48a}$$

$$\phi(f)_{d-d} = \tan^{-1} \left[\frac{2\zeta(f/f_n)^3}{1 - (f/f_n)^2 + 4\zeta^2(f/f_n)^2} \right] \tag{2.48b}$$

Note that $H(f)_{d-d}$ is dimensionless. This particular function is often called a *transmissibility function*. Plots of $|H(f)|_{d-d}$ and $\phi(f)_{d-d}$ are presented in Figure 2.5.

From Figure 2.5, it is seen that the gain factor displays a single peak similar to the example for a force input illustrated in Figure 2.3. However, the details of the gain factor as well as the phase factor in Figure 2.5 are quite different from the factors in Figure 2.3.

Other Input and Output Combinations.   The previous two examples indicate how two different frequency response functions are applicable to the same simple mechanical system, depending upon the type of input to be considered. Actually, a different frequency response function is generally required for every different combination of input and output parameters which might be desired. For example, the relative output of the system $z(t) = y(t) - x(t)$ to a foundation motion input might be of interest for some applications. Perhaps it is desired to interpret motion inputs and/or outputs in terms of velocities or accelerations rather than displacements. A slightly different frequency response function would be required for each case. To illustrate this point, the various possible gain factors for the simple mechanical system in Figure 2.1 for twenty-one different combinations of input and output parameters are presented in Table 2.1.

Table 2.1   Summary of Gain Factors for Simple Mechanical System

Values for the Gain Factor $|H(f)|$ of a Simple Mechanical System as a Function of the Input and Output Parameters		Foundation Motion Input (see Fig. 2.4 for model)			Force Input (see Fig. 2.2 for model) Force (in displacement units)
		Displacement $x(t)$ in.	Velocity $\dot{x}(t)$ in./sec	Acceleration $\ddot{x}(t)$ in./sec.^{2}	$x(t) = F(t)/k$ in.
In terms of displacement output, in.	Absolute displacement $y(t)$	$\dfrac{D_1}{D_2}$	$\dfrac{D_1}{2\pi f D_2}$	$\dfrac{D_1}{4\pi^2 f^2 D_2}$	$\dfrac{1}{D_2}$
	Relative displacement $z(t) = y(t) - x(t)$	$\dfrac{f^2}{f_n{}^2 D_2}$	$\dfrac{f}{2\pi f_n{}^2 D_2}$	$\dfrac{1}{4\pi^2 f_n{}^2 D_2}$	
In terms of velocity output, in./sec.	Absolute velocity $\dot{y}(t)$	$\dfrac{2\pi f D_1}{D_2}$	$\dfrac{D_1}{D_2}$	$\dfrac{D_1}{2\pi f D_2}$	$\dfrac{2\pi f}{D_2}$
	Relative velocity $\dot{z}(t) = \dot{y}(t) - \dot{x}(t)$	$\dfrac{2\pi f^3}{f_n{}^2 D_2}$	$\dfrac{f^2}{f_n{}^2 D_2}$	$\dfrac{f}{2\pi f_n{}^2 D_2}$	
In terms of acceleration output, in./sec.^{2}.	Absolute acceleration $\ddot{y}(t)$	$\dfrac{4\pi^2 f^2 D_1}{D_2}$	$\dfrac{2\pi f D_1}{D_2}$	$\dfrac{D_1}{D_2}$	$\dfrac{4\pi^2 f^2}{D_2}$
	Relative acceleration $\ddot{z}(t) = \ddot{y}(t) - \ddot{x}(t)$	$\dfrac{4\pi^2 f^4}{f_n{}^2 D_2}$	$\dfrac{2\pi f^3}{f_n{}^2 D_2}$	$\dfrac{f^2}{f_n{}^2 D_2}$	

$$D_1 = \sqrt{1 + [2\zeta(f/f_n)]^2} \qquad\qquad D_2 = \sqrt{[1 - (f/f_n)^2]^2 + [2\zeta(f/f_n)]^2}$$

$$f_n = \frac{1}{2\pi}\sqrt{\frac{k}{m}} \qquad\qquad\qquad \zeta = \frac{c}{2\sqrt{km}}$$

2.4.2   Electrical Systems

Assume a simple electrical circuit can be represented by a lumped parameter system consisting of an inductor, a resistor, and a capacitor. Further assume that the input to the system is a potential difference as shown in Figure 2.6. In this figure, C is a capacitance in farads, R is a resistance in ohms, L is an inductance in henries, $e(t)$ is an applied potential in volts, and $i(t)$ is the resulting current in amperes. Note that $i(t) = dq(t)/dt$ where $q(t)$ is charge in coulombs.

Assume the input of interest is an applied voltage and the output of interest is the resulting charge. As for the case of mechanical systems in Section 2.4.1, the first step toward establishing a proper frequency response function is to determine the differential equation describing the

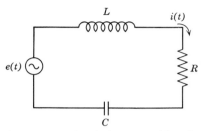

Figure 2.6 Electrical system with voltage input.

system. From basic circuit theory, the sum of all potential differences across the circuit elements must equal zero. That is,

$$e(t) + e_C(t) + e_R(t) + e_L(t) = 0 \qquad (2.49)$$

where $e_C(t) = -\dfrac{1}{C}q(t) = $ potential difference across capacitor $\qquad$ (2.49a)

$$e_R(t) = -R\dot{q}(t) = \text{potential difference across resistor} \qquad (2.49b)$$

$$e_L(t) = -L\ddot{q}(t) = \text{potential difference across inductor} \qquad (2.49c)$$

Hence the differential equation for this system is

$$L\ddot{q}(t) + R\dot{q}(t) + \frac{1}{C}q(t) = e(t) \qquad (2.50)$$

Note the similarity between Eq. (2.50) and the equation of motion for a force excited mechanical system given by Eq. (2.28). Using the same analysis procedures outlined in Section 2.4.1, it follows directly that the frequency response function for this simple electrical system is

$$H(f)_{e-q} = \left[\frac{1}{C} - (2\pi f)^2 L + j2\pi f R\right]^{-1} \qquad (2.51)$$

where the subscript $e - q$ means that this particular $H(f)$ relates a voltage input to a charge output. Note that $H(f)_{e-q}$ has the units of coulombs/volt.

The plot for $H(f)_{e-q}$ would be identical to the plot for the mechanical frequency response function $H(f)_{f-d}$ presented in Figure 2.3, where the damping ratio ζ and the undamped natural frequency f_n for the electrical circuit are given as follows.

$$\zeta = \frac{R}{2}\sqrt{\frac{C}{L}} \qquad (2.52a)$$

$$f_n = \frac{1}{2\pi}\sqrt{\frac{1}{LC}} \qquad (2.52b)$$

It should now be clear that a direct analogy may be made between mechanical and electrical systems as presented in Table 2.2.

Table 2.2   Analogous Terms for Mechanical and Electrical Systems

	Electrical System with a Voltage Input	Mechanical System with a Force Input
Input	Voltage, $e(t)$	Force, $F(t)$
Output	Charge, $q(t)$ Current, $i(t) = dq/dt$	Displacement, $y(t)$ Velocity, $v(t) = dy/dt$
Constant parameters	Inductance, L Resistance, R Capacitance, C	Mass, m Damping, c Compliance, $1/k$

A more common frequency response function for electrical systems is one which relates a voltage input to a current output. This particular frequency response function is given by

$$H(f)_{e-i} = \left[R + j\left(2\pi f L - \frac{1}{2\pi f C} \right) \right]^{-1} \qquad (2.53)$$

where $H(f)_{e-i}$ has the units of amperes/volt. The reciprocal of Eq. (2.53), which may be denoted by $H(f)_{i-e}$, is called an *impedance function*.

$$H(f)_{i-e} = R + j\left(2\pi f L - \frac{1}{2\pi f C} \right) \qquad (2.54)$$

Note that the mechanical analogy to Eq. (2.54) is given from Table 2.2 by $H(f)_{v-f}$ as follows.

$$H(f)_{v-f} = c + j\left(2\pi f m - \frac{k}{2\pi f} \right) \qquad (2.55)$$

The function in Eq. (2.55) is often called a mechanical impedance function because of its analogy to the common electrical impedance function.

2.4.3   Other Systems

By the same analytical procedures outlined in Section 2.4.1, an appropriate frequency response function can be developed, at least in theory, for any clearly defined stable physical system (that is, any system whose dynamic behavior can be described by an explicit equation). Moreover, the frequency response functions for different physical systems will often display analogous parameters, just as illustrated for mechanical and electrical systems in Section 2.4.2. A summary of analogous characteristics for several common physical systems is presented in Table 2.3.

Table 2.3   Analogous Characteristics for Several Physical Systems

System	Input	Output	Constant Parameters		
Electrical	Voltage	Current	Inductance	Resistance	Capacitance
Mechanical (translational)	Force	Velocity	Mass	Damping	Compliance
Mechanical (rotational)	Torque	Angular velocity	Moment of inertia	Angular damping	Angular compliance
Acoustical	Pressure	Particle velocity	Inertance (acoustical mass)	Acoustical damping	Acoustical capacitance
Thermo	Temperature	Heat flow	—	Thermo resistance	Thermo capacitance
Magnetic	Magneto-motive force	Flux	—	Reluctance	—

2.5   Practical Considerations

The analytical determination of frequency response functions for physical systems has been illustrated in Section 2.4. To facilitate the development and clarification of basic ideas, examples were limited to simple mechanical and electrical systems. It should not be implied from these examples that the analytical determination of frequency response functions for actual physical systems is always so easy. In fact, such determinations in practice are often difficult and sometimes not even feasible.

Consider, for example, an actual mechanical system in the form of a continuous elastic structure where the various parameters (mass, damping, and stiffness) are distributed rather than lumped as hypothetically assumed for the examples in Section 2.4.1. Such a mechanical system would have many different possible input and output points which might be of interest. Furthermore, the frequency response function for each input-output combination would generally display many peaks representing many resonant frequencies, as opposed to a single resonance as illustrated for the examples in Section 2.4.1. For relatively uncomplicated continuous structures such as uniform beams and plates, appropriate frequency response functions may still be established with reasonable accuracy by direct analytical procedures. For more complicated structures, however, considerable effort may be required to obtain only rough approximations for desired frequency response functions.

Physiological systems present even more difficult problems. For example, consider the system represented by the human brain where the input of interest is some psychological stimulus and the output of interest is an electroencephalogram. The determination of an appropriate frequency response function for this system by direct analytical procedures is not possible because a definition of the detailed mechanics for the system in question (the brain) is presently beyond the state of the art.

Because of these problems, frequency response functions for actual physical systems are usually determined, or at least confirmed, by empirical procedures. The most straightforward empirical approach is to subject the system to a sinusoidal input, and measure the output amplitude and phase as the input frequency is varied. From Section 2.3, the ratio of the output to input amplitudes at any given frequency equals the gain factor, and the phase of the output relative to the input at any given frequency equals the phase factor.

Unfortunately, situations occur where it is not convenient and/or practical to contrive a sinusoidal version of the input of interest. For example, how would one create a sinusoidal state for some physiological or psychological stimulus which constitutes an input for a physiological system of interest? Even for these cases, however, it may often be possible to establish frequency response functions by analysis of outputs to transient and random inputs. These matters are developed in detail in Chapter 3 and elsewhere.

3

MATHEMATICAL THEORY FOR
ANALYZING RANDOM DATA

This chapter is an exposition of basic mathematical ideas for analyzing random data, which extends the treatment in Chapter 1. Elementary and advanced concepts from random process theory are developed from first principles to form a proper foundation for the application of these ideas to analysis problems. Most of the results stated in this chapter are applicable only to stationary data. Special techniques for analyzing properties of nonstationary data are developed in Chapter 9.

3.1 Probability Fundamentals for Random Variables

3.1.1 Sets and Set Functions

The underlying concept in probability theory is that of a *set*, defined as a collection of objects (also called points or elements) about which it is possible to determine whether any particular object is a member of the set. In particular, the possible outcomes of an experiment (or a measurement) represent a set of *points* called the *sample space*. These points may be grouped together in various ways, called *events*, and under suitable conditions *probability functions* may be assigned to each. These probabilities always lie between zero and one, the probability of an impossible event being zero and the probability of the certain event being one. Sample spaces are either finite or infinite.

To provide a foundation for probability functions defined on sets, a very brief summary is given of basic set operations and definitions. This background will be assumed whenever required in later material dealing with random variables and will not be considered further. Basic set operations follow:

The *union* of two sets A and B is the set of points which belong to A or to B or to both, and is denoted by

$$A \cup B \quad \text{or} \quad A + B$$

The *intersection* of two sets A and B is the set of points which belong both to A and to B, and is denoted by

$$A \cap B \quad \text{or} \quad A \cdot B$$

The set A is said to be a *subset* of the set B, denoted by

$$A \subseteq B$$

if every point belonging to A also belongs to B. Two sets A and B are *equal*, denoted by

$$A = B$$

if and only if $A \subseteq B$ and $B \subseteq A$. If one assumes that $B \subseteq A$, then the *difference* set

$$A - B$$

consists of points in A which are not in B.

The *complement* of a set A, denoted by A_c, is the difference set

$$A_c = S - A$$

where S is the whole *universal set* or *sample space* of all possible points under consideration. The *null* set ϕ is the set containing no points, and is the complement of the universal set S, namely

$$\phi = S - S$$

Two sets A and B are said to be *disjoint* if their intersection is the null set, written

$$A \cap B = \phi$$

An *infinite sum* of sets A_n, $n = 1, 2, 3, \ldots$, denoted by

$$\bigcup_{n=1}^{\infty} A_n \quad \text{or} \quad \sum_{n=1}^{\infty} A_n$$

is the set containing points which lie in *any* one of the sets A_n. An *infinite product* of sets A_n, $n = 1, 2, 3, \ldots$, denoted by

$$\bigcap_{n=1}^{\infty} A_n \quad \text{or} \quad \prod_{n=1}^{\infty} A_n$$

is the set containing points which lie in *every* one of the sets A_n.

A class of subsets $\{A\}$ from a sample space S is said to be a *completely additive class of sets*, denoted by the symbol E, if the following properties hold:

1. The null set ϕ belongs to E.
2. A in E implies $A_c = S - A$ in E.
3. A_n in E implies $\bigcup_n A_n$ in E (n may be finite or countable).

It follows that a completely additive class E of subsets $\{A\}$ from a sample space S is *closed* under finite or countable operations of sums, products, and complements. The term "closed" means that new sets formed out of sets of E under the above operations still belong to E.

A *set function* $f(A)$ is a real-valued function which associates a real number with a set A. The function $f(A)$ is a set function on an arbitrary class of subsets $\{A\}$ from a sample space S if $f(A)$ assigns a real number to every subset A in $\{A\}$. The term events may be used for subsets.

3.1.2 Probability Functions

Now consider a completely additive class of subsets $\{A\}$ in S, denoted by the symbol E. A set function $P(A)$ defined for all A in E is said to be a *probability function* if the following properties hold.

1. $P(A) \geq 0$ for all A in E.
2. $P(\phi) = 0$ and $P(S) = 1$.
3. If A_n is any finite or countable collection of mutually disjoint events in E, then

$$P\left(\bigcup_n A_n\right) = \sum_n P(A_n)$$

For situations where two events A and B may have overlapping points, the probability of their union event $(A \cup B)$ is given by

$$P(A \cup B) = P(A) + P(B) - P(A \cap B)$$

When A and B are disjoint, called *mutually exclusive*, so that $A \cap B = \phi$,

$$P(A \cup B) = P(A) + P(B)$$

For situations where $P(A) \neq 0$ and $P(B) \neq 0$,

$$P(A \mid B) = \frac{P(A \cap B)}{P(B)} \qquad P(B \mid A) = \frac{P(A \cap B)}{P(A)}$$

where $P(A \mid B)$ is defined as the *conditional probability* of A given that B has occurred. Similarly, $P(B \mid A)$ is defined as the conditional probability of B given that A has occurred. Two events A and B are said to be (*statistically*) *independent* if

$$P(A \cap B) = P(A)P(B)$$

It follows here that

$$P(A \mid B) = P(A) \quad \text{and} \quad P(B \mid A) = P(B)$$

3.1.3 One Random Variable

Consider a sample space of points representing the possible outcomes of a particular experiment (or measurement). A *random variable* $x(k)$ is a set function defined for points k from the sample space; that is, a random variable $x(k)$ is a real number between $-\infty$ and $+\infty$ which is associated to each sample point k that might occur. Stated another way, the random outcome of an experiment, indexed by k, can be represented by a real number $x(k)$, called the random variable. All possible experimental events which might occur constitute a completely additive class of sets, and a probability measure may be assigned to each event.

Let $x(k)$ denote a certain random variable. Then for any fixed number x, the random event $x(k) \leq x$ is defined as the set of possible outcomes k such that $x(k) \leq x$. In terms of the underlying probability measure in the sample space, one may define a (first-order) *cumulative probability distribution function $P(x)$* as the probability which is assigned to the set of points k satisfying the desired inequality $x(k) \leq x$. Observe that the set of points k satisfying $x(k) \leq x$ is a subset of the totality of all points k which satisfy $x(k) \leq \infty$. In notation form,

$$P(x) = \text{Prob } [x(k) \leq x] \qquad (3.1)$$

Clearly,

$$P(a) \leq P(b) \qquad \text{if } a \leq b \qquad (3.2)$$

$$P(-\infty) = 0 \qquad P(\infty) = 1 \qquad (3.3)$$

If the random variable assumes a continuous range of values (which will be assumed hereafter), then a (first-order) *probability density function $p(x)$* may be defined by the differential relation

$$p(x)\, dx = \text{Prob } [x < x(k) \leq x + dx] \qquad (3.4)$$

Note that

$$p(x) \geq 0 \qquad (3.5)$$

$$\int_{-\infty}^{\infty} p(x)\, dx = 1 \qquad (3.6)$$

$$P(x) = \int_{-\infty}^{x} p(\xi)\, d\xi \qquad \frac{dP(x)}{dx} = p(x) \qquad (3.7)$$

To handle discrete cases like Example 3.1, the probability density function $p(x)$ is permitted to include delta functions. Plots of first-order probability density functions are shown in Figure 1.13.

***Example* 3.1. Discrete Distribution.** Suppose an experiment consists of tossing a single coin where the two possible outcomes, called heads and tails, are assumed to occur with equal probability ($\frac{1}{2}$). The random variable $x(k)$ for this example takes on only two discrete values, x (heads) and x (tails), to which arbitrary real numbers may be assigned. Specifically, let x (heads) $= a$ and x (tails) $= b$ where a and b are real numbers with, say $b > a$. With these choices for $x(k)$, it follows that the probability distribution function

$$P(x) = \begin{cases} 0 & x < a \\ \frac{1}{2} & a \leq x < b \\ 1 & x \geq b \end{cases}$$

The discrete probability density function is given by

$$p(x) = \tfrac{1}{2}\delta(x - a) + \tfrac{1}{2}\delta(x - b)$$

where $\delta(x - a)$ and $\delta(x - b)$ are delta functions.

***Example* 3.2. Uniform (Rectangular) Distribution.** Suppose an experiment consists of choosing a point at random in the interval $[a, b]$, including the end points. A continuous random variable $x(k)$ for this example may be defined by the numerical value of the chosen point. The corresponding probability distribution function becomes

$$P(x) = \begin{cases} 0 & x < a \\ \dfrac{x - a}{b - a} & a \leq x \leq b \\ 1 & x > b \end{cases}$$

The uniform (rectangular) probability density function is given by

$$\begin{aligned} p(x) &= (b - a)^{-1} & a \leq x \leq b \\ &= 0 & \text{otherwise} \end{aligned}$$

This concludes Example 3.2.

The random variable $x(k)$ may take on values in the range $-\infty$ to $+\infty$. The *mean value* (also called *expected value* or *average value*) of $x(k)$ is obtained by an appropriate limiting operation when each value assumed by $x(k)$ is multiplied by its probability of occurrence. This gives

$$E[x(k)] = \int_{-\infty}^{\infty} x\, p(x)\, dx = \mu_x \tag{3.8}$$

where $E[\ ]$ represents the expected value over the index k of the term inside the brackets. Similarly, the expected value of any real single-valued continuous function $g(x)$ of the random variable $x(k)$ is given by

$$E[g(x(k))] = \int_{-\infty}^{\infty} g(x)\, p(x)\, dx \tag{3.9}$$

where $p(x)$ is the probability density function associated with $x(k)$. In particular, for $g(x) = x^2$, the *mean square value* of $x(k)$ is given by

$$E[x^2(k)] = \int_{-\infty}^{\infty} x^2\, p(x)\, dx = \Psi_x^{\,2} \tag{3.10}$$

The *variance* of $x(k)$ is defined by the mean square value of $x(k)$ about its mean value. Here, $g(x) = (x - \mu_x)^2$, and

$$E[(x(k) - \mu_x)^2] = \int_{-\infty}^{\infty} (x - \mu_x)^2 p(x)\, dx = \Psi_x^2 - \mu_x^2 = \sigma_x^2 \qquad (3.11)$$

By definition, the *standard deviation* of $x(k)$, denoted by σ_x, is the positive square root of the variance. The standard deviation is measured in the same units as the mean value.

Suppose that $x(k)$ is a random variable with probability density function $p(x)$, and that $g(x)$ is any real single-valued continuous function of x. The probability density function $p(g)$ associated with the random variable $g(x(k)) = g(k)$ may now be determined for cases where the derivative dg/dx exists and is not equal to zero. To allow for multivalued inverse functions, assume that the inverse function $x(g)$ is a real n-valued function of g, where n is an integer. For these cases,

$$p(g)\, dg = \text{Prob } [g < g(x(k)) \le g + dg]$$
$$= n\, \text{Prob } [x < x(k) \le x + dx] = n\, p(x)\, dx \qquad (3.12)$$

Hence when $dg/dx \ne 0$,

$$p(g) = n\, p(x) \left| \frac{dx}{dg} \right| = \frac{n\, p(x)}{|dg/dx|} \qquad (3.13)$$

When using this formula, it is necessary to replace the variable x on the right-hand side by its equivalent g.

Example 3.3. Sine Wave Distribution.   A sine wave of fixed amplitude X and fixed frequency f_0 may be considered to be a random variable if its initial phase angle $\theta = \theta(k)$ is a random variable. In particular, consider t to be fixed at some value t_0, and let the sine wave random variable be represented by

$$x(k) = x(\theta) = X \sin [2\pi f_0 t_0 + \theta(k)]$$

Suppose that $\theta(k)$ has a uniform probability density function $p(\theta)$ given by

$$p(\theta) = (2\pi)^{-1} \qquad 0 \le \theta \le 2\pi$$
$$= 0 \qquad \qquad \text{otherwise}$$

What is the sine wave probability density function $p(x)$ for $x(k)$?

For this example, the direct function $x(\theta)$ is single-valued, but the inverse function $\theta(x)$ is double-valued. From Eq. (3.13), with θ replacing x, and x replacing g,

$$p(x) = \frac{2p(\theta)}{dx/d\theta} \qquad \text{for } \frac{dx}{d\theta} \ne 0$$

where

$$\frac{dx}{d\theta} = X \cos(2\pi f_0 t_0 + \theta) = X\sqrt{1 - \sin^2(2\pi f_0 t_0 + \theta)} = \sqrt{X^2 - x^2}$$

Thus
$$p(x) = (\pi\sqrt{X^2 - x^2})^{-1} \qquad |x| < X$$
$$= 0 \qquad\qquad\qquad |x| \geq X \qquad (3.14a)$$

which is the same as Eq. (1.24). The corresponding sine wave probability distribution function is given by

$$P(x) = 0 \qquad\qquad\qquad\qquad\qquad x < -X$$
$$= \int_{-X}^{x} p(\xi)\, d\xi = \frac{1}{\pi}\left(\frac{\pi}{2} + \sin^{-1}\frac{x}{X}\right) \qquad -X \leq x \leq X \quad (3.14b)$$
$$= 1 \qquad\qquad\qquad\qquad\qquad x > X$$

***Example* 3.4. Tchebycheff Inequality for Unknown Distribution.**
Suppose that $x(k)$ is an arbitrary random variable with mean value μ_x, mean square value Ψ_x^2 and variance σ_x^2. Suppose that its first-order probability density function, which may be unknown, is $p(x)$. Then

$$\Psi_x^2 = \int_{-\infty}^{\infty} x^2 p(x)\, dx \geq \int_{|x| \geq \epsilon} x^2 p(x)\, dx \geq \epsilon^2 \int_{|x| \geq \epsilon} p(x)\, dx$$

since the integrand is non-negative, and since $x^2 \geq \epsilon^2$ at every point in the right-hand region of integration. This proves

$$\text{Prob}\,[|x(k)| > \epsilon] = \int_{|x| \geq \epsilon} p(x)\, dx \leq \frac{\Psi_x^2}{\epsilon^2} \qquad (3.15)$$

Replace now $x(k)$ by $x(k) - \mu_x$. Then Ψ_x^2 is replaced by σ_x^2, and Eq. (3.15) becomes

$$\text{Prob}\,[|x(k) - \mu_x| \geq \epsilon] \leq \frac{\sigma_x^2}{\epsilon^2} \qquad (3.15a)$$

In particular, if $\epsilon = c\sigma_x$, then

$$\text{Prob}\,[|x(k) - \mu_x| \geq c\sigma_x] \leq \frac{1}{c^2} \qquad (3.15b)$$

which is equivalent to

$$\text{Prob}\,[|x(k) - \mu_x| \leq c\sigma_x] \geq 1 - \frac{1}{c^2} \qquad (3.15c)$$

Any of the forms of Eq. (3.15) are known as the *Tchebycheff inequality*.

3.1.4   Two Random Variables

Consider next two random variables $x(k)$ and $y(k)$ where k represents points in a suitable sample space. Let $P(x)$ and $P(y)$ be two distinct distribution functions associated with $x(k)$ and $y(k)$, respectively. The *joint* (*second-order*) *cumulative distribution function* $P(x, y)$ is defined to be the probability which is associated with the subset of points k in the sample space satisfying simultaneously both of the inequalities $x(k) \leq x$ and $y(k) \leq y$. The totality of all points k satisfies the inequalities $x(k) \leq \infty$ and $y(k) \leq \infty$. In notation form,

$$P(x, y) = \text{Prob } [x(k) \leq x \quad \text{and} \quad y(k) \leq y] \tag{3.16}$$

Clearly,

$$P(-\infty, y) = 0 = P(x, -\infty) \qquad P(\infty, \infty) = 1 \tag{3.17}$$

As before, assuming the random variables to be continuous, the joint (cumulative) probability distribution function $P(x, y)$ should not be confused with the *joint* (*second-order*) *probability density function* $p(x, y)$ which is defined by the differential relation

$$p(x, y) \, dx \, dy = \text{Prob } [x < x(k) \leq x + dx \quad \text{and} \quad y < y(k) \leq y + dy] \tag{3.18}$$

Note that

$$p(x, y) \geq 0 \tag{3.19}$$

$$\iint\limits_{-\infty}^{\infty} p(x, y) \, dx \, dy = 1 \tag{3.20}$$

$$P(x, y) = \int_{-\infty}^{y} \int_{-\infty}^{x} p(\xi, \eta) \, d\xi \, d\eta \qquad \frac{\partial}{\partial y}\left[\frac{\partial P(x, y)}{\partial x}\right] = p(x, y) \tag{3.21}$$

The first-order probability density functions are given by

$$p(x) = \int_{-\infty}^{\infty} p(x, y) \, dy$$

$$p(y) = \int_{-\infty}^{\infty} p(x, y) \, dx \tag{3.22}$$

An example of a joint probability density function is given in Figure 1.18.

Two random variables $x(k)$ and $y(k)$ are said to be (*statistically*) *independent* if

$$P(x, y) = P(x) \, P(y) \tag{3.23}$$

It follows that

$$p(x, y) = p(x) \, p(y) \tag{3.24}$$

The *expected value* of any real single-valued continuous function $g(x, y)$ of the two random variables $x(k)$ and $y(k)$ is given by

$$E[g(x, y)] = \int\!\!\int_{-\infty}^{\infty} g(x, y)p(x, y) \, dx \, dy \qquad (3.25)$$

For example, if $g(x, y) = (x(k) - \mu_x)(y(k) - \mu_y)$ where μ_x and μ_y are the mean values of $x(k)$ and $y(k)$, respectively, this defines the *covariance* C_{xy} between $x(k)$ and $y(k)$. That is,

$$C_{xy} = E[(x(k) - \mu_x)(y(k) - \mu_y)] = E[x(k)y(k)] - E[x(k)]E[y(k)]$$

$$= \int\!\!\int_{-\infty}^{\infty} (x - \mu_x)(y - \mu_y) \, p(x, y) \, dx \, dy \qquad (3.26)$$

Note that $C_{xx} = \sigma_x^2$, the variance of $x(k)$, as defined in Eq. (3.11).

A simple relation exists between the covariance of $x(k)$ and $y(k)$ and the standard deviations of $x(k)$ and $y(k)$ as expressed by the inequality

$$|C_{xy}| \leq \sigma_x \sigma_y \qquad (3.27)$$

Thus the magnitude of the covariance between $x(k)$ and $y(k)$ is less than or equal to the product of the standard deviation of $x(k)$ multiplied by the standard deviation of $y(k)$. This is proved later, following Eq. (3.50).

It follows from the above result that the normalized quantity

$$\rho_{xy} = \frac{C_{xy}}{\sigma_x \sigma_y} \qquad (3.28)$$

known as the *correlation coefficient*, will lie between -1 and $+1$. Random variables $x(k)$ and $y(k)$ whose correlation coefficient is zero are said to be *uncorrelated*. This concept is quite distinct from the previous definition of *independent* random variables. Note that if $x(k)$ and $y(k)$ are independent random variables, then, from Eq. (3.20),

$$E[x(k) \, y(k)] = \int\!\!\int_{-\infty}^{\infty} xy \, p(x, y) \, dx \, dy$$

$$= \int_{-\infty}^{\infty} x \, p(x) \, dx \int_{-\infty}^{\infty} y \, p(y) \, dy = E[x(k)] \, E[y(k)] \qquad (3.29)$$

Hence C_{xy} and, in turn, ρ_{xy} equal zero so that *independent random variables are also uncorrelated*. The converse statement is not true in general; that is, *uncorrelated random variables are not necessarily independent*. However, for physically important situations involving two or more normally

(Gaussian) distributed random variables, being mutually uncorrelated does imply independence. This is proved later, following Eq. (3.66).

The *conditional probability density function* of $x(k)$, given that $y(k)$ is between y and $y + dy$, may be defined by the differential relation

$$p(x \mid y) \, dx = \text{Prob} \; [x < x(k) \le x + dx \mid \text{given that } y < y(k) \le y + dy]$$

$$(3.30)$$

or

$$p(x \mid y) = \frac{p(x, y)}{p(y)} \quad \text{assuming } p(y) \ne 0 \tag{3.31}$$

For independent random variables, this simplifies to

$$p(x \mid y) = \frac{p(x) \, p(y)}{p(y)} = p(x) \tag{3.32}$$

In words, the conditional probability density function for $x(k)$ given $y(k)$ is now the same as the original probability density function for $x(k)$ alone.

These ideas may be extended in a straightforward manner to handle situations of three or more random variables where higher order probability distributions would be involved.

***Example* 3.5. Distribution for Sum of Two Random Variables.**   Suppose $x(k)$ and $y(k)$ are two random variables with a joint probability density function $p(x, y)$. Determine the first-order probability density function $p(z)$ for the sum random variable

$$z(k) = x(k) + y(k)$$

For each fixed value of x, the corresponding $y = z - x$. This gives

$$p(x, y) = p(x, z - x)$$

For each fixed value of z, the values of x may range from $-\infty$ to ∞. Hence one obtains

$$p(z) = \int_{-\infty}^{\infty} p(x, z - x) \, dx$$

Thus the desired sum first-order probability density function requires knowledge of the input joint probability density function. If $x(k)$ and $y(k)$ are independent random variables with first-order probability density functions $p_1(x)$ and $p_2(y)$, respectively, then $p(x, y) = p_1(x)p_2(y) = p_1(x) \, p_2(z - x)$, and

$$p(z) = \int_{-\infty}^{\infty} p_1(x)p_2(z - x) \, dx$$

3.1.5   Gaussian (Normal) Distribution

A random variable $x(k)$ is said to follow a *Gaussian* (or *normal*) distribution if its probability density function is given by

$$p(x) = \left(b\sqrt{2\pi}\right)^{-1} \exp\left[-\frac{(x-a)^2}{2b^2}\right] \tag{3.33}$$

where a is any real constant and b is any positive constant. It is verified easily that a and b constitute the mean value and standard deviation of the random variable $x(k)$ since

$$E[x(k)] = \int_{-\infty}^{\infty} x\, p(x)\, dx = a = \mu_x$$

$$E[(x(k) - a)^2] = \int_{-\infty}^{\infty} (x - a)^2\, p(x)\, dx = b^2 = \sigma_x^2$$

Thus the normal probability density function should be expressed by

$$p(x) = \left(\sigma_x\sqrt{2\pi}\right)^{-1} \exp\left[-\frac{(x-\mu_x)^2}{2\sigma_x^2}\right] \tag{3.34}$$

The normal probability distribution function is, by definition,

$$P(x) = \left(\sigma_x\sqrt{2\pi}\right)^{-1} \int_{-\infty}^{x} \exp\left[-\frac{(\xi - \mu_x)^2}{2\sigma_x^2}\right] d\xi \tag{3.35}$$

Using simple numerical methods, or from tables, it is now convenient to determine the probability that the normal random variable $x(k)$ will assume values in any desired range. In particular,

$$P(\mu_x + c\sigma_x) - P(\mu_x - c\sigma_x) = \text{Prob}\left[\mu_x - c\sigma_x < x(k) \leq \mu_x + c\sigma_x\right]$$

represents the probability that $x(k)$ will be within plus and minus c standard deviations of the mean value. For $c = 1$, 2, and 3, the probabilities are 68.3, 95.4 and 99.7 per cent, respectively. Working the other way, for a 90 per cent probability interval about the mean value, $c = 1.645$.

The importance of the normal distribution in physical problems may be attributed in part to the *Central Limit Theorem*, Refs. 18, 20, which asserts that this distribution will result quite generally from the sum of a large number of independent random variables acting together.

To be a bit more specific, let $x_1(k)$, $x_2(k)$, ..., $x_N(k)$ be N mutually independent random variables whose individual distributions are not specified and may be different. Let μ_i and σ_i^2 be the mean value and variance of each random variable $x_i(k)$, $i = 1, 2, ..., N$. Consider the sum random variable

$$x(k) = \sum_{i=1}^{N} a_i\, x_i(k)$$

where a_i are arbitrary fixed constants. Now, the mean value μ_x and variance σ_x^2 become, using the later result of Eq. (3.116),

$$\mu_x = E[x(k)] = E\left[\sum_{i=1}^{N} a_i x_i(k)\right] = \sum_{i=1}^{N} a_i E[x_i(k)] = \sum_{i=1}^{N} a_i \mu_i$$

$$\sigma_x^2 = E[(x(k) - \mu_x)^2] = E\left[\sum_{i=1}^{N} a_i(x_i(k) - \mu_i)\right]^2 = \sum_{i=1}^{N} a_i^2 \sigma_i^2$$

The last expression is a result of the mutual independence of $x_i(k)$ with $x_j(k)$ for $i \neq j$. The Central Limit Theorem states that under fairly common conditions, the sum random variable $x(k)$ will be normally distributed as $N \to \infty$ with the above mean value μ_x and variance σ_x^2.

Consider now N random variables $x_1(k), x_2(k), \ldots, x_N(k)$ which may be correlated. Denote their respective mean values, variances, and co-variances by

$$\mu_i = E[x_i(k)]$$

$$\sigma_i^2 = E[(x_i(k) - \mu_i)^2]$$

$$C_{ij} = E[(x_i(k) - \mu_i)(x_j(k) - \mu_j)] \qquad C_{ii} = \sigma_i^2$$

Their joint distribution is said to follow an *N-dimensional Gaussian (normal) distribution* if the associated N-fold probability density function is given by

$$p(x_1, x_2, \ldots, x_N) = \frac{\exp\left[(-1/2\,|C|) \sum_{i,\,j=1}^{N} |C_{ij}|\,(x_i - \mu_i)(x_j - \mu_j)\right]}{(2\pi)^{N/2}\,|C|^{\frac{1}{2}}} \tag{3.36}$$

where C is the covariance matrix of the C_{ij} defined below, $|C|$ is the determinant of C, and $|C_{ij}|$ is the cofactor of C_{ij} in determinant $|C|$. To be explicit,

$$C = \begin{bmatrix} C_{11} & C_{12} & \cdots & C_{1N} \\ C_{21} & C_{22} & \cdots & C_{2N} \\ \cdot & \cdot & & \cdot \\ \cdot & \cdot & & \cdot \\ \cdot & \cdot & & \cdot \\ C_{N1} & C_{N2} & \cdots & C_{NN} \end{bmatrix}$$

and the cofactor $|C_{ij}|$ of any element C_{ij} is defined to be the determinant of order $N - 1$ formed by omitting the ith row and jth column of C, multiplied by $(-1)^{i+j}$.

The outstanding feature of the N-dimensional normal distribution is that all of its properties are determined solely from knowledge of the various mean values μ_i and covariances C_{ij}. For $N = 1$, this function reduces to

$$p(x_1) = (\sigma_1\sqrt{2\pi})^{-1} \exp\left[-\frac{(x_1 - \mu_1)^2}{2\sigma_1^2} \right] \qquad (3.36a)$$

which is the (first-order) normal probability density function defined previously in Eq. (3.34).

For $N = 2$, there results the joint (second-order) normal probability density function

$$p(x_1, x_2) = \frac{\exp\left\{ [2(1 - \rho_{12}^2)]^{-1}\left[\left(\dfrac{x_1 - \mu_1}{\sigma_1}\right)^2 - 2\rho_{12}\left(\dfrac{x_1 - \mu_1}{\sigma_1}\right)\left(\dfrac{x_2 - \mu_2}{\sigma_2}\right) + \left(\dfrac{x_2 - \mu_2}{\sigma_2}\right)^2 \right] \right\}}{2\pi\sigma_1\sigma_2\sqrt{1 - \rho_{12}^2}}$$

$$(3.36b)$$

where $\rho_{12} = C_{12}/\sigma_1\sigma_2$ is the correlation coefficient between $x_1(k)$ and $x_2(k)$. Observe that when $x_1(k)$ and $x_2(k)$ are uncorrelated so that $\rho_{12} = 0$, one obtains

$$p(x_1, x_2) = p(x_1)\, p(x_2)$$

which shows that $x_1(k)$ and $x_2(k)$ are also independent. This result is not true for arbitrary distributions.

Similar formulas may be written down for higher-order cases where $N = 3, 4, 5, \ldots$. For arbitrary N, it follows quite easily that if all different pairs of normally distributed random variables are mutually uncorrelated (that is, $\rho_{ij} = 0$ whenever $i \neq j$), then these random variables are mutually independent in the probability sense. That is,

$$p(x_1, x_2, \ldots, x_N) = p(x_1)p(x_2) \cdots p(x_N)$$

The importance of the N-dimensional normal distribution in physical problems, analogous to the common one-dimensional normal distribution, is due in part to the *Multidimensional Central Limit Theorem*, Refs. 18, 20. This theorem yields the result that the vector sum of a large number of mutually independent N-dimensional random variables approaches an N-dimensional normal distribution under fairly general conditions.

A summary of equations for some special probability density functions which are used in theoretical studies is presented in Table 3.1.

Table 3.1   Special Probability Density Functions

Type	Probability Density Function
Discrete	$p(x) = A\,\delta(x - a) + B\,\delta(x - b) + \cdots + N\,\delta(x - n)$ where $A + B + \cdots + N = 1$
Uniform (rectangular)	$p(x) = (b - a)^{-1}, \quad a \le x \le b; \qquad$ otherwise zero
Sine wave	$p(x) = \left(\pi\sqrt{X^2 - x^2}\,\right)^{-1}, \quad |x| < X; \qquad$ otherwise zero
Gaussian (normal)	$p(x) = \left(\sigma_x\sqrt{2\pi}\,\right)^{-1} e^{-(x - \mu_x)^2/2\sigma_x^2}$
Rayleigh	$p(x) = \dfrac{x}{c^2}\,e^{-x^2/2c^2}, \quad x \ge 0; \qquad$ otherwise zero
Maxwell	$p(x) = \dfrac{x^2}{c^3}\sqrt{\dfrac{2}{\pi}}\,e^{-x^2/2c^2}, \quad x \ge 0; \qquad$ otherwise zero
Truncated	Assume original $p_1(x)$ defined over $(-\infty, \infty)$. Truncated $p(x) = Cp_1(x), \quad a \le x \le b; \qquad$ otherwise zero where $\displaystyle\int_{-\infty}^{\infty} p(x)\,dx = C\int_a^b p_1(x)\,dx = 1$
Clipped	Assume original $p_1(x)$ defined over $(-\infty, \infty)$. Clipped $\begin{aligned} p(x) &= p_1(x) & a < x < b \\ &= A\,\delta(x - a) & x = a \\ &= B\,\delta(x - b) & x = b \\ &= 0 & x < a \text{ or } x > b \end{aligned}$ where $\displaystyle\int_{-\infty}^{\infty} p(x)\,dx = \int_a^b p_1(x)\,dx + A + B = 1$

3.2 Stationary Random Processes

A *random process* $\{x_k(t)\}$, $-\infty < t < \infty$ (also called a *stochastic process*), denoted by the symbol $\{\}$, is an ensemble of real-valued (or complex-valued) functions which can be characterized through its probability structure. For convenience, the variable t will be interpreted as time in the following discussion. Each particular function $x_k(t)$, where t is variable and k is fixed, is called a sample function. In actual practice, a sample function (or some time history record of finite length from a sample function) may be thought of as the observed result of a single experiment. The possible number of experiments represents a sample space of index k which may be countable or uncountable. For any N and any fixed times $t_1, t_2, \ldots, t_N$, the quantities $x_k(t_1), x_k(t_2), \ldots, x_k(t_N)$, represent N random variables over the index k. It is required that there exist a well-defined N-dimensional probability distribution function for every N. An ensemble of sample functions forming a random process is displayed in Figure 1.10.

A particular sample function $x_k(t)$, in general, would not be suitable for representing the entire random process $\{x_k(t)\}$ to which it belongs. Under certain conditions to be described later, however, it turns out that for the special class of ergodic random processes, it is possible to derive desired statistical information about the entire random process from appropriate analysis of a single arbitrary sample function. For the situation of a pair of random processes $\{x_k(t)\}$ and $\{y_k(t)\}$, the corresponding problem is to estimate joint statistical properties of the two random processes from proper analysis of an arbitrary pair of sample functions $x_k(t)$ and $y_k(t)$.

Consider two arbitrary random processes $\{x_k(t)\}$ and $\{y_k(t)\}$. The first statistical quantities of interest are the ensemble *mean values* at arbitrary fixed values of t, where $x_k(t)$ and $y_k(t)$ are random variables over the index k. These are defined as in Eq. (3.8) by

$$\mu_x(t) = E[x_k(t)]$$
$$\mu_y(t) = E[y_k(t)]$$

(3.37)

In general, these mean values are different at different times, and must be calculated separately for every t of interest. That is,

$$\mu_x(t_1) \neq \mu_x(t_2) \qquad \text{if } t_1 \neq t_2$$
$$\mu_y(t_1) \neq \mu_y(t_2) \qquad \text{if } t_1 \neq t_2$$

(3.38)

The next statistical quantities of interest are the *covariance functions* at arbitrary fixed values of $t_1 = t$ and $t_2 = t + \tau$. These are defined by

$$C_x(t, t + \tau) = E[(x_k(t) - \mu_x(t))(x_k(t + \tau) - \mu_x(t + \tau))]$$
$$C_y(t, t + \tau) = E[(y_k(t) - \mu_y(t))(y_k(t + \tau) - \mu_y(t + \tau))]$$
(3.39)

$$C_{xy}(t, t + \tau) = E[(x_k(t) - \mu_x(t))(y_k(t + \tau) - \mu_y(t + \tau))] \qquad (3.40)$$

In general, these quantities are different for different combinations of t_1 and t_2. Observe that at $\tau = 0$ $(t_1 = t_2 = t)$,

$$C_x(t, t) = E[(x_k(t) - \mu_x(t))^2] = \sigma_x^2(t)$$
$$C_y(t, t) = E[(y_k(t) - \mu_y(t))^2] = \sigma_y^2(t)$$
(3.41)

$$C_{xy}(t, t) = E[(x_k(t) - \mu_x(t))(y_k(t) - \mu_y(t))] = C_{xy}(t) \qquad (3.42)$$

Thus the covariance functions $C_x(t, t)$ and $C_y(t, t)$ represent the ordinary variances of $\{x_k(t)\}$ and $\{y_k(t)\}$ at a fixed value of t, while $C_{xy}(t, t)$ represents the covariance between $\{x_k(t)\}$ and $\{y_k(t)\}$. As before, different results would generally be obtained for different values of t

Other statistical quantities can be defined over the ensemble which involve fixing three or more times. The probability structure of the random processes is thus described in finer and finer detail. However, if $\{x_k(t)\}$ and $\{y_k(t)\}$ form a two-dimensional Gaussian distribution at a fixed value of t, then $\{x_k(t)\}$ and $\{y_k(t)\}$ are separately Gaussian. The mean values and co-variance functions listed above then provide a complete description of the underlying probability structure. For this reason, the main emphasis in this chapter is concerned only with these two statistical quantities and their relationships to spectral density functions.

If the mean values $\mu_x(t)$ and $\mu_y(t)$, together with the covariance functions $C_x(t, t + \tau)$, $C_y(t, t + \tau)$, and $C_{xy}(t, t + \tau)$, yield the same results for all fixed values of t (that is, are independent of time translations), then the random processes $\{x_k(t)\}$ and $\{y_k(t)\}$ are said to be *weakly stationary*. If all possible probability distributions involving $\{x_k(t)\}$ and $\{y_k(t)\}$ are independent of time translations, then the processes are said to be *strongly stationary*. Since the mean values and covariance functions are conse-quences only of the first- and second-order probability distributions, it follows that the class of strongly stationary random processes is a subclass of the class of weakly stationary random processes. For Gaussian random processes, however, weak stationarity implies strong stationarity since all possible probability distributions may be derived from the mean values and covariance functions. Thus, for Gaussian random processes, these two stationary concepts coincide.

Random processes which are not stationary are said to be *nonstationary*, and are the subject matter of Chapter 9. The probability structure of non-stationary random processes, as well as stationary processes, is discussed in Section 9.1.

3.2.1 Correlation (Covariance) Functions

For stationary random processes $\{x_k(t)\}$ and $\{y_k(t)\}$, which will be considered henceforth in this chapter, the mean values become constants independent of t. That is, for all t,

$$\mu_x = E[x_k(t)] = \int_{-\infty}^{\infty} x\, p(x)\, dx$$

$$\mu_y = E[y_k(t)] = \int_{-\infty}^{\infty} y\, p(y)\, dy$$

(3.43)

where $p(x)$ and $p(y)$ are the first-order probability density functions associated with the random variables $x_k(t)$ and $y_k(t)$, respectively. The covariance functions for stationary random processes are also independent of t.

For arbitrary fixed t and τ, define

$$R_x(\tau) = E[x_k(t)\, x_k(t + \tau)]$$

$$R_y(\tau) = E[y_k(t)\, y_k(t + \tau)]$$

(3.44)

$$R_{xy}(\tau) = E[x_k(t)\, y_k(t + \tau)]$$

(3.45)

where R is introduced instead of C to distinguish between these special expressions and those presented in Eqs. (3.39) and (3.40). For nonzero mean values, R is different from C. The quantities $R_x(\tau)$ and $R_y(\tau)$ are called the *autocorrelation functions* of $\{x_k(t)\}$ and $\{y_k(t)\}$, respectively, whereas $R_{xy}(\tau)$ is called the *cross-correlation function* between $\{x_k(t)\}$ and $\{y_k(t)\}$.

A necessary and sufficient condition that $R_x(\tau)$ be the autocorrelation function of a weakly stationary random process $\{x_k(t)\}$ is that $R_x(\tau) = R_x(-\tau)$, and that $R_x(\tau)$ be a non-negative definite function, Ref. 11, p. 519. One can prove also that $R_x(\tau)$ will be a continuous function of τ if it is continuous at the origin. Similarly the cross-correlation function $R_{xy}(\tau)$ will be continuous for all τ if $R_x(\tau)$ or $R_y(\tau)$ is continuous at the origin.

For a pair of stationary random processes $\{x_k(t)\}$ and $\{y_k(t)\}$, the joint probability density function $p(x_1, x_2)$ for the pair of random variables, $x_1 = x_k(t)$ and $x_2 = x_k(t + \tau)$, is independent of t, and the joint probability density function $p(y_1, y_2)$ associated with the pair of random variables $y_1 = y_k(t)$ and $y_2 = y_k(t + \tau)$ is independent of t. This is also true for the joint probability density function $p(x_1, y_2)$ associated with the pair of random variables $x_1 = x_k(t)$ and $y_2 = y_k(t + \tau)$. In terms of these probability density functions

$$R_x(\tau) = \int\limits_{-\infty}^{\infty}\!\!\int x_1 x_2\, p(x_1,\, x_2)\, dx_1\, dx_2$$

$$R_y(\tau) = \int\limits_{-\infty}^{\infty}\!\!\int y_1 y_2\, p(y_1,\, y_2)\, dy_1\, dy_2 \qquad (3.46)$$

$$R_{xy}(\tau) = \int\limits_{-\infty}^{\infty}\!\!\int x_1 y_2\, p(x_1,\, y_2)\, dx_1\, dy_2$$

For arbitrary values of μ_x and μ_y, the covariance functions are related to the correlation functions by the equations

$$C_x(\tau) = R_x(\tau) - \mu_x{}^2$$
$$C_y(\tau) = R_y(\tau) - \mu_y{}^2 \qquad (3.47)$$
$$C_{xy}(\tau) = R_{xy}(\tau) - \mu_x\mu_y$$

Thus correlation functions are identical with covariance functions when the mean values are zero.

From the stationary hypothesis, it follows that the autocorrelation functions $R_x(\tau)$ and $R_y(\tau)$ are even functions of τ. That is,

$$R_x(-\tau) = R_x(\tau)$$
$$R_y(-\tau) = R_y(\tau) \qquad (3.48)$$

while the cross-correlation function is neither odd nor even, but satisfies the relation

$$R_{xy}(-\tau) = R_{yx}(\tau) \qquad (3.49)$$

Examples of autocorrelation and cross-correlation functions are given in Figures 1.15 and 1.20. The useful relation stated in Eq. (1.48) will now be proved.

Cross-Correlation Inequality.　An upper bound for the cross-correlation function is given by the inequality

$$|R_{xy}(\tau)|^2 \le R_x(0)\, R_y(0) \qquad (3.50)$$

which may be proved as follows. For any real constants a and b, the expected value

$$E[(a\, x(t) + b\, y(t + \tau))^2] \ge 0$$

since only non-negative quantities are being considered. This is equivalent to

$$a^2 R_x(0) + 2ab\, R_{xy}(\tau) + b^2\, R_y(0) \geq 0$$

Hence, assuming $b \neq 0$,

$$\left(\frac{a}{b}\right)^2 R_x(0) + 2\left(\frac{a}{b}\right) R_{xy}(\tau) + R_y(0) \geq 0$$

This is a quadratic equation in a/b without real roots since the right-hand side is non-negative. Therefore, the discriminant of this quadratic equation in a/b must be nonpositive. That is,

$$\text{Discriminant} = 4R_{xy}{}^2(\tau) - 4R_x(0)\, R_y(0) \leq 0$$

Thus

$$R_{xy}{}^2(\tau) = |R_{xy}(\tau)|^2 \leq R_x(0)\, R_y(0)$$

as stated in Eq. (3.50). This completes the proof.

By considering $x(t) - \mu_x$ and $y(t + \tau) - \mu_y$ instead of $x(t)$ and $y(t + \tau)$, the same proof gives the cross-covariance inequality

$$|C_{xy}(\tau)|^2 \leq C_x(0)\, C_y(0) \tag{3.51}$$

When $x(t) = y(t)$, one obtains $|R_x(\tau)| \leq R_x(0)$ and $|C_x(\tau)| \leq C_x(0)$ for all τ. It follows from Eq. (3.51) that a *correlation function coefficient* (*normalized cross-covariance function*) may be defined by

$$\rho_{xy}(\tau) = \frac{C_{xy}(\tau)}{\sqrt{C_x(0)\, C_y(0)}} \tag{3.52}$$

and satisfies, for all τ,

$$-1 \leq \rho_{xy}(\tau) \leq 1 \tag{3.53}$$

If the mean values μ_x and μ_y are zero, then $\rho_{xy}(\tau)$ becomes

$$\rho_{xy}(\tau) = \frac{R_{xy}(\tau)}{\sqrt{R_x(0)\, R_y(0)}} \tag{3.54}$$

The function $\rho_{xy}(\tau)$ measures the degree of linear dependence between $\{x_k(t)\}$ and $\{y_k(t)\}$ for a displacement of τ in $\{y_k(t)\}$ relative to $\{x_k(t)\}$. A proof of this property for $\tau = 0$ is given in Section 3.5.5.

In summary, the correlation properties of stationary random processes $\{x_k(t)\}$, $\{y_k(t)\}$ may be described by the four functions $R_x(\tau)$, $R_y(\tau)$, $R_{xy}(\tau)$, and $R_{yx}(\tau)$. These need be calculated only for values of $\tau \geq 0$, since symmetry properties from Eqs. (3.48) and (3.49) yield results for $\tau < 0$.

***Example* 3.6. Autocorrelation Function for Sine Wave Process.** Suppose $\{x_k(t)\} = \{X \sin [2\pi f_0 t + \theta(k)]\}$ is a sine wave process in which X and f_0

are constants and $\theta(k)$ is a random variable with a uniform probability density function $p(\theta)$ over $(0, 2\pi)$. Determine the autocorrelation function $R_x(\tau)$.

Here, for any fixed value of t, the random variable

$$x_k(t) = X \sin [2\pi f_0 t + \theta(k)] = x_1(\theta)$$

$$x_k(t + \tau) = X \sin [2\pi f_0(t + \tau) + \theta(k)] = x_2(\theta)$$

From Eq. (3.44),

$$R_x(\tau) = E[x_k(t) \, x_k(t + \tau)] = E[x_1(\theta) \, x_2(\theta)]$$

with

$$p(\theta) = (2\pi)^{-1} \quad 0 \le \theta \le 2\pi; \qquad \text{otherwise zero}$$

Hence

$$R_x(\tau) = \frac{X^2}{2\pi} \int_0^{2\pi} \sin (2\pi f_0 t + \theta) \sin [2\pi f_0(t + \tau) + \theta] \, d\theta$$

$$= \frac{X^2}{2} \cos 2\pi f_0 \tau$$

giving the autocorrelation function for a sine wave stationary random process, as stated in Eq. (1.31).

Example 3.7. Autocorrelation Function for Rectangular Wave Process. Consider a physical situation where a sample function $x_k(t)$ from a random rectangular wave process $\{x_k(t)\}$ is restricted so as to assume only values of c or $-c$, where the number of changes of sign in an interval $(t, t + \tau)$ occur at random and independent times with an average density of λ. Assume also that what happens inside an interval $(t, t + \tau)$ is independent of what happens outside the interval. Define.

$$A_n = \text{Event [exactly } n \text{ changes of sign fall inside } (t, t + \tau)]$$

This type of physical situation follows a Poisson distribution, Ref. 1, p. 90, where the probability of event A_n is

$$P(A_n) = \frac{\lambda |\tau|^n}{n!} e^{-\lambda |\tau|}$$

Determine the autocorrelation function for $\{x_k(t)\}$.

The autocorrelation function may be calculated as follows. An individual product term $x_k(t) x_k(t + \tau)$ equals c^2 if $x_k(t)$ and $x_k(t + \tau)$ are of the same sign, and it equals $-c^2$ if they are of opposite sign. The total probability for c^2 is given by the sum $P(A_0) + P(A_2) + P(A_4) + \cdots$, and the total probability for $-c^2$ is given by the sum $P(A_1) + P(A_3) + P(A_5) + \cdots$.

Hence

$$R_x(\tau) = E[x_k(t)\, x_k(t + \tau)] = c^2 \sum_{n=0}^{\infty} (-1)^n\, P(A_n)$$

$$= c^2 e^{-\lambda|\tau|} \sum_{n=1}^{\infty} (-1)^n \frac{\lambda\, |\tau|^n}{n!} = c^2 e^{-2\lambda|\tau|}$$

***Example* 3.8. Autocorrelation Function for Sum of Two Stationary Processes.** Assume that a random process $\{y_k(t)\}$ is the sum of two stationary processes $\{x_{1,k}(t)\}$ and $\{x_{2,k}(t)\}$ such that each sample function

$$y_k(t) = a_1 x_{1,k}(t) + a_2 x_{2,k}(t)$$

where a_1 and a_2 are constants. Assume also that $\{x_{1,k}(t)\}$ and $\{x_{2,k}(t)\}$ may be correlated. Determine the autocorrelation function $R_y(\tau)$.

From Eq. (3.44), one obtains

$$
\begin{aligned}
R_y(\tau) &= E[y_k(t)\, y_k(t + \tau)] \\
&= E[(a_1 x_{1,k}(t) + a_2 x_{2,k}(t))(a_1 x_{1,k}(t + \tau) + a_2 x_{2,k}(t + \tau))] \\
&= a_1^2\, E[x_{1,k}(t)\, x_{1,k}(t + \tau)] + a_1 a_2\, E[x_{1,k}(t)\, x_{2,k}(t + \tau)] \\
&\quad + a_1 a_2\, E[x_{2,k}(t)\, x_{1,k}(t + \tau)] + a_2^2\, E[x_{2,k}(t)\, x_{2,k}(t + \tau)] \\
&= a_1^2\, R_{x_1}(\tau) + a_1 a_2 [R_{x_1 x_2}(\tau) + R_{x_2 x_1}(\tau)] + a_2^2\, R_{x_2}(\tau)
\end{aligned}
$$

Thus the sum autocorrelation function requires knowledge of the input cross-correlation functions as well as their autocorrelation functions.

3.2.2 Spectral Decomposition

The spectral density functions corresponding to the correlation functions discussed previously can be defined directly by taking Fourier transforms. Conditions are assumed which guarantee that these autocorrelation functions will have a Fourier transform. This approach yields two-sided spectral density functions which exist for frequencies over $(-\infty, \infty)$. An alternate way to obtain one-sided physically realizable spectral density functions for frequencies over $(0, \infty)$ is discussed in Sections 1.3.4 and 1.4.3, where the data are filtered, squared, and averaged. These results apply to ergodic random processes and are the same as the Fourier transform results when the negative frequency terms are folded over into the positive frequency terms. Before explaining these ideas, it is instructive to consider the spectral decomposition of a stationary random process by assuming that each sample function has a Fourier transform. This heuristic treatment shows why spectral density functions should be defined as Fourier transforms of correlation functions, as is done in the next section.

The spectral decomposition of a stationary random process $\{x_k(t)\}$ will now be developed assuming that each sample function $x_k(t)$ of the random process has a complex Fourier transform $X_k(f)$, such that

$$X_k(f) = \int_{-\infty}^{\infty} x_k(t) \, e^{-j2\pi ft} \, dt \tag{3.55a}$$

and conversely,

$$x_k(t) = \int_{-\infty}^{\infty} X_k(f) \, e^{j2\pi ft} \, df \tag{3.55b}$$

A sufficient set of conditions for this to occur is that $x_k(t)$ and its derivative $\dot{x}_k(t)$ be piecewise continuous in every finite interval (a, b) and that $|x_k(t)|$ be integrable over $(-\infty, \infty)$. These conditions can always be satisfied in practical problems by conceptually setting functions $x_k(t)$ equal to zero outside some arbitrarily high range of t (that is, making them truncated functions of finite duration).

Similarly, every sample function $y_k(t)$ from a stationary random process $\{y_k(t)\}$ will be assumed to have a complex Fourier transform $Y_k(f)$ where

$$Y_k(f) = \int_{-\infty}^{\infty} y_k(t) \, e^{-j2\pi ft} \, dt$$

$$y_k(t) = \int_{-\infty}^{\infty} Y_k(f) \, e^{j2\pi ft} \, df$$

Thus the original pair of real-valued random processes, $\{x_k(t)\}$ and $\{y_k(t)\}$, may be described in terms of two new complex-valued random processes, $\{X_k(f)\}$ and $\{Y_k(f)\}$. Note that the parameter f replaces t, but the sample space is still indexed by k.

***Example* 3.9. Fourier Transforms for Constants and Periodic Functions.** The cases of a constant and a periodic function can be given special treatment by using delta functions. If $x_k(t) = 1$, a constant, then the Fourier transform relation

$$1 = \int_{-\infty}^{\infty} X_k(f) \, e^{j2\pi ft} \, df \tag{3.56}$$

implies that

$$X_k(f) = \delta(f) = \int_{-\infty}^{\infty} e^{-j2\pi ft} \, dt \tag{3.57}$$

where $\delta(f)$ is the *delta function* defined by Eq. (3.57) and the properties

$$\delta(f) = 0 \quad \text{for} \quad f \neq 0 \qquad\qquad \delta(0) = \infty \tag{3.57a}$$

$$\int_{-\epsilon}^{\epsilon} \delta(f) \, df = 1 \quad \text{for any} \quad \epsilon > 0 \qquad \delta(-f) = \delta(f) \tag{3.57b}$$

$$\int_{-\epsilon}^{\epsilon} F(f) \, \delta(f) \, df = F(0) \qquad \text{for any function } F(f) \tag{3.57c}$$

If $x_k(t) = e^{j2\pi f_0 t}$, a complex-valued periodic function, then

$$e^{j2\pi f_0 t} = \int_{-\infty}^{\infty} X_k(f)\, e^{j2\pi f t}\, df$$

Hence

$$1 = \int_{-\infty}^{\infty} X_k(f)\, e^{j2\pi(f-f_0)t}\, df = \int_{-\infty}^{\infty} X_k(f+f_0)\, e^{j2\pi f t}\, df$$

which yields

$$X_k(f+f_0) = \delta(f)$$

equivalent to

$$X_k(f) = \delta(f-f_0)$$

Now, for a cosine function,

$$x_c(t) = \cos 2\pi f_0 t = \tfrac{1}{2}(e^{j2\pi f_0 t} + e^{-j2\pi f_0 t}) \tag{3.58a}$$

It follows that its Fourier transform is

$$X_c(f) = \tfrac{1}{2}[\delta(f-f_0) + \delta(f+f_0)] \tag{3.58b}$$

Similarly, a sine function

$$x_s(t) = \sin 2\pi f_0 t = \tfrac{1}{2}(e^{j2\pi f_0 t} - e^{-j2\pi f_0 t}) \tag{3.59a}$$

has a Fourier transform

$$X_s(f) = \tfrac{1}{2}[\delta(f-f_0) - \delta(f+f_0)] \tag{3.59b}$$

This concludes Example 3.9.

If $\{x_k(t)\}$ and $\{y_k(t)\}$ have mean values of zero for all t, it follows that the mean values of their Fourier transforms $\{X_k(f)\}$ and $\{Y_k(f)\}$ will be zero for all f. That is

$$E[X_k(f)] = E[Y_k(f)] = 0$$

Since $x_k(t)$ is real, it may be expressed in terms of the complex conjugate $X_k^*(f)$ by

$$x_k(t) = \int_{-\infty}^{\infty} X_k^*(f)\, e^{-j2\pi f t}\, df$$

The squared value from the above and Eq. (3.55b) is now

$$x_k^2(t) = \int_{-\infty}^{\infty} X_k^*(f)\, e^{-j2\pi f t}\, df \int_{-\infty}^{\infty} X_k(g)\, e^{j2\pi g t}\, dg$$

$$= \iint_{-\infty}^{\infty} X_k^*(f)\, X_k(g)\, e^{j2\pi(g-f)t}\, dg\, df$$

The expected value of $x_k^2(t)$ is thus given by

$$E[x_k^2(t)] = \iint\limits_{-\infty}^{\infty} E[X_k^*(f)\, X_k(g)]\, e^{j2\pi(g-f)t}\, dg\, df = R_x(0) \qquad (3.60)$$

where the assumption that $\{x_k(t)\}$ is a stationary random process yields $E[x_k^2(t)] = R_x(0)$, independent of t.

From separate considerations, the *power spectral density function* $S_x(f)$ associated with a stationary random process $\{x_k(t)\}$, where f ranges over $(-\infty, \infty)$, may be defined by the relation

$$R_x(0) = E[x_k^2(t)] = \int_{-\infty}^{\infty} S_x(f)\, df \qquad (3.61)$$

which indicates how the mean square value of $\{x_k(t)\}$ is distributed over the infinite frequency range $(-\infty, \infty)$. In particular, $S_x(f)\, df$ represents the mean square value lying in the frequency range $(f, f + df)$ so that $S_x(f)$ is real and non-negative for all f.

Since these last two equations must be equivalent, one obtains

$$S_x(f) = \int_{-\infty}^{\infty} E[X_k^*(f)\, X_k(g)]\, e^{j2\pi(g-f)t}\, dg \qquad (3.62)$$

Equation (3.62) is satisfied for all t by the requirement that

$$E[X_k^*(f)\, X_k(g)] = S_x(f)\delta(f - g) \qquad (3.63)$$

where $\delta(f - g)$ is a delta function defined by Eq. (3.57).

The preceding discussion helps to justify the fact, in agreement with the more rigorous analysis of Ref. 11, p. 527, that pairs of complex random variables $X(f)$, $X(g)$, $Y(f)$, $Y(g)$ associated with stationary random processes satisfy the relations

$$E[X_k^*(f)\, X_k(g)] = S_x(f)\,\delta(f - g)$$
$$E[Y_k^*(f)\, Y_k(g)] = S_y(f)\,\delta(f - g) \qquad (3.64)$$
$$E[X_k^*(f)\, Y_k(g)] = S_{xy}(f)\,\delta(f - g)$$

where $S_x(f)$ and $S_y(f)$ are called the *two-sided power spectral density functions* of the random processes $\{x_k(t)\}$ and $\{y_k(t)\}$, respectively, and $S_{xy}(f)$ is called the *two-sided cross-spectral density function* between $\{x_k(t)\}$ and $\{y_k(t)\}$. The frequency variable f ranges over $(-\infty, \infty)$, accounting for the two-sided designation.

Equation (3.64) represents correlation functions in the complex frequency domain, analogous to the correlation functions in the time domain of Eqs. (3.44) and (3.45). In particular, Eq. (3.64) shows that the complex random variables $\{X_k(f)\}$ and $\{Y_k(f)\}$ are both individually and mutually uncorrelated when $f \neq g$. This property is characteristic for stationary random processes, and is not satisfied by general nonstationary processes.

It is now quite straightforward to derive the correspondence between these two-sided *stationary* spectral density functions $S_x(f)$, $S_y(f)$, $S_{xy}(f)$, and the *stationary* correlation functions $R_x(\tau)$, $R_y(\tau)$, $R_{xy}(\tau)$. The results are

$$R_x(\tau) = \int_{-\infty}^{\infty} S_x(f)\, e^{j2\pi f\tau}\, df$$

$$R_y(\tau) = \int_{-\infty}^{\infty} S_y(f)\, e^{j2\pi f\tau}\, df \tag{3.65}$$

$$R_{xy}(\tau) = \int_{-\infty}^{\infty} S_{xy}(f)\, e^{j2\pi f\tau}\, df \tag{3.66}$$

proving that the functions are Fourier transform pairs. Consequently, either set of functions theoretically yields the other set.

Proof of Equation (3.65).   To prove Eq. (3.65), one would proceed by the following steps.

$$x(t) = \int_{-\infty}^{\infty} X^*(f)\, e^{-j2\pi ft}\, df$$

$$x(t+\tau) = \int_{-\infty}^{\infty} X(g)\, e^{j2\pi g(t+\tau)}\, dg$$

$$x(t)\, x(t+\tau) = \iint_{-\infty}^{\infty} X^*(f)\, X(g)\, e^{j2\pi(g-f)t}\, e^{j2\pi g\tau}\, dg\, df$$

$$R_x(\tau) = E[x(t)\, x(t+\tau)] = \iint_{-\infty}^{\infty} E[X^*(f)\, X(g)]\, e^{j2\pi(g-f)t}\, e^{j2\pi g\tau}\, dg\, df$$

$$= \iint_{-\infty}^{\infty} S_x(f)\, \delta(f-g)\, e^{j2\pi(g-f)t}\, e^{j2\pi g\tau}\, dg\, df$$

$$= \int_{-\infty}^{\infty} S_x(f)\, e^{j2\pi f\tau}\, df$$

This concludes the proof. A similar proof yields Eq. (3.66).

The inverse relations to Eqs. (3.65) and (3.66) are

$$S_x(f) = \int_{-\infty}^{\infty} R_x(\tau) e^{-j2\pi f\tau} d\tau$$

$$S_y(f) = \int_{-\infty}^{\infty} R_y(\tau) e^{-j2\pi f\tau} d\tau$$

$$(3.67)$$

$$S_{xy}(f) = \int_{-\infty}^{\infty} R_{xy}(\tau) e^{-j2\pi f\tau} d\tau \qquad (3.68)$$

From the symmetry properties of stationary correlation functions Eqs. (3.48) and (3.49), it follows that

$$S_x(-f) = S_x(f)$$

$$S_y(-f) = S_y(f)$$

$$(3.69)$$

$$S_{xy}(-f) = S_{xy}*(f) = S_{yx}(f) \qquad (3.70)$$

These equations state that two-sided power spectral density functions are real, non-negative, and even functions of f, whereas cross-spectral density functions are complex-valued functions of f.

The above relations for the real-valued two-sided power spectral density functions $S_x(f)$ and $S_y(f)$ may be simplified to

$$S_x(f) = \int_{-\infty}^{\infty} R_x(\tau) \cos 2\pi f\tau \, d\tau = 2\int_{0}^{\infty} R_x(\tau) \cos 2\pi f\tau \, d\tau$$

$$S_y(f) = \int_{-\infty}^{\infty} R_y(\tau) \cos 2\pi f\tau \, d\tau = 2\int_{0}^{\infty} R_y(\tau) \cos 2\pi f\tau \, d\tau$$

$$(3.71)$$

whereas

$$R_x(\tau) = 2\int_{0}^{\infty} S_x(f) \cos 2\pi f\tau \, df$$

$$R_y(\tau) = 2\int_{0}^{\infty} S_y(f) \cos 2\pi f\tau \, df$$

$$(3.72)$$

3.2.3 Spectral Density Functions

It will now be assumed that $R_x(\tau)$, $R_y(\tau)$, and $R_{xy}(\tau)$ exist, and that they have Fourier transforms $S_x(f)$, $S_y(f)$, and $S_{xy}(f)$ as given by Eqs. (3.67) and (3.68). A sufficient condition for the existence of these Fourier transforms is that both $|R_x(\tau)|$ and $|R_y(\tau)|$ are integrable over $(-\infty, \infty)$. This is a weaker requirement than assuming that each sample function in $\{x_k(t)\}$ and $\{y_k(t)\}$ have a Fourier transform as was done in the last section, and so it is applicable to a wider class of problems. Thus a proper theoretical way to define (power or cross) spectral density functions is by the

Fourier transform relation, where f varies over $(-\infty, \infty)$,

$$S(f) = \int_{-\infty}^{\infty} R(\tau)\, e^{-j2\pi f\tau}\, d\tau \tag{3.73}$$

which will exist if $R(\tau)$ exists and if

$$\int_{-\infty}^{\infty} |R(\tau)|\, d\tau < \infty$$

The inverse Fourier transform gives

$$R(\tau) = \int_{-\infty}^{\infty} S(f)\, e^{j2\pi f\tau}\, df \tag{3.74}$$

All the properties follow as stated previously. To handle practical problems, both $R(\tau)$ and $S(f)$ are permitted to include delta functions.

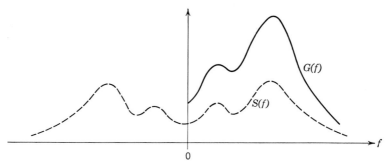

Figure 3.1   One-sided and two-sided spectral density function.

The *physically realizable one-sided* power spectral density functions, $G_x(f)$ and $G_y(f)$, where f varies only over $(0, \infty)$, are defined by

$$G_x(f) = 2S_x(f), \quad 0 \le f < \infty \qquad \text{otherwise zero}$$
$$G_y(f) = 2S_y(f), \quad 0 \le f < \infty \qquad \text{otherwise zero} \tag{3.75}$$

These are the quantities measured by direct filtering procedures in practice. For mathematical calculations, however, the use of $S_x(f)$ and $S_y(f)$ defined over $(-\infty, \infty)$ and exponentials with imaginary exponents often simplifies the analysis. It is important to be able to deal properly with both these representations, and both will be used in this book. See Figure 3.1.

In terms of the one-sided physically realizable power spectral density functions $G_x(f)$ and $G_y(f)$, the correspondence with the stationary correlation functions $R_x(\tau)$ and $R_y(\tau)$ becomes, from Eqs. (3.72) and (3.75),

$$G_x(f) = 4\int_0^\infty R_x(\tau)\cos 2\pi f\tau\, d\tau \qquad 0 \le f < \infty$$

$$G_y(f) = 4\int_0^\infty R_y(\tau)\cos 2\pi f\tau\, d\tau \qquad 0 \le f < \infty$$

(3.76)

Conversely,

$$R_x(\tau) = \int_0^\infty G_x(f)\cos 2\pi f\tau\, df$$

$$R_y(\tau) = \int_0^\infty G_y(f)\cos 2\pi f\tau\, df$$

(3.77)

When dealing with delta functions at the origin, it is convenient to let the lower limit of integration, zero, be approached from below. In particular, for $R(\tau) = c^2$, this allows the corresponding $G(f)$ to be represented by $G(f) = c^2\,\delta(f)$.

The *physically realizable one-sided* cross-spectral density function, $G_{xy}(f)$, where f varies only over $(0, \infty)$ is defined by

$$G_{xy}(f) = 2S_{xy}(f), \quad 0 \le f < \infty \qquad \text{otherwise zero} \qquad (3.78)$$

From Eq. (3.68),

$$G_{xy}(f) = 2\int_{-\infty}^\infty R_{xy}(\tau)\, e^{-j2\pi f\tau}\, d\tau = C_{xy}(f) - j\, Q_{xy}(f) \qquad (3.79)$$

where $C_{xy}(f)$ is called the *co-spectrum*, and $Q_{xy}(f)$ is called the *quad-spectrum*. In terms of $C_{xy}(f)$ and $Q_{xy}(f)$, the cross-correlation function

$$R_{xy}(\tau) = \int_0^\infty [C_{xy}(f)\cos 2\pi f\tau + Q_{xy}(f)\sin 2\pi f\tau]\, df \qquad (3.80)$$

From Eqs. (3.79) and (3.49), one obtains

$$C_{xy}(f) = \int_0^\infty [R_{xy}(\tau) + R_{yx}(\tau)]\cos 2\pi f\tau\, d\tau = C_{xy}(-f)$$

$$Q_{xy}(f) = \int_0^\infty [R_{xy}(\tau) - R_{yx}(\tau)]\sin 2\pi f\tau\, d\tau = -Q_{xy}(-f)$$

(3.81)

Thus $C_{xy}(f)$ is a real-valued even function of f, whereas $Q_{xy}(f)$ is a real-valued odd function of f. In terms of $G_{xy}(f)$ and $G_{yx}(f)$,

$$C_{xy}(f) = \tfrac{1}{2}[G_{xy}(f) + G_{yx}(f)]$$

$$Q_{xy}(f) = \tfrac{j}{2}[G_{xy}(f) - G_{yx}(f)]$$

(3.82)

An alternative way to describe $S_{xy}(f)$ is by the complex polar form

$$S_{xy}(f) = |S_{xy}(f)| \, e^{-j\theta_{xy}(f)} \qquad -\infty < f < \infty \qquad (3.83)$$

containing an absolute magnitude and phase angle. Similarly,

$$G_{xy}(f) = |G_{xy}(f)| \, e^{-j\theta_{xy}(f)} \qquad 0 \leq f < \infty \qquad (3.84)$$

In terms of $C_{xy}(f)$ and $Q_{xy}(f)$,

$$|G_{xy}(f)| = \sqrt{C_{xy}^2(f) + Q_{xy}^2(f)} \qquad (3.85)$$

$$\theta_{xy}(f) = \tan^{-1}\left[\frac{Q_{xy}(f)}{C_{xy}(f)}\right] \qquad (3.86)$$

A cross-spectrum inequality analogous to the cross-correlation inequality of Eq. (3.50) is proved in the following discussion. Examples of power spectral and cross-spectral density functions are displayed in Figures 1.16 and 1.21. The phase angle $\theta_{xy}(f)$ is explained further in Figure 5.4.

Cross-Spectrum Inequality.   From Eq. (3.50), the cross-correlation inequality, it is known that for $\tau = 0$,

$$|R_{xy}(0)|^2 \leq R_x(0) \, R_y(0)$$

From Eqs. (3.65) and (3.66), this is equivalent to

$$\left| \int_{-\infty}^{\infty} S_{xy}(f)\,df \right|^2 \leq \int_{-\infty}^{\infty} S_x(g)\,dg \int_{-\infty}^{\infty} S_y(f)\,df = \int\!\!\int_{-\infty}^{\infty} S_x(g)\,S_y(f)\,dg\,df$$

Now

$$\left| \int_{-\infty}^{\infty} S_{xy}(f)\,df \right|^2 = \int_{-\infty}^{\infty} S_{xy}(g)\,dg \left[\int_{-\infty}^{\infty} S_{xy}(f)\,df \right]^*$$

$$= \int\!\!\int_{-\infty}^{\infty} S_{xy}(g)\,S_{xy}^*(f)\,dg\,df$$

Hence, for all f and g,

$$S_{xy}(g)\,S_{xy}^*(f) \leq S_x(g)\,S_y(f) \qquad (3.87)$$

Setting $g = f$ yields the two-sided spectra result

$$|S_{xy}(f)|^2 \leq S_x(f)\,S_y(f) \qquad (3.88)$$

For the corresponding one-sided spectra, it follows that

$$|G_{xy}(f)|^2 \leq G_x(f)\,G_y(f) \qquad (3.89)$$

This completes the proof. A normalized cross-spectral density function, known as the coherence function, may now be defined. This is discussed in Section 3.4.2.

In summary, the spectral properties of stationary random processes $\{x_k(t)\}$ and $\{y_k(t)\}$ may be described by the three functions $S_x(f)$, $S_y(f)$, $S_{xy}(f)$, or by the four functions $S_x(f)$, $S_y(f)$, $C_{xy}(f)$, $Q_{xy}(f)$, which need be calculated only for $f \geq 0$, since the symmetry properties from Eqs. (3.69), (3.70), and (3.81) yield results for $f < 0$.

***Example* 3.10. Bandwidth Limited White Noise.** By definition, bandwidth limited white noise is a random process with a constant power spectral density function defined by

$$G_x(f) = a \qquad 0 \leq f_0 - (B/2) \leq f \leq f_0 + (B/2)$$
$$= 0 \qquad \text{otherwise}$$

where f_0 is the center frequency, B is the bandwidth, and a is a constant. From Eq. (3.77), it follows that the associated autocorrelation function is

$$R_x(\tau) = \int_{f_0-(B/2)}^{f_0+(B/2)} a \cos 2\pi f \tau \, df = a B \left(\frac{\sin \pi B\tau}{\pi B\tau} \right) \cos 2\pi f_0 \tau$$

For the special case where $f_0 = B/2$, these equations become

$$G_x(f) = a \qquad 0 \leq f \leq B$$
$$= 0 \qquad \text{otherwise}$$

and

$$R_x(\tau) = a B \left(\frac{\sin 2\pi B\tau}{2\pi B\tau} \right)$$

In a theoretical limiting case when $G_x(f) = a$ for all frequencies, the process is called *white noise*. For this case, $R_x(\tau) = a\,\delta(\tau)$, where $\delta(\tau)$ is the usual delta function.

***Example* 3.11. Power Spectrum for Sum of Two Stationary Processes.** Determine the one-sided power spectral density function for the sum of the two stationary random processes considered in Example 3.8. From Example 3.8, the sum autocorrelation function

$$R_y(\tau) = a_1^2 R_{x_1}(\tau) + a_1 a_2 [R_{x_1 x_2}(\tau) + R_{x_2 x_1}(\tau)] + a_2^2 R_{x_2}(\tau)$$

It follows from Eqs. (3.76) and (3.79) that

$$G_y(f) = a_1^2 G_{x_1}(f) + a_1 a_2 [G_{x_1 x_2}(f) + G_{x_2 x_1}(f)] + a_2^2 G_{x_2}(f)$$

Thus the sum power spectral density function requires knowledge of the input cross-spectral density functions as well as their power spectral density functions.

Tables 3.2 and 3.3 present a summary of equations for some special stationary autocorrelation functions and related one-sided power spectral density functions which are used in theoretical studies.

Table 3.2   Special Autocorrelation Functions

Type		Autocorrelation Function
Constant		$R_x(\tau) = c^2$
Sine wave		$R_x(\tau) = \dfrac{X^2}{2}\cos 2\pi f_0 \tau$
White noise		$R_x(\tau) = a\,\delta(\tau)$
Low-pass, white noise		$R_x(\tau) = a\,B\left(\dfrac{\sin 2\pi B\tau}{2\pi B\tau}\right)$
Band-pass white noise		$R_x(\tau) = a\,B\left(\dfrac{\sin \pi B\tau}{\pi B\tau}\right)\cos 2\pi f_0 \tau$
Exponential		$R_x(\tau) = e^{-a|\tau|}$
Exponential cosine		$R_x(\tau) = e^{-a|\tau|}\cos 2\pi f_0 \tau$
Exponential cosine, exponential sine		$R_x(\tau) = e^{-a|\tau|}(b\cos 2\pi f_0 \tau + c\sin 2\pi f_0\,|\tau|)$

86

Table 3.3   Special Power Spectral Density Functions

Type	(One-Sided) Power Spectral Density Function
Constant	$G_x(f) = c^2\,\delta(f)$
Sine wave	$G_x(f) = \dfrac{X^2}{2}\,\delta(f - f_0)$
White noise	$G_x(f) = a,\quad f \geq 0;\qquad \text{otherwise zero}$
Low-pass white noise	$G_x(f) = a,\quad 0 \leq f \leq B;\qquad \text{otherwise zero}$
Band-pass white noise	$G_x(f) = a,\quad 0 < f_0 - (B/2) \leq f \leq f_0 + (B/2)$ otherwise zero
Exponential	$G_x(f) = \dfrac{4a}{a^2 + 4\pi^2 f^2}$
Exponential cosine	$G_x(f) = 2a\left[\dfrac{1}{a^2 + 4\pi^2(f + f_0)^2} + \dfrac{1}{a^2 + 4\pi^2(f - f_0)^2}\right]$
Exponential cosine, exponential sine	$G_x(f) = \dfrac{2ab + 4\pi c(f + f_0)}{a^2 + 4\pi^2(f + f_0)^2} + \dfrac{2ab - 4\pi c(f - f_0)}{a^2 + 4\pi^2(f - f_0)^2}$

3.2.4   Ergodic Random Processes

Consider two weakly stationary random processes $\{x_k(t)\}$ and $\{y_k(t)\}$ with two arbitrary sample functions $x_k(t)$ and $y_k(t)$. These stationary random processes are said to be *weakly ergodic* if the mean values and covariance (correlation) functions, which are defined by certain *ensemble averages* in Section 3.2.1, may be calculated by performing corresponding *time averages* on the arbitrary pair of sample functions. In this way the underlying statistical structure of the weakly stationary random processes may be determined quite simply from an available sample pair without the need for collecting a considerable amount of data.

To be more specific, the mean values of the individual sample functions $x_k(t)$ and $y_k(t)$, when computed by a time average, may be represented by

$$\mu_x(k) = \lim_{T \to \infty} \frac{1}{T} \int_0^T x_k(t)\, dt$$

$$\mu_y(k) = \lim_{T \to \infty} \frac{1}{T} \int_0^T y_k(t)\, dt$$

$$(3.90)$$

Observe that the answer is no longer a function of t since t has been averaged out. In general, however, the answer is a function of the particular sample function chosen, as denoted by the index k.

The cross-covariance function and cross-correlation function between $x_k(t)$ and $y_k(t + \tau)$, when computed by a time average, are defined by the expression

$$\begin{aligned}
C_{xy}(\tau, k) &= \lim_{T \to \infty} \frac{1}{T} \int_0^T [x_k(t) - \mu_x(k)][y_k(t + \tau) - \mu_y(k)]\, dt \\
&= \lim_{T \to \infty} \frac{1}{T} \int_0^T x_k(t)\, y_k(t + \tau)\, dt - \mu_x(k)\, \mu_y(k) \\
&= R_{xy}(\tau, k) - \mu_x(k)\, \mu_y(k)
\end{aligned}$$

$$(3.91)$$

The autocovariance functions and autocorrelation functions are defined by

$$\begin{aligned}
C_x(\tau, k) &= \lim_{T \to \infty} \frac{1}{T} \int_0^T [x_k(t) - \mu_x(k)][x_k(t + \tau) - \mu_x(k)]\, dt \\
&= R_x(\tau, k) - \mu_x^2(k) \\
C_y(\tau, k) &= \lim_{T \to \infty} \frac{1}{T} \int_0^T [y_k(t) - \mu_y(k)][y_k(t + \tau) - \mu_y(k)]\, dt \\
&= R_y(\tau, k) - \mu_y^2(k)
\end{aligned}$$

$$(3.92)$$

These quantities should now be compared with the previously defined ensemble mean values μ_x, μ_y, and ensemble covariance functions $C_x(\tau)$, $C_y(\tau)$, $C_{xy}(\tau)$ for stationary random processes developed in Section 3.2.1. If it turns out that, independent of k,

$$\mu_x(k) = \mu_x$$
$$\mu_y(k) = \mu_y$$

(3.93)

$$C_x(\tau, k) = C_x(\tau)$$
$$C_y(\tau, k) = C_y(\tau)$$

(3.94)

$$C_{xy}(\tau, k) = C_{xy}(\tau)$$

(3.95)

then the random processes $\{x_k(t)\}$ and $\{y_k(t)\}$ are said to be *weakly ergodic*. If all ensemble averaged statistical properties of $\{x_k(t)\}$ and $\{y_k(t)\}$, not just the means and covariances, are deducible from corresponding time averages, then the random processes are said to be *strongly ergodic*. Thus strong ergodicity implies weak ergodicity, but not conversely. No distinction between these concepts exists for Gaussian random processes.

For an arbitrary random process to be ergodic, it must first be stationary. Each sample function must then be representative of all the others in the sense described above so that it does not matter which particular sample function is used in the time-averaging calculations. This restriction serves to eliminate many stationary random processes from ergodicity.

Example **3.12. Nonergodic Stationary Random Process.** A simple example of a nonergodic stationary random process follows. Consider a hypothetical random process $\{x_k(t)\}$ composed of sinusoidal sample functions such that

$$\{x_k(t)\} = \{X(k) \sin [2\pi f t + \phi(k)]\}$$

Let the amplitude $X(k)$ and the phase angle $\phi(k)$ be random variables which take on a different set of values for each sample function. If $\phi(k)$ is uniformly distributed, the properties of the process computed over the ensemble at specific times will be independent of time; hence the process is stationary. However, the properties computed by time averaging over individual sample functions are not always the same. For example, the autocovariance (or autocorrelation) function for each sample function is given here by

$$C_x(\tau, k) = \frac{X^2(k)}{2} \sin 2\pi f \tau$$

Since $X(k)$ is a function of k, $C_x(\tau, k) \neq C_x(\tau)$. Hence the random process is nonergodic.

There are two important classes of random processes which one can state in advance will be ergodic. The first ergodic class is the class of stationary Gaussian random processes whose power spectral density functions are absolutely continuous, Ref. 11, p. 532; that is, no sharp lines (delta functions) appear in the power spectra corresponding to infinite mean square densities at discrete frequencies. The second ergodic class (a special case of the first class) is the class of stationary Gaussian Markov processes; a Markov process is one whose relationship to the past does not extend beyond the immediately preceding observation. The autocorrelation function of a stationary Gaussian Markov process may be shown to be of a simple exponential form, Ref. 11, p. 233.

Sufficient conditions for a random process to be ergodic are as follows.

I. A sufficient condition for an arbitrary random process to be weakly ergodic is that it be weakly stationary, and that the time averages $\mu_x(k)$ and $C_x(\tau, k)$ be the same for all sample functions k.

The proof of this result is as follows. By definition,

$$\mu_x(k) = \lim_{T \to \infty} \frac{1}{T} \int_0^T x_k(t)\, dt$$

By hypothesis, $\mu_x(k)$ is independent of k. Hence the expected value over k is the same as an individual estimate, namely,

$$E[\mu_x(k)] = \mu_x(k)$$

Also, as will be proved in Eq. (3.116), expected values commute with linear operations. Hence

$$E[\mu_x(k)] = \lim_{T \to \infty} \frac{1}{T} \int_0^T E[x_k(t)]\, dt$$

$$= \lim_{T \to \infty} \frac{1}{T} \int_0^T \mu_x\, dt = \mu_x$$

The assumption of weak stationarity is used in setting $E[x_k(t)] = \mu_x$. Thus

$$\mu_x(k) = \mu_x$$

Similarly,

$$C_x(\tau, k) = C_x(\tau)$$

since the hypothesis that $C_x(\tau, k)$ is independent of k yields

$$E[C_x(\tau, k)] = C_x(\tau, k)$$

while the stationary hypothesis yields

$$E[C_x(\tau, k)] = C_x(\tau)$$

This completes the proof.

II. A sufficient condition for a Gaussian random process to be ergodic is that it be weakly stationary, and the autocovariance function $C_x(\tau)$ has the following four integrable properties.

$$\int_{-\infty}^{\infty} |C_x(\tau)|\, d\tau < \infty \qquad \int_{-\infty}^{\infty} C_x^{\,2}(\tau)\, d\tau < \infty$$

$$\int_{-\infty}^{\infty} |\tau C_x(\tau)|\, d\tau < \infty \qquad \int_{-\infty}^{\infty} |\tau|\, C_x^{\,2}(\tau)\, d\tau < \infty \tag{3.96}$$

The proof of this result is contained in later Sections 5.3.1 and 5.3.2. It is shown that time averages for mean value estimates and autocovariance function estimates are independent of the particular sample record when the above four integrable properties on $C_x(\tau)$ are satisfied. This result then follows from the preceding result. In practice, these conditions are frequently satisfied, justifying the assumption of ergodicity.

3.2.5 Gaussian Random Processes

The formal definition of a Gaussian random process is as follows. A random process $\{x_k(t)\}$ is said to be a Gaussian random process if, for every set of fixed times $\{t_n\}$, the random variables $x_k(t_n)$ follow a multidimensional normal distribution as defined by Eq. (3.36).

Gaussian random processes are quite prevalent in physical problems, and often may be mathematically predicted by the multidimensional Central Limit Theorem. Also, one may show that if a Gaussian process undergoes a linear transformation, then the output will still be a Gaussian process. This property is quite important in various engineering processing of physical data which is considered to be Gaussian.

Consider a time history $x(t)$ which is a sample function from an ergodic Gaussian random process with zero mean value. Note that the index k is no longer needed since the properties of any one sample function will be representative of all other sample functions. From the ergodic property, the timewise behavior of $x(t)$ over a long period of time will exhibit the same statistical characteristics as corresponding ensemble averages at various fixed times. As a consequence, it follows that the probability density function associated with the instantaneous values of $x(t)$ that will occur over a long time interval is given by the Gaussian probability density function with zero mean value, as follows.

$$p(x) = \left(\sigma_x\sqrt{2\pi}\right)^{-1} e^{-x^2/2\sigma_x^2} \tag{3.97}$$

The variance $\sigma_x{}^2$ when $x(t)$ has zero mean is determined by

$$\sigma_x{}^2 = E[x^2(t)] = \int_{-\infty}^{\infty} x^2 p(x)\, dx \qquad \text{independent of } t$$

$$\approx \frac{1}{T} \int_0^T x^2(t)\, dt \qquad \text{for large } T$$

$$= \int_{-\infty}^{\infty} S_x(f)\, df = 2 \int_0^{\infty} S_x(f)\, df = \int_0^{\infty} G_x(f)\, df \qquad (3.98)$$

Thus, the Gaussian probability density function $p(x)$ is completely characterized through knowledge of $S_x(f)$ or $G_x(f)$ since they alone determine σ_x. This important result places knowledge of $S_x(f)$ or $G_x(f)$ at the forefront of much work in analysis of random records. It should be noted that no restriction is placed on the shape of the power spectral density function or its associated autocorrelation function.

If the mean value of $x(t)$ is not zero, then the underlying probability density function is given by the general Gaussian formula

$$p(x) = \left(\sigma_x \sqrt{2\pi}\right)^{-1} e^{-(x-\mu_x)^2/2\sigma_x{}^2} \qquad (3.99)$$

where the mean value

$$\mu_x = E[x(t)] = \int_{-\infty}^{\infty} x\, p(x)\, dx \qquad \text{independent of } t$$

$$\approx \frac{1}{T} \int_0^T x(t)\, dt \qquad \text{for large } T \qquad (3.100)$$

and the variance

$$\sigma_x{}^2 = E[x(t) - \mu_x]^2 = E[x^2(t)] - \mu_x{}^2 \qquad (3.101)$$

The *central moments* for any probability distribution are defined by

$$m_n{}' = E[(x - \mu_x)^n] = \int_{-\infty}^{\infty} (x - \mu_x)^n\, p(x)\, dx \qquad (3.102)$$

where the prime is used to denote central moments as opposed to ordinary moments. For the Gaussian case, where $p(x)$ is given by Eq. (3.99),

$$m_n{}' = 0 \qquad \text{if } n \text{ is an odd integer}$$

$$m_{2n}{}' = 1\ 3\ 5 \cdots (2n - 1)\sigma_x{}^{2n} \qquad \text{for } n = 0, 1, 2, 3, \ldots \qquad (3.103)$$

Thus

$$m_0{}' = 1 \qquad m_2{}' = \sigma_x{}^2 \qquad m_4{}' = 3\sigma_x{}^4 \qquad \text{etc.}$$

Assume $\{x(t)\}$ is a stationary Gaussian random process where the index k is omitted for simplicity in notation. Consider the two random variables $x_1 = x(t)$ and $x_2 = x(t + \tau)$ at an arbitrary pair of fixed times t and $t + \tau$.

Assume that x_1 and x_2 follow a two-dimensional (joint) Gaussian distribution with zero means and equal variances σ_x^2. By definition,

$$\sigma_x^2 = E[x^2(t)] = E[x^2(t + \tau)] = \int_{-\infty}^{\infty} x^2 p(x) \, dx \qquad (3.104)$$

$$R_x(\tau) = E[x(t) \, x(t + \tau)] = \rho_x(\tau)\sigma_x^2 = \iint_{-\infty}^{\infty} x_1 x_2 \, p(x_1, x_2) \, dx_1 \, dx_2 \qquad (3.105)$$

where the quantity $\rho_x(\tau)$ is defined by Eq. (3.105).

Here, letting $\rho = \rho_x(\tau)$, the joint Gaussian probability density function is given by

$$p(x_1, x_2) = \left(2\pi\sigma_x^2\sqrt{1 - \rho^2}\right)^{-1} \exp\left[\frac{-1}{2\sigma_x^2(1 - \rho^2)} (x_1^2 - 2\rho x_1 x_2 + x_2^2)\right]$$

$$(3.106)$$

One can prove directly that

$$\int_{-\infty}^{\infty} \int_{-\infty}^{\infty} p(x_1, x_2) \, dx_1 \, dx_2 = 1 \qquad (3.107)$$

Also, it follows that

$$p(x_1) = \int_{-\infty}^{\infty} p(x_1, x_2) \, dx_2 = (\sigma_x\sqrt{2\pi})^{-1} \, e^{-x_1^2/2\sigma_x^2} \qquad (3.108)$$

with a similar result for $p(x_2)$.

By definition, the two variables x_1 and x_2 are uncorrelated if $\rho = 0$. When $\rho = 0$, Eq. (3.106) becomes

$$p(x_1, x_2) = p(x_1) \, p(x_2) \qquad (3.109)$$

The conditional probability density function $p(x_2 \mid x_1)$ is defined by

$$p(x_2 \mid x_1) = \frac{p(x_1, x_2)}{p(x_1)} \qquad \text{assuming } p(x_1) \neq 0 \qquad (3.110)$$

For a Gaussian process, from Eqs. (3.106) and (3.108),

$$p(x_2 \mid x_1) = \left(\sigma_x\sqrt{1 - \rho^2}\sqrt{2\pi}\right)^{-1} \exp\left[\frac{-(x_2 - \rho x_1)^2}{2\sigma_x^2(1 - \rho^2)}\right] \qquad (3.111)$$

Thus the conditional probability density function of x_2 given x_1 is *Gaussian*, with mean value ρx_1 and variance $\sigma_x^2(1 - \rho^2)$. This provides an easy interpretation for $p(x_2 \mid x_1)$ in this case.

Consider four random variables x_1, x_2, x_3, and x_4 which follow a four-dimensional Gaussian distribution with possibly different nonzero mean values. A useful relation which can be derived from Eq. (3.36), see Ref. 18, p. 83, is

$$E[x_1 x_2 x_3 x_4] = E[x_1 x_2] \, E[x_3 x_4] + E[x_1 x_3] \, E[x_2 x_4]$$
$$+ \, E[x_1 x_4] \, E[x_2 x_3] - 2\mu_{x_1}\mu_{x_2}\mu_{x_3}\mu_{x_4} \quad (3.112)$$

Note how the fourth-order quantity in question is the product of its possible different second-order quantities. In particular, if $x_1 = x(u)$, $x_2 = y(u + \tau)$, $x_3 = x(v)$, $x_4 = y(v + \tau)$, with the stationary cross-correlation function

$$R_{xy}(\tau) = E[x(t)y(t + \tau)]$$

and equal nonzero mean values μ_x, then

$$E[x(u) \, y(u + \tau) \, x(v) \, y(v + \tau)]$$
$$= R_{xy}{}^2(\tau) + R_x(v - u)R_y(v - u) \quad (3.113)$$
$$+ \, R_{xy}(v - u + \tau)R_{yx}(v - u - \tau) - 2\mu_x{}^4$$

3.3 Linear Transformations of Random Processes

The dynamic behavior of representative linear physical systems has been discussed in practical terms in Chapter 2. It will be helpful at this time to consider very briefly the mathematical properties of linear transformations of random processes in more detail. This background will be assumed whenever required in Sections 3.4 and 3.5 which develop important input-output relationships for linear systems subjected to random inputs.

Consider an arbitrary random process $\{x_k(t)\}$. An operator A which transforms a sample function $x_k(t)$ into another function $y_k(v)$ may be written as

$$y_k(v) = A[x_k(t)] \quad (3.114)$$

where A denotes a functional operation on the term inside the brackets [ ]. The argument v may or may not be the same as t. For example, if the operation in question is differentiation, then $v = t$ and $y_k(t)$ will be a sample function from the derivative random process $\{x_k{}'(t)\}$, assuming of course that the derivative exists. A different example is when the operation in question is integration between definite limits. Here, $v = t$, and $y_k(v)$ will be a random variable over the index k, determined by $x_k(t)$ and the definite limits. The operator A can take many different forms. In the following, the sample space index k will be omitted for simplicity in notation.

The operator A is said to be *linear* and time invariant (constant parameter) if, for any set of admissible values $x_1, x_2, \ldots, x_N$ and constants $a_1, a_2, \ldots, a_N$, it follows that

$$A\left[\sum_{i=1}^{N} a_i x_i\right] = \sum_{i=1}^{N} a_i A[x_i] \tag{3.115}$$

In words, the operation is both additive and homogeneous. The admissible values here may be different sample functions at the same t, or they may be different values from the same sample function at different t.

For any linear operation where all quantities exist, the procedure of taking expected values of random variables is commutative with the linear operation. That is, for fixed t and v,

$$E[y(v)] = E[A[x(t)]] = A[E[x(t)]] \tag{3.116}$$

This result is proved easily, as follows. Assume $x(t)$ takes on N discrete values $x_1, x_2, \ldots, x_N$ and $y(v)$ takes on N corresponding discrete values $y_1, y_2, \ldots, y_N$ where $y_i = A[x_i]$. Then

$$E[y(v)] = \frac{1}{N}\sum_{i=1}^{N} y_i = \frac{1}{N}\sum_{i=1}^{N} A[x_i] \quad \text{and} \quad E[x(t)] = \frac{1}{N}\sum_{i=1}^{N} x_i$$

Now, since A is a linear operator,

$$\frac{1}{N}\sum_{i=1}^{N} A[x_i] = A\left[\frac{1}{N}\sum_{i=1}^{N} x_i\right] = A[E[x(t)]]$$

Hence

$$E[y(v)] = A[E[x(t)]]$$

The continuous case follows by letting N approach infinity and using an appropriate convergence criterion, such as Eq. (3.125). This completes the proof.

A basic result whose proof follows directly from definitions is as follows. *If $x(t)$ is from a weakly (strongly) stationary random process and if the operator A is linear and time-invariant, then $y(v) = A[x(t)]$ will form a weakly (strongly) stationary random process.*

Another result of special significance, proved in Ref. 10, p. 155, is as follows. *If $x(t)$ follows a Gaussian distribution and the operator A is linear, then $y(v) = A[x(t)]$ will also follow a Gaussian distribution.*

3.3.1 Moment Transformations

The first moment of $y(v)$ at $v = v_1$ is defined by

$$m_{1,y}(v_1) = E[y(v_1)] \tag{3.117}$$

From Eq. (3.116), letting $y(v_1) = A[x(t_1)]$,

$$m_{1,y}(v_1) = E[A[x(t_1)]] = A[E[x(t_1)]] = A[m_{1,x}(t_1)] \qquad (3.118)$$

where $m_{1,x}(t_1) = E[x(t_1)]$ is the first moment of $x(t)$ at $t = t_1$.

The second moment of $y(v)$ at $v = v_1$ is defined by

$$m_{2,y}(v_1) = E[y^2(v_1)] = E[\{A[x(t_1)]\}^2] \qquad (3.119)$$

The mixed second moment of $y(v)$ at $v = v_1$ and $v = v_2$ is defined by

$$m_{2,y}(v_1, v_2) = E[y(v_1)y(v_2)] = E[\{A[x(t_1)]\}\{A[x(t_2)]\}] \qquad (3.120)$$

and includes Eq. (3.119) as a special case. Similar definitions hold for higher-order moments.

For a stationary process $\{x(t)\}$, and a linear time invariant operator A, the first moment of $x(t)$ will be independent of t and the first moment of $y(v)$ will be independent of v. Equation (3.118) becomes

$$m_{1,y} = E[y(v)] = A[m_{1,x}] \qquad (3.121)$$

Higher-order moments of $y(v)$ will also be independent of v. The set of moments

$$m_{n,y} = E[y^n(v)] \qquad n = 1, 2, 3, \ldots, \qquad (3.122)$$

characterize the probability distribution for y and can be determined from the set of mixed higher-order moments of $x(t)$. This is shown in the next section for the case of integral transformations.

3.3.2   Integral Transformations

An integral transformation of any particular sample function $x(t)$ from an arbitrary random process $\{x(t)\}$ is defined by

$$I = \int_a^b x(t)\ \phi(t)\ dt \qquad (3.123)$$

where $\phi(t)$ is an arbitrary given function for which the integral exists. For any given $\phi(t)$ and limits (a, b), the quantity I is a random variable which depends on the particular sample function $x(t)$.

In order to investigate statistical properties of the random variable I, it is customary to break up the integration interval (a, b) into subintervals Δt, and consider the approximation linear sum

$$I_N \approx \sum_{i=1}^N x(i\,\Delta t)\ \phi(i\,\Delta t)\ \Delta t \qquad (3.124)$$

Convergence of I_N to I may now be defined by different criteria. The sequence $\{I_N\}$ is said to converge to I

1. In the *mean square sense* if

$$\lim_{N \to \infty} E[|I_N - I|^2] = 0 \qquad (3.125)$$

2. In *probability* if for every $\epsilon > 0$

$$\lim_{N \to \infty} \text{Prob} \, [|I_N - I| \geq \epsilon] = 0 \qquad (3.126)$$

From the Tchebycheff inequality of Eq. (3.15), it follows directly that convergence in the mean square sense implies convergence in probability. In practice, most integral expressions involving random variables exist by assuming convergence in the mean square sense.

Consider now the transformation of moments of $x(t)$ due to the linear integral operation. Since the average of a sum equals the sum of the averages, the first moment

$$E[I] = \mu_I \approx \sum_{i=1}^{N} \mu_x(i \, \Delta t) \, \phi(i \, \Delta t) \, \Delta t$$

On passing to an integral, one obtains

$$\mu_I = \int_a^b \mu_x \, \phi(t) \, dt \qquad (3.127)$$

This result can also be obtained directly by applying Eq. (3.121) to Eq. (3.123).

Similarly, by considering finite sums and passing to integral form, one derives for the second moment

$$E[I^2] = \Psi_I^2 = \int_a^b \int_a^b R_x(t_1, t_2) \, \phi(t_1) \, \phi(t_2) \, dt_1 \, dt_2 \qquad (3.128)$$

where $R_x(t_1, t_2) = m_{2,x}(t_1, t_2)$ and $\Psi_I^2 = m_{2,I}$. Equation (3.128) shows that the second moment of I requires knowledge of the mixed second moment of $x(t)$. Extensions of Eq. (3.128) to higher-order moments of I of order n requires an n-fold integration of mixed nth-order moments of $x(t)$. For example, using the notation of Section 3.3.1,

$$m_{3,I} = \int_a^b \int_a^b \int_a^b m_{3,x}(t_1, t_2, t_3) \, \phi(t_1) \, \phi(t_2) \, \phi(t_3) \, dt_1 \, dt_2 \, dt_3$$

3.3.3 Derivative Transformations

The derivative of a sample function $x(t)$ from an arbitrary random process $\{x(t)\}$ is defined by the linear operation

$$x'(t) = \lim_{\Delta t \to 0} \left[\frac{x(t + \Delta t) - x(t)}{\Delta t} \right] \qquad (3.129)$$

when this limit exists. For any given $x(t)$, the derivative $x'(t)$ is a sample function which depends upon $x(t)$. The following result states the conditions under which a derivative exists for *stationary* processes.

The derivative $x'(t)$ will exist in the mean square sense if and only if the stationary autocorrelation function $R_x(\tau)$ is differentiable with respect to τ at the point $\tau = 0$ with $R_x'(0) = 0$.

Reference 5, Section 5.8, contains a proof for a generalized version of this result which is applicable to nonstationary Gaussian processes. Existence in the mean square sense occurs here if the variance of the quotient of Eq. (3.129) is finite as $\Delta t \to 0$.

A consequence of this result is that if $R_x(\tau)$ has a derivative with respect to τ at $\tau = 0$, then it is necessary that this derivative equal zero.

$$R_x'(0) = 0 \tag{3.130}$$

Another general result for stationary processes is that the expected value of the derivative random process $\{x'(t)\}$ at any t must equal zero,

$$E[x'(t)] = 0 \tag{3.131}$$

This follows because $E[x'(t)] = (d/dt)E[x(t)]$ and $E[x(t)]$ is independent of t for a stationary process.

3.4   Single-Input Linear Systems

Consider a physically realizable constant parameter linear system with a weighting function $h(\tau)$ and frequency response function $H(f)$, as defined

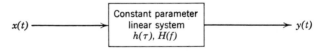

Figure 3.2   Single-input linear system.

and discussed in Chapter 2. Assume the system is subjected to a well-defined single input $x(t)$, which is from a stationary random process $\{x(t)\}$, as illustrated in Figure 3.2. The output $y(t)$ will then belong to a stationary random process $\{y(t)\}$. Various important relations between the input, the system, and the output will now be developed. Note that the index k of the sample space is omitted for simplicity in notation.

3.4.1   Correlation and Spectral Relations

As stated earlier by Eqs. (2.1) and (2.2), the output $y(t)$ is given by

$$y(t) = \int_0^\infty h(\tau)\, x(t - \tau)\, d\tau \tag{3.132}$$

If desired, the lower limit may be set equal to $-\infty$ instead of 0 to facilitate changes of variables that will be made later. However, it is understood then that $h(\tau) = 0$ for $\tau < 0$.

For a pair of times t and $t + \tau$, the product $y(t) y(t + \tau)$ is given by

$$y(t) y(t + \tau) = \int\!\!\int_0^\infty h(\xi) h(\eta) x(t - \xi) x(t + \tau - \eta) \, d\xi \, d\eta \quad (3.133)$$

Upon taking the expected value of Eq. (3.133), one obtains

$$R_y(\tau) = \int\!\!\int_0^\infty h(\xi) h(\eta) R_x(\tau + \xi - \eta) \, d\xi \, d\eta \quad\quad (3.134)$$

Note that this result is independent of t. This general result shows how to obtain the output stationary autocorrelation function from an input stationary autocorrelation function and the system weighting function entirely from operations in the time domain.

The stationary cross-correlation function $R_{xy}(\tau)$ between the input $x(t)$ and the output $y(t + \tau)$ is derived from the relation

$$x(t) y(t + \tau) = \int_0^\infty h(\xi) x(t) x(t + \tau - \xi) \, d\xi \quad\quad (3.135)$$

Upon taking the expected value of Eq. (3.135), one obtains

$$R_{xy}(\tau) = \int_0^\infty h(\xi) R_x(\tau - \xi) \, d\xi \quad\quad (3.136)$$

The transformation of Eqs. (3.134) and (3.136) to a complex-valued frequency domain by taking Fourier transforms yields the important power spectra and cross-spectra relations

$$S_y(f) = |H(f)|^2 S_x(f) \quad\quad (3.137)$$

and

$$S_{xy}(f) = H(f) S_x(f) \qu\quad\quad (3.138)$$

These formulas follow directly from definitions, together with suitable substitutions and algebraic manipulations. Note that Eq. (3.137) contains only the gain factor $|H(f)|$, while Eq. (3.138) is actually a pair of equations containing both the gain factor and the phase factor.

In terms of one-sided physically realizable spectral density functions $G_x(f)$, $G_y(f)$, and $G_{xy}(f)$, which exist only for $f \geq 0$, Eqs. (3.137) and (3.138) become

$$G_y(f) = |H(f)|^2 G_x(f) \quad\quad (3.139)$$

$$G_{xy}(f) = H(f) G_x(f) \quad\quad (3.140)$$

From Eqs. (2.24) and (3.84), Eq. (3.140) is equivalent to

$$|G_{xy}(f)| \, e^{-j\theta_{xy}(f)} = |H(f)| \, e^{-j\phi(f)} G_x(f) \qquad (3.141)$$

Thus

$$|G_{xy}(f)| = |H(f)| \, G_x(f) \qquad (3.142)$$

$$\theta_{xy}(f) = \phi(f) \qquad (3.143)$$

Equation (3.139) shows how the output spectral density function $G_y(f)$ can be determined from the input spectral density function $G_x(f)$ and the system gain factor $|H(f)|$. It follows that the output mean square value is given by

$$\Psi_y^2 = \int_0^\infty G_y(f) \, df = \int_0^\infty |H(f)|^2 \, G_x(f) \, df \qquad (3.144)$$

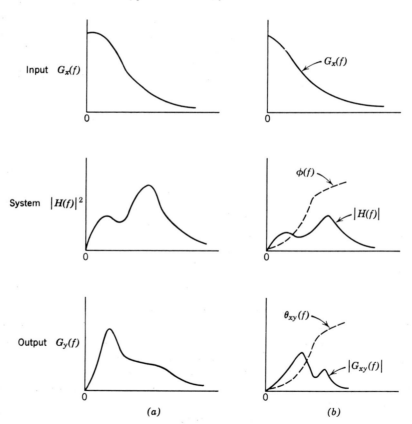

Figure 3.3   Input-output spectrum relations for linear systems: (a) power spectrum, (b) cross-spectrum.

Equation (3.139) also permits the input spectral density function to be determined from the output spectral density function and system gain factor, or the system gain factor to be determined from the input and output spectral density functions. However, Eq. (3.139) does not permit the determination of the complete frequency response function $H(f)$ for the system since this relationship does not include the system phase factor $\phi(f)$.

In order to determine the complete frequency response function of the system, one must acquire cross-spectral density function information. The relation of Eq. (3.140) provides a convenient interpretation of the cross-spectral density function in terms of $H(f)$ and $G_x(f)$. A special relation involving cross-spectra quantities which would determine the phase factor $\phi(f)$ of the system alone is

$$\frac{G_{xy}(f)}{G_{yx}(f)} = \frac{H(f)}{H^*(f)} = e^{-j2\phi(f)} \tag{3.145}$$

where $H^*(f)$ is the complex conjugate of $H(f)$. Note that Eq. (3.145) actually determines $2\phi(f)$ instead of $\phi(f)$.

The results of Eqs. (3.139) and (3.140) provide the basis for many physical applications of random process theory. Figure 3.3 illustrates how an input power spectrum, described by $G_x(f)$, is modified in passing through a linear system, described by $H(f)$.

Example **3.13. Response Properties of Low-Pass Filter to White Noise.** Assume white noise is applied to the input of a low-pass RC filter with a time constant $K = RC$. Determine the output power spectral density function, the output mean square value, and the output autocorrelation function.

The frequency response function for the low-pass RC filter is

$$H(f) = (1 + j2\pi Kf)^{-1} = |H(f)| \, e^{-j\phi(f)}$$

corresponding to a weighting function of

$$h(\tau) = \frac{1}{K} e^{-\tau/K} \qquad \tau \geq 0$$

$$= 0 \qquad \tau < 0$$

Here

$$|H(f)| = [1 + (2\pi Kf)^2]^{-\frac{1}{2}}$$

$$\phi(f) = \tan^{-1}(2\pi Kf)$$

From Eqs. (3.142) and (3.144), if $G_x(f)$ is white noise where $G_x(f) = a$, a constant for all $f \geq 0$,

$$G_y(f) = |H(f)|^2 G_x(f) = \frac{a}{1 + (2\pi Kf)^2} \qquad 0 \leq f < \infty$$

$$\Psi_y^2 = \int_0^\infty G_y(f) \, df = \int_0^\infty \frac{a}{1 + (2\pi Kf)^2} \, df = \frac{a}{4K}$$

Equation (3.77) yields

$$R_y(\tau) = \int_0^\infty G_y(f) \cos 2\pi f \tau \, df = \frac{a}{4K} e^{-|\tau|/K}$$

Example 3.14. Response Properties of Low-Pass Filter to Sine Wave. Assume a sine wave with power spectral density function $G_x(f) = (X^2/2) \, \delta(f - f_0)$ where $f_0 > 0$ is applied to the low-pass RC filter of Example 3.13. Determine the output power spectral density function, the output mean square value, and the output autocorrelation function.

For this problem,

$$G_y(f) = |H(f)|^2 G_x(f) = \frac{(X^2/2) \, \delta(f - f_0)}{1 + (2\pi Kf)^2}$$

$$\Psi_y^2 = \int_0^\infty G_y(f) \, df = \frac{X^2/2}{1 + (2\pi K f_0)^2}$$

$$R_y(\tau) = \int_0^\infty G_y(f) \cos 2\pi f \tau \, df = \frac{X^2/2}{1 + (2\pi K f_0)^2} \cos 2\pi f_0 \tau$$

Example 3.15. Force Input–Displacement Output System. Determine the output power spectral density function, the output autocorrelation function, and the output mean square value when the input is white noise, for the force input and displacement output system of Figure 2.2. These results apply also to other analogous systems, as discussed in Chapter 2.

Assume $G_x(f) = a$. Then, from Eq. (2.34a) or Table 2.1, when the force is expressed in displacement units, that is, $x(t) = F(t)/k$, the output power spectral density function becomes

$$G_y(f) = |H(f)|^2_{f-d} a = \frac{a}{[1 - (f/f_n)^2]^2 + (2\zeta f/f_n)^2} \qquad 0 \leq f < \infty$$

The corresponding output autocorrelation function is given by

$$R_y(\tau) = \frac{a\pi f_n e^{-2\pi f_n \zeta |\tau|}}{4\zeta} \left[\cos \left(2\pi f_n \sqrt{1 - \zeta^2} \, \tau \right) \right.$$
$$\left. + \frac{\zeta}{\sqrt{1 - \zeta^2}} \sin \left(2\pi f_n \sqrt{1 - \zeta^2} \, |\tau| \right) \right] \qquad (3.146)$$

The output mean square value is

$$\Psi_y^2 = \int_0^\infty G_y(f)\, df = R_y(0) = \frac{a\pi f_n}{4\zeta}$$

***Example* 3.16. Displacement Input–Displacement Output System.**
Determine the output power spectral density function, the output auto-correlation function, and the output mean square value when the input is white noise, for the displacement input and displacement output system of Figure 2.4. These results apply also to other analogous systems, as discussed in Chapter 2.

Assume $G_x(f) = a$. Then, from Eq. (2.48a), or Table 2.1, the output power spectral density function becomes

$$G_y(f) = |H(f)|_{a-a}^2 = \frac{a[1 + (2\zeta f/f_n)^2]}{[1 - (f/f_n)^2]^2 + (2\zeta f/f_n)^2}$$

The corresponding output autocorrelation function is given by

$$R_y(\tau) = \frac{a\pi f_n(1 + 4\zeta^2)}{4\zeta}\, e^{-2\pi f_n \zeta |\tau|}\left[\cos\left(2\pi f_n\sqrt{1 - \zeta^2}\,\tau\right)\right.$$

$$\left. + \frac{\zeta(1 - 4\zeta^2)}{\sqrt{1 - \zeta^2}\,(1 + 4\zeta^2)}\,\sin\left(2\pi f_n\sqrt{1 - \zeta^2}\,|\tau|\right)\right] \quad (3.147)$$

The output mean square value is

$$\Psi_y^2 = \int_0^\infty G_y(f)\, df = R_y(0) = \frac{a\pi f_n(1 + 4\zeta^2)}{4\zeta}$$

The importance of exponential-cosine and exponential-sine autocorrelation functions for many physical problems are apparent from the last two examples.

3.4.2 Coherence Functions

The coherence function between the input $x(t)$ and the output $y(t)$ is a real-valued quantity defined by

$$\gamma_{xy}^2(f) = \frac{|G_{xy}(f)^2|}{G_x(f)\, G_y(f)} = \frac{|S_{xy}(f)|^2}{S_x(f)\, S_y(f)} \quad (3.148)$$

where the G's are the one-sided measurable spectra, and the S's are the two-sided theoretical spectra defined previously. From Eqs. (3.88) or (3.89), the coherence function satisfies for all f

$$0 \leq \gamma_{xy}^2(f) \leq 1 \quad (3.149)$$

which is analogous to the square of the correlation function coefficient $\rho_{xy}{}^2(\tau)$ defined by Eqs. (3.52) or (3.54).

For a constant parameter linear system, Eqs. (3.139) and (3.142) apply and may be substituted into Eq. (3.148) to obtain

$$\gamma_{xy}{}^2(f) = \frac{|H(f)|^2 G_x{}^2(f)}{G_x(f)\,|H(f)|^2 G_x(f)} = 1 \tag{3.150}$$

Hence, for the ideal case of a constant parameter linear system with a single clearly defined input and output, the coherence function will be unity.

If $x(t)$ and $y(t)$ are completely unrelated, the coherence function will be zero. If the coherence function is greater than zero but less than unity, one or more of three possible situations exist.

(a) Extraneous noise is present in the measurements.
(b) The system relating $x(t)$ and $y(t)$ is not linear.
(c) $y(t)$ is an output due to an input $x(t)$ as well as to other inputs.

Methods for evaluating effects of situation (a) using ordinary coherence functions are developed in Section 5.4.7. Methods for evaluating situation (b) are discussed in Ref. 17. Methods for evaluating situation (c) are discussed in Section 3.5.

For applications of coherence functions to problems of estimating linear frequency response functions, one may consider the coherence function to be the ratio of two different measures of the square of the system gain factor. From Eq. (3.139), one measure is given by

$$|H(f)|_1^2 = \frac{G_y(f)}{G_x(f)} \tag{3.151}$$

From Eq. (3.140), the second measure is given by

$$|H(f)|_2^2 = \frac{|G_{xy}(f)|^2}{G_x{}^2(f)} \tag{3.152}$$

Now, their ratio gives the coherence function as follows.

$$\frac{|H(f)|_2^2}{|H(f)|_1^2} = \frac{|G_{xy}{}^2(f)|^2}{G_x(f)\,G_y(f)} = \gamma_{xy}{}^2(f) \tag{3.153}$$

In practice, measured values of Eq. (3.153) will be between zero and unity. The gain factor estimate of Eq. (3.151), based upon power spectra calculations of input and output, will be a biased estimate for all cases except when the coherence function equals unity. The gain factor estimate of Eq. (3.152), however, based upon the input power spectrum and the cross-spectrum between input and output, will be a biased estimate if extraneous noise is present at the input, but will be an unbiased estimate if extraneous noise is present at the output only. In particular, Eq. (3.152) provides an unbiased estimate for the frequency response function gain factors in multiple input problems when the inputs are uncorrelated (incoherent), as proved in Eq. (3.171). These matters are discussed further in Sections 5.4.6 and 5.7.5 where it is shown how the accuracy of unbiased frequency response function estimates increases as the coherence function approaches unity.

3.5   Multiple-Input Linear Systems

Constant parameter linear systems responding to multiple inputs from stationary random processes will now be considered. It will be assumed that N inputs are occurring with a single output being measured. For convenience, two-sided spectral quantities $S(f)$ will be used in the developments instead of one-sided measurable spectral quantities $G(f)$. All the resulting formulas will be valid when the S's are replaced by their corresponding G's.

3.5.1   Autocorrelation and Power Spectral Relations

Consider N constant parameter linear systems with N clearly defined inputs $x_i(t)$, $i = 1, 2, 3, \ldots, N$ and one measured output $y(t)$, as illustrated in Figure 3.4. The output may be considered as the sum of the N outputs $y_i(t)$, $i = 1, 2, 3, \ldots, N$. That is,

$$y(t) = \sum_{i=1}^{N} y_i(t) \tag{3.154}$$

where $y_i(t)$ is defined as that part of the output which is produced by the ith input when all the other inputs are zero.

Let the function $h_i(\tau)$ be defined as the weighting function which is associated with the input $x_i(t)$. Hence, from Eq. (2.1), $y_i(t)$ is given by

$$y_i(t) = \int_0^\infty h_i(\tau) \, x_i(t - \tau) \, d\tau \tag{3.155}$$

Moreover, the frequency response function is given by Eq. (2.22) and the relation between Fourier transforms of the input and output is given by Eq. (2.23). That is,

$$Y_i(f) = H_i(f) \, X_i(f) \tag{3.156}$$

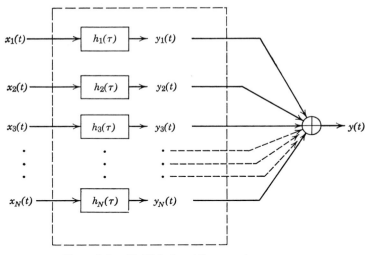

Figure 3.4   Multiple-input linear system.

where $H_i(f)$ is the frequency response function corresponding to $h_i(\tau)$. The Fourier transform, $Y(f)$, of the total output then is

$$Y(f) = \sum_{i=1}^{N} Y_i(f) = \sum_{i=1}^{N} H_i(f)\, X_i(f) \qquad (3.157)$$

Assume next that the $x_i(t)$ are sample functions from different stationary random processes with mean values of μ_i. Here, independent of t,

$$\mu_i = E[x_i(t)] \qquad (3.158)$$

where each $x_i(t)$ is defined over an appropriate sample space. Recalling that the expected value operator is linear, the expected value of $y(t)$ then is obtained as

$$\mu_y = E[y(t)] = E\left[\sum_{i=1}^{N} \int_0^\infty h_i(\tau)\, x_i(t-\tau)\, d\tau \right]$$

$$= \sum_{i=1}^{N} \int_0^\infty h_i(\tau)\, E[x_i(t-\tau)]\, d\tau$$

$$= \sum_{i=1}^{N} \mu_i \int_0^\infty h_i(\tau)\, d\tau = \sum_{i=1}^{N} \mu_i\, H_i(0) \qquad (3.159)$$

Equation (3.159) is a general result for arbitrary μ_i. If each $\mu_i = 0$, then $\mu_y = 0$.

The autocorrelation function, $R_y(\tau)$, may also be computed. Assuming that the process is stationary, one finds

$$R_y(\tau) = E[y(t)\, y(t + \tau)] = E\left[\sum_i y_i(t) \sum_j y_j(t + \tau)\right]$$

$$= E\left[\sum_i \sum_j \int_0^\infty h_i(\xi)\, x_i(t - \xi)\, d\xi \int_0^\infty h_j(\eta) x_j(t + \tau - \eta)\, d\eta\right]$$

$$= \sum_i \sum_j \iint_0^\infty h_i(\xi)\, h_j(\eta)\, E[x_i(t - \xi)\, x_j(t + \tau - \eta)]\, d\xi\, d\eta$$

$$= \sum_{i=1}^N \sum_{j=1}^N \iint_0^\infty h_i(\xi)\, h_j(\eta)\, R_{ij}(\xi - \eta + \tau)\, d\xi\, d\eta \qquad (3.160)$$

In Eq. (3.160), $R_{ij}(\tau)$ is defined as

$$R_{ij}(\tau) = R_{x_i x_j}(\tau) = E[x_i(t)\, x_j(t + \tau)] \qquad (3.161)$$

Equation (3.160) is a general result for correlated inputs.

If it is assumed that all the various inputs are mutually uncorrelated, then

$$R_{ij}(\tau) = \begin{cases} R_i(\tau) & \text{when } i = j \\ 0 & \text{when } i \neq j \end{cases} \qquad (3.162)$$

In this case, Eq. (3.160) simplifies to

$$R_y(\tau) = \sum_{i=1}^N \iint_0^\infty h_i(\xi)\, h_i(\eta)\, R_i(\xi - \eta + \tau)\, d\xi\, d\eta \qquad (3.163)$$

The power spectral density relations will now be computed. For stationary random processes, the two-sided power spectral density function $S_y(f)$ is given as the Fourier transform of the autocorrelation function $R_y(\tau)$. Thus the Fourier transform of Eq. (3.160) yields the output power spectral density function as follows.

$$S_y(f) = \int_{-\infty}^\infty e^{-j2\pi f\tau}\, R_y(\tau)\, d\tau$$

$$= \int_{-\infty}^\infty e^{-j2\pi f\tau}\left(\sum_i \sum_j \iint_0^\infty h_i(\xi)\, h_j(\eta)\, R_{ij}(\xi - \eta + \tau)\, d\xi\, d\eta\right) d\tau$$

$$(3.164)$$

To simplify Eq. (3.164), one notes that the factor $e^{-j2\pi f(\xi-\eta)} e^{j2\pi f(\xi-\eta)} = 1$ may be inserted, and the equation then becomes

$$S_y(f) = \sum_i \sum_j \int_{-\infty}^{\infty} \iint_0^{\infty} h_i(\xi) e^{j2\pi f\xi} h_j(\eta) e^{-j2\pi f\eta}$$
$$R_{ij}(\xi - \eta + \tau) e^{-j2\pi f(\xi-\eta+\tau)} d\xi \, d\eta \, d\tau \quad (3.165)$$

Now, the change of the variable $t = \xi - \eta + \tau$ and $dt = d\tau$ is made, and Eq. (3.165) may be factored to give the following general result for correlated inputs.

$$S_y(f) = \sum_i \sum_j \int_0^{\infty} h_i(\xi) e^{j2\pi f\xi} d\xi \int_0^{\infty} h_j(\eta) e^{-j2\pi f\eta} d\eta \int_{-\infty}^{\infty} R_{ij}(t) e^{-j2\pi ft} dt$$
$$= \sum_{i=1}^{N} \sum_{j=1}^{N} H_i^*(f) H_j(f) S_{ij}(f) \quad (3.166)$$

In Eq. (3.166), $S_{ij}(f)$ represents the cross-spectral density function between the inputs $x_i(t)$ and $x_j(t)$, that is, $S_{ij}(f) = S_{x_i x_j}(f)$. Realizable one-sided spectra $G_y(f)$ and $G_{ij}(f)$ can replace $S_y(f)$ and $S_{ij}(f)$ since the common factor of two cancels out.

Equation (3.166) is a generalization of the mutually uncorrelated value case where the autocorrelation function is given by Eq. (3.163). Using these assumptions, Eq. (3.166) becomes

$$S_y(f) = \sum_{i=1}^{N} |H_i(f)|^2 S_i(f) \quad (3.167)$$

3.5.2 Cross-Correlation and Cross-Spectral Relations

The cross-spectral relations corresponding to Figure 3.4 are obtained by calculating the cross-spectral density function $S_{x_i y}(f) = S_{iy}(f)$ of the output $y(t)$ with one of the inputs, say $x_i(t)$. The general result for correlated inputs is

$$S_{iy}(f) = \sum_{j=1}^{N} H_j(f) S_{ij}(f) \quad (3.168)$$

This equation is derived in a manner similar to the previous derivation of $S_y(f)$, as follows.

$$S_{iy}(f) = \int_{-\infty}^{\infty} e^{-j2\pi f\tau} R_{iy}(\tau) d\tau$$
$$= \sum_{j=1}^{N} \int_{-\infty}^{\infty} \left(\int_{-\infty}^{\infty} e^{-j2\pi f\xi} h_j(\xi) \right) e^{-j2\pi f(\tau-\xi)} R_{ij}(\tau - \xi) d\xi \, d\tau$$
$$= \sum_{j=1}^{N} H_j(f) S_{ij}(f) \quad (3.168)$$

where utilization is made of the fact that the cross-correlation function $R_{iy}(\tau)$ is given by

$$R_{iy}(\tau) = E[x_i(t)\, y(t + \tau)] = E\left[x_i(t) \sum_j \int_0^\infty x_j(t + \tau - \xi)\, h_j(\xi)\, d\xi\right]$$

$$= \sum_j \int_0^\infty h_j(\xi)\, E[x_i(t)\, x_j(t + \tau - \xi)]\, d\xi$$

$$= \sum_{j=1}^N \int_0^\infty h_j(\xi)\, R_{ij}(\tau - \xi)\, d\xi \qquad (3.169)$$

If it is assumed that the inputs are mutually uncorrelated, then Eq. (3.169) reduces to

$$R_{iy}(\tau) = \int_0^\infty h_i(\xi)\, R_i(\tau - \xi)\, d\xi \qquad (3.170)$$

Hence the cross-spectral input/output formula becomes

$$S_{iy}(f) = H_i(f)\, S_i(f) \qquad (3.171)$$

Equation (3.171) is a useful and interesting result since it implies that the frequency response characteristics for the structural path associated with the input $x_i(t)$ can be measured by means of the cross-spectra whether or not the other inputs are active, as long as the inputs are mutually uncorrelated. This result solves the problem of how to measure the individual frequency response functions for uncorrelated inputs. The statistical accuracy of the measurements can be determined from a knowledge of the coherence function as discussed in Sections 5.4.6 and 5.7.5.

3.5.3 Matrix Formulation of Results

The preceding formulas can be expressed more concisely by the use of matrix notation and, in addition, some further results become more readily apparent. First, define an N-dimensional input vector

$$\mathbf{x}(t) = [x_1(t), x_2(t), \ldots, x_N(t)] \qquad (3.172)$$

Also define an N-dimensional frequency response function vector

$$\mathbf{H}(f) = [H_1(f), H_2(f), \ldots, H_N(f)] \qquad (3.173)$$

Next define an N-dimensional cross-spectrum vector of the output $y(t)$ with the inputs $x_i(t)$,

$$\mathbf{S}_{xy}(f) = [S_{1y}(f), S_{2y}(f), \ldots, S_{Ny}(f)] \qquad (3.174)$$

where

$$S_{iy}(f) = S_{x_iy}(f) \qquad i = 1, 2, \ldots, N \qquad (3.175)$$

Finally, define the $N \times N$ matrix of cross-spectra of all the inputs $x_i(t)$ by

$$\mathbf{S}_{xx}(f) = \begin{bmatrix} S_{11}(f) & S_{12}(f) & \cdots & S_{1N}(f) \\ S_{21}(f) & S_{22}(f) & \cdots & S_{2N}(f) \\ \cdot & \cdot & & \cdot \\ \cdot & \cdot & & \cdot \\ \cdot & \cdot & & \cdot \\ S_{N1}(f) & S_{N2}(f) & \cdots & S_{NN}(f) \end{bmatrix} \tag{3.176}$$

where

$$S_{ij}(f) = S_{x_i x_j}(f) \qquad i, j = 1, 2, \ldots, N \tag{3.177}$$

The result of Eq. (3.166) may be rewritten in matrix form as

$$S_{yy}(f) = \mathbf{H}(f)\,\mathbf{S}_{xx}(f)\,\mathbf{H}^{*\prime}(f) \tag{3.178}$$

where $\mathbf{H}^{*\prime}(f)$ denotes the complex conjugate transpose vector. When fully written out, Eq. (3.178) becomes

$$S_{yy}(f) = [H_1(f), H_2(f), \ldots, H_N(f)]$$

$$\times \begin{bmatrix} S_{11}(f) & S_{12}(f) & \cdots & S_{1N}(f) \\ S_{21}(f) & S_{22}(f) & \cdots & S_{2N}(f) \\ \cdot & \cdot & & \cdot \\ \cdot & \cdot & & \cdot \\ \cdot & \cdot & & \cdot \\ S_{N1}(f) & S_{N2}(f) & \cdots & S_{NN}(f) \end{bmatrix} \begin{bmatrix} H_1^*(f) \\ H_2^*(f) \\ \cdot \\ \cdot \\ \cdot \\ H_N^*(f) \end{bmatrix} \tag{3.179}$$

The column vector on the right is the transposed complex conjugate of $\mathbf{H}(f)$, that is,

$$\mathbf{H}^{*\prime}(f) = \begin{bmatrix} H_1^*(f) \\ H_2^*(f) \\ \cdot \\ \cdot \\ \cdot \\ H_N^*(f) \end{bmatrix} \tag{3.180}$$

Note that $S_{yy}(f)$ in Eq. (3.178) is still a scalar quantity but the other quantities are not. Equation (3.178) is also a proper representation of Eq. (3.167) where the off-diagonal elements of the matrix $\mathbf{S}_{xx}(f)$ become zero for uncorrelated inputs.

In place of Eq. (3.168), the system of equations for $i = 1, 2, \ldots, N$ may be written as the matrix equation

$$\mathbf{S}_{xy}'(f) = \mathbf{S}_{xx}(f)\,\mathbf{H}'(f) \qquad (3.181)$$

This is equivalent to

$$
\begin{bmatrix}
S_{1y}(f) \\
S_{2y}(f) \\
\cdot \\
\cdot \\
\cdot \\
S_{Ny}(f)
\end{bmatrix}
=
\begin{bmatrix}
S_{11}(f) & S_{12}(f) & \cdots & S_{1N}(f) \\
S_{21}(f) & S_{22}(f) & \cdots & S_{2N}(f) \\
\cdot & \cdot & & \cdot \\
\cdot & \cdot & & \cdot \\
\cdot & \cdot & & \cdot \\
S_{N1}(f) & S_{N2}(f) & \cdots & S_{NN}(f)
\end{bmatrix}
\begin{bmatrix}
H_1(f) \\
H_2(f) \\
\cdot \\
\cdot \\
\cdot \\
H_N(f)
\end{bmatrix}
\qquad (3.182)
$$

where the column vectors are the transposed row vectors of $\mathbf{S}_{xy}(f)$ and $\mathbf{H}(f)$.

The matrix equation (3.181) may be solved for the transposed row vector $\mathbf{H}'(f)$ if $\mathbf{S}_{xy}(f)$ and $\mathbf{S}_{xx}(f)$ have been measured or are known. This is, of course, a system of N simultaneous linear equations whose solution is

$$\mathbf{H}'(f) = \mathbf{S}_{xx}^{-1}(f)\mathbf{S}_{xy}'(f) \qquad (3.183)$$

where $\mathbf{S}_{xx}^{-1}(f)$ represents the inverse matrix to $\mathbf{S}_{xx}(f)$. Equation (3.183) gives each $H_i(f)$ as a function of the input/output cross-spectra $S_{iy}(f)$ and the input/input cross-spectra $S_{ij}(f)$, and holds *whether or not the various inputs are correlated*.

The inverse matrix, $\mathbf{S}_{xx}^{-1}(f)$, is obtained by dividing the transposed adjoint matrix of $\mathbf{S}_{xx}(f)$ by its determinant Δ. The adjoint matrix of $\mathbf{S}_{xx}(f)$ is the matrix obtained by substituting the cofactor of the element $S_{ij}(f)$, denoted by Cof $S_{ij}(f)$, for the element $S_{ij}(f)$. In equation form,

$$
\begin{bmatrix}
S_{11}(f) & S_{12}(f) & \cdots & S_{1N}(f) \\
S_{21}(f) & S_{22}(f) & \cdots & S_{2N}(f) \\
\cdot & \cdot & & \cdot \\
\cdot & \cdot & & \cdot \\
\cdot & \cdot & & \cdot \\
S_{N1}(f) & S_{N2}(f) & \cdots & S_{NN}(f)
\end{bmatrix}^{-1}
$$

$$
= \frac{1}{\Delta}
\begin{bmatrix}
\text{Cof } S_{11}(f) & \text{Cof } S_{21}(f) & \cdots & \text{Cof } S_{N1}(f) \\
\text{Cof } S_{12}(f) & \text{Cof } S_{22}(f) & \cdots & \text{Cof } S_{N2}(f) \\
\cdot & \cdot & & \cdot \\
\cdot & \cdot & & \cdot \\
\cdot & \cdot & & \cdot \\
\text{Cof } S_{1N}(f) & \text{Cof } S_{2N}(f) & \cdots & \text{Cof } S_{NN}(f)
\end{bmatrix}
\qquad (3.184)
$$

3.5.4   Special Case of Two Inputs

Consider a two-input linear system as pictured in Figure 3.5 where $x_1(t)$ and $x_2(t)$ may be correlated. Assume one desires to determine the frequency response functions for the systems from spectral density information. For this case, Eq. (3.168) states

$$S_{1y}(f) = H_1(f)\, S_{11}(f) + H_2(f)\, S_{12}(f)$$
$$S_{2y}(f) = H_1(f)\, S_{21}(f) + H_2(f)\, S_{22}(f)$$

(3.185)

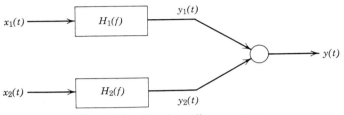

Figure 3.5   Two-input linear system.

The solutions for $H_1(f)$ and $H_2(f)$, assuming $\gamma_{12}^2(f) \neq 1$, are

$$H_1(f) = \frac{S_{1y}(f)\left[1 - \dfrac{S_{12}(f)\, S_{2y}(f)}{S_{22}(f)\, S_{1y}(f)}\right]}{S_{11}(f)[1 - \gamma_{12}^2(f)]}$$

(3.186)

$$H_2(f) = \frac{S_{2y}(f)\left[1 - \dfrac{S_{21}(f)\, S_{1y}(f)}{S_{11}(f)\, S_{2y}(f)}\right]}{S_{22}(f)[1 - \gamma_{12}^2(f)]}$$

(3.187)

where

$$\gamma_{12}^2(f) = \frac{|S_{12}(f)|^2}{S_{11}(f)\, S_{22}(f)}$$

(3.188)

For the special case when $\gamma_{12}^2(f) = 0$, the terms $S_{12}(f)$ and $S_{21}(f)$ are zero also, and Eqs. (3.186) and (3.187) reduce to the usual relations

$$H_1(f) = \frac{S_{1y}(f)}{S_{11}(f)}$$

(3.189)

$$H_2(f) = \frac{S_{2y}(f)}{S_{22}(f)}$$

(3.190)

The case when $\gamma_{12}^2(f) = 1$ must be handled separately. A coherence function of unity between $x_1(t)$ and $x_2(t)$ implies complete linear dependence between them. Hence one would consider a linear system existing between them, as illustrated below. The implication is that the first input $x_1(t)$ is

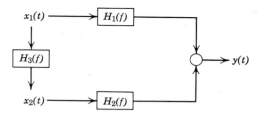

actually taking two different paths to arrive at the output $y(t)$. For this situation, a single frequency response function $H(f)$ will relate $y(t)$ to $x_1(t)$, namely,

$$x_1(t) \longrightarrow \boxed{H(f)} \longrightarrow y(t)$$

where

$$H(f) = H_1(f) + H_2(f)\,H_3(f)$$

In a general case where $\gamma_{12}^2(f) \neq 0$ or 1, the denominator in Eq. (3.186) is the spectrum of the residual process $\{\Delta x_1(t)\}$ resulting from $\{x_1(t)\}$ after a linear least-squares prediction of $\{x_1(t)\}$ from $\{x_2(t)\}$ has been subtracted from $\{x_1(t)\}$. Similarly, the numerator in Eq. (3.186) is the cross-spectrum of the residual processes $\{\Delta y(t)\}$ and $\{\Delta x_1(t)\}$, where $\{\Delta y(t)\}$ is the residual process resulting from $\{y(t)\}$ after a linear least-squares prediction of $\{y(t)\}$ from $\{x_2(t)\}$ has been subtracted from $\{y(t)\}$. These statements will now be explained by analogy from basic regression analysis theory in the next section.

3.5.5   Residual Random Variables

Consider any two real-valued stationary random processes $\{x(t)\}$ and $\{y(t)\}$. For fixed t, the quantities $x(t)$ and $y(t)$ are random variables over the sample space in question. For simplicity in notation, assume that the mean values are zero. A linear prediction $\hat{y}(t)$ of $y(t)$ from $x(t)$ can here be described by

$$\hat{y}(t) = c\,x(t) \tag{3.191}$$

where c is a constant to be determined. For least-squares prediction, the constant c is to be chosen so that the mean square error

$$\epsilon = E[(y(t) - \hat{y}(t))^2] = E[(y(t) - c\,x(t))^2]$$
$$= E[y^2(t)] - 2c\,E[x(t)\,y(t)] + c^2\,E[x^2(t)] \tag{3.192}$$

is a minimum over all possible choices of c. A necessary condition for c to satisfy is

$$\frac{\partial \epsilon}{\partial c} = 0 \tag{3.193}$$

and leads to the simple result

$$c = \frac{E[x(t)\, y(t)]}{E[x^2(t)]} = \frac{R_{xy}}{R_{xx}} \tag{3.194}$$

where $R_{xx} = R_{xx}(0)$ is the autocorrelation function of $\{x(t)\}$ at $\tau = 0$, and $R_{xy} = R_{xy}(0)$ is the cross-correlation function between $\{x(t)\}$ and $\{y(t)\}$ at $\tau = 0$. As defined by Eqs. (3.44) and (3.45),

$$R_{xx}(0) = E[x(t)\, x(t)] = R_{xx} \tag{3.195}$$

$$R_{xy}(0) = E[x(t)\, y(t)] = R_{xy} \tag{3.196}$$

The *residual (conditioned) random variable* $\Delta y(t)$ of $y(t)$ from $x(t)$ is defined by

$$\Delta y(t) = y(t) - \hat{y}(t) = y(t) - \left(\frac{R_{xy}}{R_{xx}}\right) x(t) \tag{3.197}$$

It follows that the autocorrelation function of $\{\Delta y(t)\}$ at $\tau = 0$ is given by $R_{\Delta y \Delta y} = R_{\Delta y \Delta y}(0)$, where

$$R_{\Delta y \Delta y}(0) = E[\Delta y(t)\, \Delta y(t)] = R_{yy}(1 - \rho_{xy}^2) = R_{\Delta y \Delta y} \tag{3.198}$$

The term $R_{yy} = R_{yy}(0)$ is the autocorrelation function of $\{y(t)\}$ at $\tau = 0$. Since the mean values are assumed to be zero, the quantity $\rho_{xy}^2 = \rho_{xy}^2(0)$ is the square of the function defined previously by Eq. (3.54), as follows.

$$\rho_{xy}^2(0) = \frac{R_{xy}^2(0)}{R_{xx}(0)\, R_{yy}(0)} = \frac{R_{xy}^2}{R_{xx}\, R_{yy}} = \rho_{xy}^2 \tag{3.199}$$

It satisfies the inequality

$$0 \leq \rho_{xy}^2 \leq 1 \tag{3.200}$$

When $\rho_{xy}^2 = 0$, then $R_{\Delta y \Delta y} = R_{yy}$, and there is no linear dependence between $x(t)$ and $y(t)$. When $\rho_{xy}^2 = 1$, then $R_{\Delta y \Delta y} = 0$, and $x(t)$ and $y(t)$ are completely linear related.

Consider now any three real-valued random variables $x_1(t)$, $x_2(t)$, and $y(t)$, from stationary random processes with zero mean values, where $x_1(t)$ and $x_2(t)$ may be correlated. For any fixed t, this can represent the situation in Figure 3.4. Here, in order to measure $H_1(f)$ properly, one should calculate the residual random variable of $x_1(t)$ from $x_2(t)$, as well as the residual random variable of $y(t)$ from $x_2(t)$. Analogous to Eq. (3.197), these residual random variables are

$$\Delta x_1(t) = x_1(t) - \left(\frac{R_{21}}{R_{22}}\right) x_2(t) \tag{3.201}$$

$$\Delta y(t) = y(t) - \left(\frac{R_{2y}}{R_{22}}\right) x_2(t) \tag{3.202}$$

Analogous to Eq. (3.198), the autocorrelation functions for $\{\Delta x_1(t)\}$ and $\{\Delta y(t)\}$ at $\tau = 0$ are

$$R_{\Delta x_1 \Delta x_1} = R_{11}(1 - \rho_{21}{}^2) \tag{3.203}$$

$$R_{\Delta y \Delta y} = R_{yy}(1 - \rho_{2y}{}^2) \tag{3.204}$$

where

$$\rho_{21}{}^2 = \frac{R_{21}{}^2}{R_{22} R_{11}} \qquad \rho_{2y}{}^2 = \frac{R_{2y}{}^2}{R_{22} R_{yy}} \tag{3.205}$$

$$R_{21} = E[x_2(t) \, x_1(t)] \qquad R_{2y} = E[x_2(t) \, y(t)] \tag{3.206}$$

The terms R_{11} and R_{22} are special cases of Eq. (3.206).

The cross-correlation function $R_{\Delta x_1 \Delta y} = R_{\Delta x_1 \Delta y}(0)$ between $\{\Delta x_1(t)\}$ and $\{\Delta y(t)\}$ at $\tau = 0$ is given by

$$R_{\Delta x_1 \Delta y}(0) = E[\Delta x_1(t) \, \Delta y(t)] = R_{\Delta x_1 \Delta y} \tag{3.207}$$

Substitution of Eqs. (3.201) and (3.202) into Eq. (3.207) yields

$$R_{\Delta x_1 \Delta y} = R_{1y}\left[1 - \frac{R_{12} R_{2y}}{R_{22} R_{1y}}\right] \tag{3.208}$$

An accepted notation for the quantity defined by Eq. (3.208) is

$$R_{\Delta x_1 y \Delta y} = R_{1y.2} \tag{3.209}$$

indicating that the residuals $\Delta x_1(t)$ and $\Delta y(t)$ are obtained by subtracting from $x_1(t)$ and $y(t)$ their respective linear least-squares prediction from $x_2(t)$. Similarly, this notation replaces the previous quantities in Eqs. (3.203) and (3.204) by

$$R_{\Delta x_1 \Delta x_1} = R_{11.2} \tag{3.210}$$

$$R_{\Delta y \Delta y} = R_{yy.2} \tag{3.211}$$

Since mean values are assumed to be zero, a partial correlation function coefficient at $\tau = 0$ can now be defined by its squared value

$$\rho^2_{1y.2} = \frac{R^2_{1y.2}}{R_{11.2} R_{yy.2}} \tag{3.212}$$

which satisfies the inequality

$$0 \leq \rho^2_{1y.2} \leq 1 \tag{3.213}$$

When mean values are not zero, definitions in this section are stated in terms of covariance functions instead of correlation functions.

3.5.6 Partial Coherence Functions for Two Inputs

Assume that $x(t)$ and $y(t)$ are real-valued random variables from stationary random processes $\{x(t)\}$ and $\{y(t)\}$. Let $X(f)$ and $Y(f)$ be their associated complex-valued random variables, as developed in Section 3.2.2. For real-valued random variables, the cross-correlation function $R_{xy}(0)$ is simply the expected value of the product $x(t) y(t)$. For corresponding complex-valued random variables, the cross-correlation function becomes the expected value of the product $X^*(f) Y(f)$, where one variable is replaced by its complex conjugate. Hence Eqs. (3.196) and (3.199) are analogous heuristically to

$$R_{xy}(f) = E[X^*(f) Y(f)] \tag{3.214}$$

$$\rho_{xy}{}^2(f) = \frac{|R_{xy}(f)|^2}{R_{xx}(f) R_{yy}(f)} \tag{3.215}$$

where $R_{xx}(f)$ and $R_{yy}(f)$ are special cases of Eq. (3.214).

From Eq. (3.64), the two-sided cross-spectral density function $S_{xy}(f)$ may be related to $R_{xy}(f)$ in Eq. (3.214), with similar expressions relating the power spectral density functions $S_{xx}(f)$ and $S_{yy}(f)$ to $R_{xx}(f)$ and $R_{yy}(f)$. From Eq. (3.148), it follows that the *ordinary coherence function* $\gamma_{xy}{}^2(f)$ may be related to Eq. (3.215) where

$$\gamma_{xy}{}^2(f) = \frac{|S_{xy}(f)|^2}{S_{xx}(f) S_{yy}(f)} \tag{3.216}$$

Consider now the two-input linear system of Figure 3.4 where the inputs $x_1(t)$ and $x_2(t)$ may be correlated. The *partial coherence function* between $x_1(t)$ and $y(t)$, with $x_2(t)$ removed at every t by least-squares prediction from $x_1(t)$ and $y(t)$, is analogous to Eq. (3.212), and is defined by

$$\gamma^2_{1y.2}(f) = \frac{|S_{1y.2}(f)|^2}{S_{11.2}(f) S_{yy.2}(f)} \tag{3.217}$$

The terms in Eq. (3.217) are called *residual* (or *conditioned*) *spectra*, and are defined by

$$S_{1y.2}(f) = S_{1y}(f)\left[1 - \frac{S_{12}(f)\,S_{2y}(f)}{S_{22}(f)\,S_{1y}(f)}\right] \tag{3.218}$$

$$S_{11.2}(f) = S_{11}(f)[1 - \gamma_{12}^2(f)] \tag{3.219}$$

$$S_{yy.2}(f) = S_{yy}(f)[1 - \gamma_{2y}^2(f)] \tag{3.220}$$

$$\gamma_{12}^2(f) = \frac{|S_{12}(f)|^2}{S_{11}(f)\,S_{22}(f)} \tag{3.221}$$

$$\gamma_{2y}^2(f) = \frac{|S_{2y}(f)|^2}{S_{22}(f)\,S_{yy}(f)} \tag{3.222}$$

Since $\gamma_{1y.2}^2(f)$ is a coherence function, it satisfies the inequality

$$0 \le \gamma_{1y.2}^2(f) \le 1 \tag{3.223}$$

The *residual* (*conditioned*) *spectral matrix*, between $x_1(t)$ and $y(t)$ is defined by

$$\mathbf{S}_{xy.2}(f) = \begin{bmatrix} S_{yy.2}(f) & S_{y1.2}(f) \\ S_{1y.2}(f) & S_{11.2}(f) \end{bmatrix} \tag{3.224}$$

where $S_{y1.2}(f)$ is the complex conjugate of $S_{1y.2}(f)$. The frequency response function $H_1(f)$ of Eq. (3.186) may now be calculated by the ratio of the two terms

$$H_1(f) = \frac{S_{1y.2}(f)}{S_{11.2}(f)} \tag{3.225}$$

The partial coherence function of Eq. (3.217) involves all four terms.

For an arbitrary two-input linear system where the inputs may be correlated, $S_{1y}(f)$ and $S_{2y}(f)$ are given by Eq. (3.185), whereas $S_{yy}(f)$ is given by Eq. (3.166). Specifically,

$$\begin{aligned} S_{yy}(f) = |H_1(f)|^2\,S_{11}(f) + H_1^*(f)\,H_2(f)\,S_{12}(f) \\ + H_2^*(f)\,H_1(f)\,S_{21}(f) + |H_2(f)|^2\,S_{22}(f) \end{aligned} \tag{3.226}$$

The ordinary coherence functions are

$$\gamma_{1y}^2(f) = \frac{|H_1(f)\,S_{11}(f) + H_2(f)\,S_{12}(f)|^2}{S_{11}(f)\,S_{yy}(f)} \tag{3.227}$$

$$\gamma_{2y}^2(f) = \frac{|H_1(f)\,S_{21}(f) + H_2(f)\,S_{22}(f)|^2}{S_{22}(f)\,S_{yy}(f)} \tag{3.228}$$

and may or may not be unity, depending upon the particular situation. Both erroneous high ordinary coherence and erroneous low ordinary coherence can occur. Under ideal conditions, however, assuming $H_1(f) \neq 0$ and $\gamma_{12}^2(f) \neq 1$, the partial coherence function of Eq. (3.217) will be exactly unity, since Eqs. (3.218), (3.219), and (3.220) become

$$S_{1y.2}(f) = H_1(f) S_{11}(f)[1 - \gamma_{12}^2(f)]$$
$$S_{11.2}(f) = S_{11}(f)[1 - \gamma_{12}^2(f)] \tag{3.229}$$
$$S_{yy.2}(f) = |H_1(f)|^2 S_{11}(f)[1 - \gamma_{12}^2(f)]$$

Thus the partial coherence function of Eq. (3.217),

$$\gamma_{1y.2}^2(f) = 1 \qquad \text{for all } f, \tag{3.230}$$

will reveal a true linear relationship even when this is not apparent from the ordinary coherence function, *regardless of whether or not the two inputs are correlated*.

For the special case when the two inputs are uncorrelated, $S_{12}(f)$ and $\gamma_{12}(f) = 0$. Here, the ordinary coherence functions become

$$\gamma_{1y}^2(f) = \frac{|H_1(f)|^2 S_{11}(f)}{|H_1(f)|^2 S_{11}(f) + |H_2(f)|^2 S_{22}(f)} \tag{3.231}$$

$$\gamma_{2y}^2(f) = \frac{|H_2(f)|^2 S_{22}(f)}{|H_1(f)|^2 S_{11}(f) + |H_2(f)|^2 S_{22}(f)} \tag{3.232}$$

Thus, for the uncorrelated two-input case, the sum

$$\gamma_{1y}^2(f) + \gamma_{2y}^2(f) = 1 \tag{3.233}$$

proving that each of these ordinary coherence functions will be strictly less than unity if the other is nonzero.

3.5.7 General Case of Multiple Inputs

Consider first the special case of two inputs. Define an augmented spectral matrix of $x_1(t)$, $x_2(t)$, and $y(t)$ by

$$\mathbf{S}_{yxx} = \begin{bmatrix} S_{yy} & S_{y1} & S_{y2} \\ S_{1y} & S_{11} & S_{12} \\ \hline S_{2y} & S_{21} & S_{22} \end{bmatrix} \tag{3.234}$$

where the dependence upon f is omitted for simplicity in notation. As in Eq. (3.224), the residual spectral matrix between $x_1(t)$ and $y(t)$ is defined by

$$\mathbf{S}_{xy.2} = \begin{bmatrix} S_{yy.2} & S_{y1.2} \\ S_{1y.2} & S_{11.2} \end{bmatrix} \tag{3.235}$$

Then, relative to the dotted blocks in S_{yxx}, one can verify that

$$\mathbf{S}_{xy.2} = \begin{bmatrix} S_{yy} & S_{y1} \\ S_{1y} & S_{11} \end{bmatrix} - \begin{bmatrix} S_{y2} \\ S_{12} \end{bmatrix} [S_{22}]^{-1} [S_{2y} \quad S_{21}] \qquad (3.236)$$

$$= \begin{bmatrix} S_{yy} - \dfrac{S_{y2} S_{2y}}{S_{22}}, & S_{y1} - \dfrac{S_{y2} S_{21}}{S_{22}} \\[3mm] S_{1y} - \dfrac{S_{12} S_{2y}}{S_{22}}, & S_{11} - \dfrac{S_{12} S_{21}}{S_{22}} \end{bmatrix} \qquad (3.237)$$

Equation (3.237) indicates how to calculate the terms in the residual matrix. The frequency response function $H_1(f)$ and its associated partial coherence function are now found by using Eqs. (3.225) and (3.217).

For a general case of N inputs, define an augmented $(N + 1, N + 1)$ spectral matrix of the N inputs $x_i(t)$ and the output $y(t)$ by

$$\mathbf{S}_{yxx} = \begin{bmatrix} S_{yy} & S_{y1} & S_{y2} & S_{y3} & \cdots & S_{yN} \\ S_{1y} & S_{11} & S_{12} & S_{13} & \cdots & S_{1N} \\ \hline S_{2y} & S_{21} & S_{22} & S_{23} & \cdots & S_{2N} \\ S_{3y} & S_{31} & S_{32} & S_{33} & \cdots & S_{3N} \\ \cdot & \cdot & \cdot & \cdot & & \cdot \\ \cdot & \cdot & \cdot & \cdot & & \cdot \\ \cdot & \cdot & \cdot & \cdot & & \cdot \\ S_{Ny} & S_{N1} & S_{N2} & S_{N3} & \cdots & S_{NN} \end{bmatrix} \qquad (3.238)$$

where the dependence upon f is once again omitted for simplicity in notation. The problem of interest is to: (1) determine the frequency response function $H_1(f)$, and (2) determine the partial coherence function between $x_1(t)$ and $y(t)$ when linear least-squares prediction of $x_1(t)$ and $y(t)$ from the sum of the other inputs are removed from $x_1(t)$ and $y(t)$. By symmetry, similar results follow for $H_2(f)$, $H_3(f)$, ..., $H_N(f)$, and for the corresponding partial coherence functions.

The solution to this general problem is discussed in Ref. 17, and is as follows. Partition the spectral matrix S_{yxx} as indicated by the dashed lines so that

$$\mathbf{S}_{yxx} = \left[\begin{array}{c|c} \mathbf{A}(2, 2) & \mathbf{B}(2, N-1) \\ \hline \mathbf{C}(N-1, 2) & \mathbf{D}(N-1, N-1) \end{array} \right] \qquad (3.239)$$

where $\mathbf{A}(2, 2)$, $\mathbf{B}(2, N - 1)$, $\mathbf{C}(N - 1, 2)$, and $\mathbf{D}(N - 1, N - 1)$ are submatrices with either 2 or $N - 1$ rows and columns, as defined below:

$$\mathbf{A}(2, 2) = \begin{bmatrix} S_{yy} & S_{y1} \\ S_{1y} & S_{11} \end{bmatrix} \tag{3.240}$$

$$\mathbf{B}(2, N - 1) = \begin{bmatrix} S_{y2} & S_{y3} & \cdots & S_{yN} \\ S_{12} & S_{13} & \cdots & S_{1N} \end{bmatrix} \tag{3.241}$$

$$\mathbf{C}(N - 1, 2) = \begin{bmatrix} S_{2y} & S_{21} \\ S_{3y} & S_{31} \\ \cdot & \cdot \\ \cdot & \cdot \\ \cdot & \cdot \\ S_{Ny} & S_{N1} \end{bmatrix} \tag{3.242}$$

$$\mathbf{D}(N - 1, N - 1) = \begin{bmatrix} S_{22} & S_{23} & \cdots & S_{2N} \\ S_{32} & S_{33} & \cdots & S_{3N} \\ \cdot & \cdot & & \cdot \\ \cdot & \cdot & & \cdot \\ \cdot & \cdot & & \cdot \\ S_{N2} & S_{N3} & \cdots & S_{NN} \end{bmatrix} \tag{3.243}$$

Define the residual (conditioned) spectral matrix between $x_1(t)$ and $y(t)$ by

$$\mathbf{S}_{xy.23\ldots N} = \begin{bmatrix} S_{yy.23\ldots N} & S_{y1.23\ldots N} \\ S_{1y.23\ldots N} & S_{11.23\ldots N} \end{bmatrix} \tag{3.244}$$

From the matrices $\mathbf{A}$, $\mathbf{B}$, $\mathbf{C}$, and $\mathbf{D}$, the four terms in $\mathbf{S}_{xy.23\ldots N}$ can be determined by carrying out the operations

$$\mathbf{S}_{xy.23\cdots N} = \mathbf{A} - \mathbf{B}\mathbf{D}^{-1}\mathbf{C} \tag{3.245}$$

where $\mathbf{D}^{-1}$ is the inverse of the matrix $\mathbf{D}$.

Now the frequency response function is given by the ratio of two of the terms in the residual matrix

$$H_1(f) = \frac{S_{1y.23\ldots N}(f)}{S_{11.23\ldots N}(f)} \tag{3.246}$$

and the partial coherence function is given by the ratio

$$\gamma^2_{1y.23\ldots N}(f) = \frac{|S_{1y.23\ldots N}(f)|^2}{S_{11.23\ldots N}(f)\, S_{yy.23\ldots N}(f)} \tag{3.247}$$

These same results hold if all two-sided spectral quantities, $S(f)$, are replaced by one-sided spectral quantities, $G(f)$. Further discussion of these ideas appears in Sections 5.7 and 7.5. Multiple coherence functions are defined in Section 5.7.1 which include partial coherence functions as special cases.

3.5.8 Application of Partial Coherence Functions

For the multiple-input problem, the partial coherence function, rather than the ordinary coherence function, gives a quantitative indication of the degree of linear dependence between a given input and the output. As mentioned previously, this is due to the fact that the computation of the partial coherence amounts to determining the coherence between two variables when the effects of extraneous variables have been subtracted out. When the effects of extraneous variables are not considered properly, the computation of ordinary coherences alone can lead to erroneous conclusions about the nature of the system. An example of erroneous high coherence is shown in Figure 3.6.

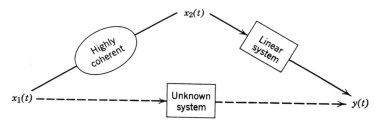

Figure 3.6   Example of erroneous high coherence.

Assume that a coherence function value near unity is computed between the two variables $x_1(t)$ and $y(t)$. One would be inclined to believe that there is a physical linear system relating these two variables as input and output. But suppose there is a third variable $x_2(t)$ which is highly coherent with $x_1(t)$ and also passes through a linear system to make up $y(t)$. In this type of situation, the high coherence computed between $x_1(t)$ and $y(t)$ might only be a reflection of the fact that $x_2(t)$ is highly coherent with $x_1(t)$, and $x_2(t)$ is related via a linear system to $y(t)$. In reality there may be no physical system between $x_1(t)$ and $y(t)$ at all. If the partial coherence function is computed between $x_1(t)$ and $y(t)$ in the situation, it might turn out to be a very small number near zero. Both the ordinary and the partial coherence between $x_2(t)$ and $y(t)$, however, would prove to be near unity.

Alternatively, the opposite situation can exist. An example of erroneous low coherence is shown in Figure 3.7. In this case, assume that $x_1(t)$ and $x_2(t)$ are uncorrelated, and that both pass through physically existing linear systems to make up $y(t)$. Hence, if one computes the ordinary coherence between $x_1(t)$ and $y(t)$, it would appear less than unity since there would be a contribution due to $x_2(t)$. This contribution, for practical purposes, would appear as a noise component at the output $y(t)$. The same thing would hold true if the ordinary coherence is computed between $x_2(t)$ and $y(t)$, with $x_1(t)$ appearing as a noise component in this case. In either of these situations, the true relation between $x_1(t)$ and $y(t)$, or between $x_2(t)$ and $y(t)$, is linear and the coherence should be one. If the partial coherence between $x_1(t)$ and $y(t)$ is computed, the effects of $x_2(t)$ would be subtracted out from $x_1(t)$ and $y(t)$, and the true coherence of unity would be uncovered. The same statements hold true when computing the partial coherence between $x_2(t)$ and $y(t)$.

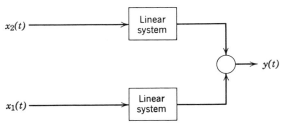

Figure 3.7 Example of erroneous low coherence.

Another application of coherence and partial coherence functions to the analysis of the response of complicated systems is the following. Consider the situation where one has measured a set of response variables which represent stationary random processes at different points of a system. Assume that no prior information is available to determine which of the measured responses may be considered as inputs and which as outputs. By means of the coherence and partial coherence functions, linear relationships between the various responses may be established. A study of the peaks in the cross-correlation functions will indicate time lags between the various response points and thus input-to-output direction. For example, if a peak in the cross-correlation function $R_{x_i x_j}(\tau)$, between $x_i(t)$ and $x_j(t)$, occurred at a positive value $\tau = +\tau_0$, then $x_i(t)$ would be considered an input. If the peak occurred at a negative value $\tau = -\tau_0$, then $x_j(t)$ would be the input.

It should be mentioned that the linear relationships established by the methods indicated above are not necessarily unique. This follows from the fact that different linear systems with different input-output relationships may produce identical coherence and partial coherence functions. However, from other considerations, the correct structure of the system may be inferred in many cases.

4

STATISTICAL TECHNIQUES
FOR EVALUATING DATA

Pertinent concepts of random process theory and its applications to the description and analysis of random data are developed in Chapter 3. Beyond these basic ideas of random process theory, the evaluation of random data often involves certain numerical manipulations where statistical techniques are required. This chapter will review and illustrate various statistical ideas which have wide applications to commonly occurring data evaluation problems. The intent is to supply the reader with a minimum background in terminology and certain techniques of applied statistics which are relevant to later discussions and to general applications.

4.1 Sample Values and Parameter Estimation

Consider a random variable $x(k)$ which may take on values in the range $-\infty$ to ∞. Any number of different parameters might be used to describe this random variable. For example, two descriptive parameters would be the mean value and variance which, from Chapter 3, are given by

$$\mu_x = E[x(k)] = \int_{-\infty}^{\infty} x \, p(x) \, dx \tag{4.1}$$

$$\sigma_x^2 = E[(x(k) - \mu_x)^2] = \int_{-\infty}^{\infty} (x - \mu_x)^2 \, p(x) \, dx \tag{4.2}$$

where $p(x)$ is the probability density function for the variable $x(k)$. These two parameters for $x(k)$ cannot, of course, be precisely determined in practice since an exact knowledge of the probability density function will not generally be available. Hence one must be content with an estimate for the mean value and variance based upon a finite number of observed values.

123

One possible method (there are others) for estimating the mean value and variance of $x(k)$ based upon N independent observed values would be as follows.

$$\bar{x} = \hat{\mu}_x = \frac{1}{N} \sum_{i=1}^{N} x_i \tag{4.3}$$

$$s_b^2 = \hat{\sigma}_x^2 = \frac{1}{N} \sum_{i=1}^{N} (x_i - \bar{x})^2 \tag{4.4}$$

Here, $\bar{x}$ and s_b^2 are the *sample mean* and *sample variance*, respectively. The hats ($\wedge$) over $\hat{\mu}_x$ and $\hat{\sigma}_x^2$ indicate that these sample parameters are being used as estimators for the mean value and variance of $x(k)$. The subscript on s_b^2 means that this is a biased variance estimate (to be discussed later). The number of values used to compute the estimates (sample values) is called the *sample size*.

The specific sample values in Eqs. (4.3) and (4.4) are not the only quantities which might be used to estimate the mean value and variance of a random variable $x(k)$. For example, reasonable estimates for the mean value and variance would also be obtained by dividing the summations in Eqs. (4.3) and (4.4) by $N - 1$ instead of N. Estimators are never clearly right or wrong since they are defined somewhat arbitrarily. Nevertheless, certain estimators can be judged as being "good" estimators, or "better" estimators than others.

Three principal factors can be used to establish the quality or "goodness" of an estimator. First, it is desirable that the expected value of the estimator be equal to the parameter being established. That is,

$$E[\hat{\Phi}] = \Phi \tag{4.5}$$

where $\hat{\Phi}$ is an estimator for the parameter Φ. If this is true, the estimator is said to be *unbiased*. Second, it is desirable that the mean square error of the estimator be smaller than for other possible estimators. That is,

$$E[(\hat{\Phi}_1 - \Phi)^2] \leq E[(\hat{\Phi}_i - \Phi)^2] \tag{4.6}$$

where $\hat{\Phi}_1$ is the estimator of interest and $\hat{\Phi}_i$ is any other possible estimator. If this is true, the estimator is said to be more *efficient* than other possible estimators. Third, it is desireable that the estimator approach the parameter being estimated with a probability approaching unity as the sample size becomes large. That is, for any $\epsilon > 0$,

$$\lim_{N \to \infty} \text{Prob} \left[|\hat{\Phi} - \Phi| \geq \epsilon \right] = 0 \tag{4.7}$$

If this is true, the estimator is said to be *consistent*. It follows from the Tchebycheff inequality of Eq. (3.36) that a sufficient (but not necessary) condition to meet the requirements of Eq. (4.7) is

$$\lim_{N \to \infty} E[(\hat{\Phi} - \Phi)^2] = 0 \qquad (4.8)$$

Consider the example of the mean value and variance estimators given by Eqs. (4.3) and (4.4). The expected value for the sample mean $\bar{x}$ is

$$E[\bar{x}] = E\left[\frac{1}{N}\sum_{i=1}^{N} x_i\right] = \frac{1}{N} E\left[\sum_{i=1}^{N} x_i\right] = \frac{1}{N}(N\mu_x) = \mu_x \qquad (4.9)$$

Hence the estimator $\hat{\mu}_x = \bar{x}$ is *unbiased*. The expected value for the sample variance s_b^2 is

$$E[s_b^2] = E\left[\frac{1}{N}\sum_{i=1}^{N}(x_i - \bar{x})^2\right] = \frac{1}{N} E\left[\sum_{i=1}^{N}(x_i - \bar{x})^2\right]$$

However,

$$\sum_{i=1}^{N}(x_i - \bar{x})^2 = \sum_{i=1}^{N}(x_i - \mu_x + \mu_x - \bar{x})^2$$

$$= \sum_{i=1}^{N}(x_i - \mu_x)^2 - 2(\bar{x} - \mu_x)\sum_{i=1}^{N}(x_i - \mu_x) + \sum_{i=1}^{N}(\bar{x} - \mu_x)^2$$

$$= \sum_{i=1}^{N}(x_i - \mu_x)^2 - 2(\bar{x} - \mu_x)N(\bar{x} - \mu_x) + N(\bar{x} - \mu_x)^2$$

$$= \sum_{i=1}^{N}(x_i - \mu_x)^2 - N(\bar{x} - \mu_x)^2$$

Since $E[(x_i - \mu_x)^2] = \sigma_x^2$ and $E[(\bar{x} - \mu_x)^2] = \sigma_x^2/N$, it follows that

$$E[s_b^2] = \frac{1}{N}(N\sigma_x^2 - \sigma_x^2) = \frac{(N-1)}{N}\sigma_x^2 \qquad (4.10)$$

Hence the estimator $\hat{\sigma}_x^2 = s_b^2$ is *biased*. Although the sample variance s_b^2 is a biased estimator for σ_x^2, it is a consistent estimator, as will be proved in Sections 5.3.2. The sample mean $\bar{x}$ is consistent as well as unbiased, as will be proved in Section 5.3.1. Both sample values can be shown to be efficient.

From the results in Eq. (4.10), it is clear that an unbiased estimator for

σ_x^2 may be obtained by computing a slightly different sample variance as follows.

$$s^2 = \hat{\sigma}_x^2 = \frac{1}{N-1} \sum_{i=1}^{N} (x_i - \bar{x})^2 \tag{4.11}$$

The quantity defined in Eq. (4.11) is an *unbiased* estimator for σ_x^2, as well as an efficient and consistent estimator. For this reason, the sample variance defined in Eq. (4.11) is usually considered a "better" estimator than the sample variance given by Eq. (4.4). The sample variance defined in Eq. (4.11) will be used henceforth as an estimator for the true variance of a random variable.

4.2   Important Probability Distribution Functions

Examples of several theoretical probability distribution functions are given in Section 3.1.5. The most important of these distribution functions from the viewpoint of applied statistics is the *normal* (Gaussian) distribution. There are three other distribution functions associated with normally distributed random variables that have wide applications as statistical tools. These are the χ^2 distribution, the t distribution, and the F distribution. Each of these three, along with the normal distribution, will now be defined and discussed. Applications for each as an analysis tool will be covered in later sections.

4.2.1   Normal Distribution

The most important type of random variable, which arises in both applied and theoretical statistics, is that variable $x(k)$ which has a probability *density* function given by

$$p(x) = (\sigma_x\sqrt{2\pi})^{-1} e^{-(x-\mu_x)^2/2\sigma_x^2} \tag{4.12a}$$

The corresponding probability *distribution* function for the variable $x(k)$ is given by

$$P(x) = \int_{-\infty}^{x} p(\xi) \, d\xi \tag{4.12b}$$

The distribution function defined in Eq. (4.12) is called the *normal* or *Gaussian* distribution.

A convenient form for the normal distribution is obtained by using the standardized variable $z(k)$ given by

$$z(k) = \frac{x(k) - {}_x\mu}{\sigma_x} \tag{4.13}$$

When Eq. (4.13) is substituted into Eqs. (4.12a) and (4.12b), a standardized normal density function and distribution function with zero mean and unit variance ($\mu_z = 0$; $\sigma_z^2 = 1$) are obtained as follows.

$$p(z) = (\sqrt{2\pi})^{-1} e^{-z^2/2} \tag{4.14a}$$

$$P(z) = \int_{-\infty}^{z} p(\xi) \, d\xi \tag{4.14b}$$

It is desirable for later applications to denote the value of $z(k)$, which corresponds with a specific probability $P(z) = 1 - \alpha$, by z_α. That is,

$$P(z_\alpha) = \int_{-\infty}^{z_\alpha} p(z) \, dz = \text{Prob} \, [z(k) \leq z_\alpha] = 1 - \alpha \tag{4.15a}$$

or

$$1 - P(z_\alpha) = \int_{z_\alpha}^{\infty} p(z) \, dz = \text{Prob} \, [z(k) > z_\alpha] = \alpha \tag{4.15b}$$

The value of z_α which satisfies Eq. (4.15) is called the 100α *percentage point.*

The density function $p(z)$ is unimodal, monotonic about the mode, and symmetric with inflection points at ± 1, as illustrated in Figure 4.1(a). The corresponding distribution function $P(z)$ is illustrated in Figure 4.1(b). A limited tabulation is presented for the ordinates of the standardized normal density function in Table 4.6, and for the areas under the standardized normal density function in Table 4.7, at the end of this chapter.

As discussed in Section 3.1.5, the normal distribution derives much of its usefulness from the well-known Central Limit Theorem, which essentially states that sums of independent random variables under fairly general conditions will be approximately normally distributed, regardless of the underlying distributions. Since many physically observed phenomena in practice actually represent the net effect of numerous contributing variables, the normal distribution constitutes a good approximation to commonly occurring distribution functions.

4.2.2   Chi-Square Distribution

Let $z_1(k), z_2(k), z_3(k), \ldots, z_N(k)$ be N independent random variables, each of which has a normal distribution with zero mean and unit variance. Let a new random variable be defined as

$$\chi_n^2 = z_1^2(k) + z_2^2(k) + z_3^2(k) + \cdots + z_N^2(k) \tag{4.16}$$

The random variable χ_n^2 is the chi-square variable with n degrees of freedom. The number of *degrees of freedom*, n, represents the number of independent or "free" squares entering into the expression. The probability density function for χ_n^2 is given by

$$p(\chi^2) = [2^{n/2} \, \Gamma(n/2)]^{-1}(\chi^2)^{((n/2)-1)} \, e^{-\chi^2/2} \qquad \chi^2 \geq 0 \tag{4.17a}$$

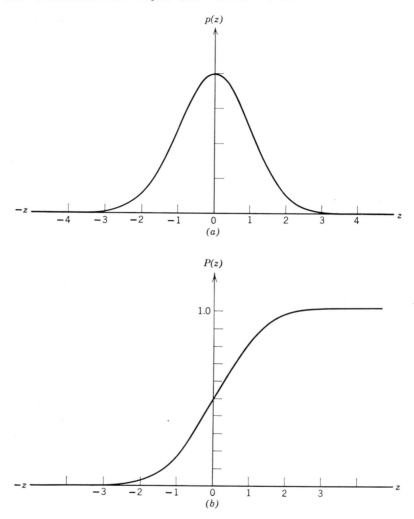

Figure 4.1 Standardized normal probability density and distribution functions. (*a*) Probability density function. (*b*) Probability distribution function.

where $\Gamma(n/2)$ is the gamma function. The corresponding distribution function for χ^2 is given by

$$P(\chi^2) = \int_{-\infty}^{\chi^2} p(\xi)\, d\xi \tag{4.17b}$$

The distribution function in Eq. (4.17) is called a *chi-square distribution* with n degrees of freedom. The 100α percentage point of the χ^2 distribution will be denoted by $\chi^2_{n;\alpha}$. That is,

$$\int_{\chi^2_{n;\alpha}}^{\infty} p(\chi^2)\, d\chi^2 = \text{Prob}\, [\chi_n{}^2 > \chi^2_{n;\alpha}] = \alpha \qquad (4.18)$$

The mean value and variance for the variable $\chi_n{}^2$ are

$$E[\chi_n{}^2] = \mu_{\chi^2} = n \qquad (4.19)$$

$$E[(\chi_n{}^2 - \mu_{\chi^2})^2] = \sigma_{\chi^2}{}^2 = 2n \qquad (4.20)$$

The density function $p(\chi^2)$ is monotonic for $n = 1$ and 2, and unimodal, monotonic about the mode, and nonsymmetric for $n > 2$, as illustrated in Figure 4.2(a). The corresponding distribution function $P(\chi^2)$ is shown in Figure 4.2(b). A limited tabulation of percentage points for the χ^2 distribution function is presented in Table 4.8 at the end of this chapter.

Several features of the chi-square distribution should be noted. First, the chi-square distribution is actually a special case of the more general gamma distribution function. Second, the square root of chi-square with two degrees of freedom (χ_2) constitutes an important special case called the *Rayleigh distribution function*, which is defined in Section 3.1.5. The Rayleigh distribution has wide applications to two-dimensional target problems. Furthermore, it is the limiting distribution function for the peak values of a narrow-band Gaussian random signal as the bandwidth approaches zero. Third, the square root of chi-square with three degrees of freedom (χ_3) constitutes another important special case which is called the *Maxwell distribution function*. The Maxwell distribution has applications to three-dimensional target problems. Fourth, a chi-square distribution approaches a normal distribution as the number of degrees of freedom becomes large. Specifically, for $n > 30$, the quantity $\sqrt{2\chi_n{}^2}$ is distributed approximately as a normal variable with a mean of $\mu = \sqrt{2n - 1}$ and a variance of $\sigma^2 = $ unity.

4.2.3   Student t Distribution

Let $y(k)$ and $z(k)$ be independent random variables such that $y(k)$ has a $\chi_n{}^2$ distribution function and $z(k)$ has a normal distribution function with zero mean and unit variance. Let a new random variable be defined as

$$t_n = \frac{z(k)}{\sqrt{y(k)/n}} \qquad (4.21)$$

The random variable t_n is the Student t variable with n degrees of freedom.

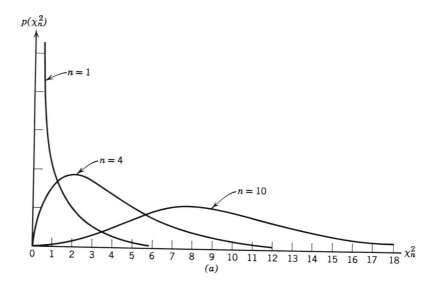

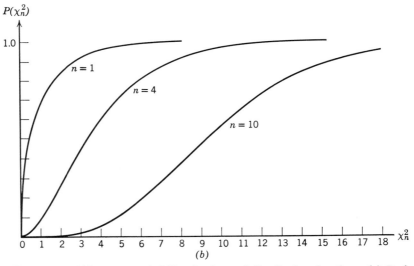

Figure 4.2 Chi-square probability density and distribution functions. (a) Probability density function. (b) Probability distribution function.

The probability density function for t_n is given by

$$p(t) = \frac{\Gamma[(n+1)/2]}{\sqrt{\pi n}\,\Gamma(n/2)}\left[1 + \frac{t^2}{n}\right]^{-(n+1)/2} \qquad (4.22a)$$

The corresponding distribution function for t_n is given by

$$P(t) = \int_{-\infty}^{t} p(\xi)\,d\xi \qquad (4.22b)$$

The distribution function in Eq. (4.22) is called a *Student t distribution with n degrees of freedom*. The 100α percentage point of the t distribution will be denoted by $t_{n;\alpha}$. That is,

$$\int_{t_{n;\alpha}}^{\infty} p(t)\,dt = \text{Prob}\,[t_n > t_{n;\alpha}] = \alpha \qquad (4.23)$$

The mean value and variance for the variable t_n are

$$E[t_n] = \mu_t = 0 \qquad \text{for} \qquad n > 1 \qquad (4.24)$$

$$E[(t_n - \mu_t)^2] = \sigma_t^2 = \frac{n}{n-2} \qquad \text{for} \qquad n > 2 \qquad (4.25)$$

The density function $p(t)$ is unimodal, monotonic about the mode, and symmetric, as illustrated in Figure 4.3(*a*). The corresponding distribution function $P(t)$ is illustrated in Figure 4.3(*b*). A limited tabulation of percentage points for the t distribution function is presented in Table 4.9 at the end of this chapter. It should be noted that the t distribution approaches a standardized normal distribution as the number of degrees of freedom, n, becomes large.

4.2.4   The F Distribution

Let $y_1(k)$ and $y_2(k)$ be independent random variables such that $y_1(k)$ has a χ^2 distribution function with n_1 degrees of freedom, and $y_2(k)$ has a χ^2 distribution function with n_2 degrees of freedom. Let a new random variable be defined as

$$F_{n_1,n_2} = \frac{y_1(k)/n_1}{y_2(k)/n_2} = \frac{y_1(k)n_2}{y_2(k)n_1} \qquad (4.26)$$

The random variable F_{n_1,n_2} is the F variable with n_1 and n_2 degrees of freedom. The probability density function for F_{n_1,n_2} is given by

$$p(F) = \frac{\Gamma[(n_1+n_2)/2](n_1/n_2)^{n_1/2}F^{(n_1/2)-1}}{\Gamma(n_1/2)\,\Gamma(n_2/2)[1+(n_1F/n_2)]^{(n_1+n_2)/2}} \qquad F \geq 0 \qquad (4.27a)$$

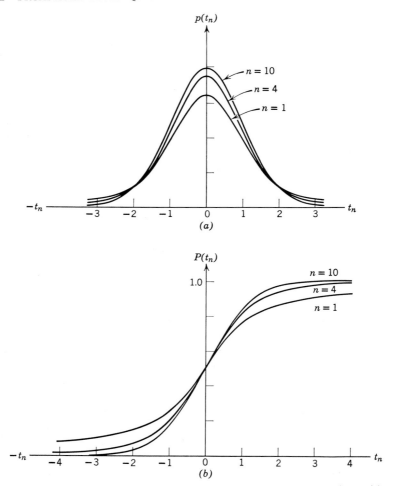

Figure 4.3   Student t probability density and distribution functions. (a) Probability density function. (b) Probability distribution function.

The corresponding distribution function for F_{n_1, n_2} is given by

$$P(F) = \int_{-\infty}^{F} p(\xi) \, d\xi \tag{4.27b}$$

The distribution function in Eq. (4.27) is called an F *distribution with* n_1 *and* n_2 *degrees of freedom.* The 100α percentage point of the F distribution will be denoted by $F_{n_1, n_2; \alpha}$. That is,

$$\int_{F_{n_1, n_2; \alpha}}^{\infty} p(F) \, dF = \text{Prob} \, [F_{n_1, n_2} > F_{n_1, n_2; \alpha}] = \alpha \tag{4.28}$$

The mean value and variance for F_{n_1, n_2} are

$$E[F_{n_1, n_2}] = \mu_F = \frac{n_2}{n_2 - 2} \qquad \text{for } n_2 > 2 \quad (4.29)$$

$$E[(F_{n_1, n_2} - \mu_F)^2] = \sigma_F^2 = \frac{2n_2^2(n_1 + n_2 - 2)}{n_1(n_2 - 2)^2(n_2 - 4)} \qquad \text{for } n_2 > 4 \quad (4.30)$$

The density function $p(F)$ is unimodal, monotonic about the mode, and nonsymmetric for $n_2 > 2$, as illustrated in Figure 4.4(*a*). The corresponding distribution function $P(F)$ is illustrated in Figure 4.4(*b*). A limited tabulation of percentage points for the F distribution function is presented in Tables 4.10(*a*), (*b*), and (*c*), at the end of this chapter. It should be noted that the statistic t_n^2, [the square of the variable defined in Eq. (4.21)], has an F distribution with $n_1 = 1$ and $n_2 = n$ degrees of freedom.

4.3 Sampling Distributions and Illustrations

Consider a random variable $x(k)$ with a probability distribution function $P(x)$. Let $x_1, x_2, \ldots, x_N$ be a sample of N observed values of $x(k)$. Any quantity computed from these sample values will also be a random variable. For example, consider the mean value $\bar{x}$ for the sample. If a series of different samples of size N were selected from the same random variable $x(k)$, the value of $\bar{x}$ computed from each sample would generally be different. Hence, the sample mean value $\bar{x}$ is also a random variable which has some probability distribution function $P(\bar{x})$. This probability distribution function is called the *sampling distribution* for the sample mean $\bar{x}$.

Some of the more common sampling distributions which often arise in practice will now be considered. These involve the probability distribution functions defined and discussed in Section 4.2. The use of these sampling distributions to establish confidence intervals and perform hypothesis tests is illustrated in Sections 4.4 and 4.5.

4.3.1 Distribution for Sample Mean with Known Variance

Consider the mean value of a sample of N independent observations from a random variable $x(k)$ as follows.

$$\bar{x} = \frac{1}{N} \sum_{i=1}^{N} x_i \qquad (4.31)$$

First consider the case where the random variable $x(k)$ is normally distributed with a mean value of μ_x and a known variance of σ_x^2. From Section 3.3, the sampling distribution for the sample mean $\bar{x}$ will also be normally distributed. From Eq. (4.9), the mean value for the sampling

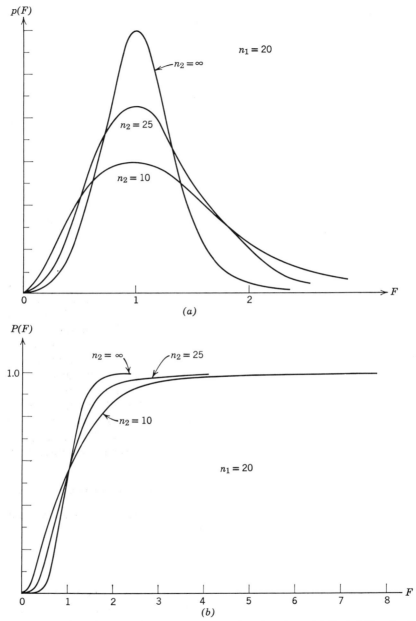

Figure 4.4 F probability density and distribution functions. (a) Probability density function. (b) Probability distribution function. Special case when $n_1 = 20$.

distribution of $\bar{x}$ is

$$\mu_{\bar{x}} = \mu_x \qquad (4.32)$$

Noting that Var $[ax] = a^2$ Var $[x]$, the variance for the sampling distribution of $\bar{x}$ is

$$\sigma_{\bar{x}}^2 = \text{Var}\left[\frac{1}{N}\sum_{i=1}^{N} x_i\right] = \frac{1}{N^2}\sum_{i=1}^{N} \sigma_x^2 = \frac{\sigma_x^2}{N} \qquad (4.33)$$

Hence, in terms of a standardized normal distribution, the following sampling distribution applies for the sample mean $\bar{x}$.

$$\frac{(\bar{x} - \mu_x)\sqrt{N}}{\sigma_x} = z(k) \qquad (4.34)$$

Here, $z(k)$ has a standardized normal distribution, as defined in Section 4.2.1. It follows that a probability statement concerning the value of a sample mean *prior* to collecting the sample may be made as follows.

$$\text{Prob}\left[\bar{x} > \left(\frac{\sigma_x z_\alpha}{\sqrt{N}} + \mu_x\right)\right] = \alpha \qquad (4.35)$$

Note that the probability statement in Eq. (4.35) is valid only prior to collecting the sample, since after a sample is collected, the probability of $\bar{x}$ being greater than any given value is either zero or one. This point will be further clarified when confidence intervals are discussed in Section 4.5.

Example **4.1.**   Assume a sample of $N = 25$ independent observations are to be collected from a normally distributed random variable $x(k)$ with a mean value of $\mu_x = 10$ and a variance of $\sigma_x^2 = 4$. Determine an interval which will include the sample mean value with a probability of 95 per cent. From Eqs. (4.32) and (4.33), the sample mean $\bar{x}$ will effectively be a single observation of a normally distributed random variable with a mean value of $\mu_{\bar{x}} = 10$ and a variance of $\sigma_{\bar{x}}^2 = \frac{4}{25}$.

To establish a 95 per cent probability interval for $\bar{x}$, let the limits of the interval be such that the probability is 2.5 per cent that $\bar{x}$ will be below the interval and 2.5 per cent that $\bar{x}$ will be above the interval (5 per cent that $\bar{x}$ will be outside the interval). From Eq. (4.34), the following probability statement applies.

$$\text{Prob}\left[z_{1-\alpha/2} < \frac{(\bar{x} - 10)5}{2} \leq z_{\alpha/2}\right] = 1 - \alpha$$

From Table 4.7, for $\alpha = 0.05$, $z_{\alpha/2} = -z_{1-\alpha/2} = z_{0.025} = 1.96$. Hence

$$\text{Prob}\left[-1.96 < \frac{(\bar{x} - 10)5}{2} \leq 1.96\right] = 0.95$$

By rearranging terms, the 95 per cent probability interval for $\bar{x}$ is obtained as follows.

$$\text{Prob } [9.216 < \bar{x} \leq 10.784] = 0.95$$

This concludes Example 4.1.

Now, consider the case where the random variable $x(k)$ is not normally distributed. From the practical implications of the Central Limit Theorem, the following result occurs. As the sample size N becomes large, the *sampling distribution for the sample mean $\bar{x}$ approaches a normal distribution regardless of the distribution for the original variable $x(k)$.* In practical terms, a normality assumption for the sampling distribution of $\bar{x}$ becomes reasonable in many cases for $N > 4$ and quite accurate in most cases for $N > 10$. Hence, for reasonably large sample sizes, Eq. (4.34) applies to the sampling distribution for the sample mean $\bar{x}$ computed for any random variable $x(k)$, regardless of its probability distribution function.

4.3.2 Distribution for Sample Variance

Consider the variance of a sample of N independent observations from a random variable $x(k)$ as follows.

$$s^2 = \frac{1}{N-1} \sum_{i=1}^{N} (x_i - \bar{x})^2 \tag{4.36}$$

If the variable $x(k)$ is normally distributed with a mean value of μ_x and a variance of σ_x^2, the following sampling distribution applies for the sample variance s^2.

$$\frac{ns^2}{\sigma_x^2} = \chi_n^2 \qquad n = N - 1 \tag{4.37}$$

Here, χ_n^2 has a chi-square distribution with $n = N - 1$ degrees of freedom, as defined in Section 4.2.2. It follows that a probability statement concerning the value of the sample variance s^2 prior to collecting the sample may be made as follows.

$$\text{Prob} \left[s^2 > \frac{\sigma_x^2 \chi_{n;\alpha}^2}{n} \right] = \alpha \tag{4.38}$$

Example 4.2. For the problem in Example 4.1, determine an interval which will include the sample variance with a probability of 95 per cent. From Eq. (4.37), the following probability statement applies.

$$\text{Prob} \left[\chi_{24;1-\alpha/2}^2 < \frac{24s^2}{4} \leq \chi_{24;\alpha/2}^2 \right] = 1 - \alpha$$

From Table 4.8, for $\alpha = 0.05$, $\chi^2_{24;1-\alpha/2} = \chi^2_{24;0.975} = 12.40$ and $\chi^2_{24;\alpha/2} = \chi^2_{24;0.025} = 39.36$. Hence

$$\text{Prob}\left[12.40 < \frac{24s^2}{4} \leq 39.36\right] = 0.95$$

By rearranging terms, the 95 per cent probability interval for s^2 is obtained as follows.

$$\text{Prob}\,[2.07 < s^2 \leq 6.56] = 0.95$$

4.3.3 Distribution for Sample Mean with Unknown Variance

Consider the mean value of a sample of N independent observations from a random variable $x(k)$, as given by Eq. (4.31). If the variable $x(k)$ is normally distributed with a mean value of μ_x and an unknown variance, the following sampling distribution applies for the sample mean $\bar{x}$.

$$\frac{(\bar{x} - \mu_x)\sqrt{N}}{s} = t_n \qquad n = N - 1 \tag{4.39}$$

Here, t_n has a Student t distribution with $n = N - 1$ degrees of freedom, as defined in Section 4.2.3. It follows that a probability statement concerning the value of the sample mean $\bar{x}$ prior to collecting the sample may be made as follows.

$$\text{Prob}\left[\bar{x} > \left(\frac{st_{n;\alpha}}{\sqrt{N}} + \mu_x\right)\right] = \alpha \tag{4.40}$$

***Example* 4.3.** Assume a sample of $N = 25$ independent observations are to be collected from a normally distributed random variable $x(k)$ with a mean value of $\mu_x = 10$ and an unknown variance. Determine an interval which will include the sample mean value with a probability of 95 per cent. From Eq. (4.39), the following probability statement applies.

$$\text{Prob}\left[t_{24;1-\alpha/2} < \frac{(\bar{x} - 10)5}{s} \leq t_{24;\alpha/2}\right] = 1 - \alpha$$

From Table 4.9, for $\alpha = 0.05$, $t_{24;\alpha/2} = -t_{24;1-\alpha/2} = t_{24;0.025} = 2.064$. Hence,

$$\text{Prob}\left[-2.064 < \frac{(\bar{x} - 10)5}{s} \leq 2.064\right] = 0.95$$

By rearranging terms, the 95 per cent probability interval for $\bar{x}$ is obtained as follows.

$$\text{Prob}\,[(10 - 0.413s) < \bar{x} \leq (10 + 0.413s)] = 0.95$$

Note that the exact numerical probability statement based on the t distribution is not possible since the sample variance s is unknown prior to collecting the sample.

4.3.4 Distribution for Ratio of Two Sample Variances

Consider the variances of two samples, one consisting of N_x independent observations of a random variable $x(k)$, and the other consisting of N_y observations of a random variable $y(k)$, as given by Eq. (4.36). If the variable $x(k)$ is normally distributed with a mean value of μ_x and a variance of σ_x^2, and the variable $y(k)$ is normally distributed with a mean value of μ_y and a variance of σ_y^2, then the following sampling distribution applies for the sampling variances s_x^2 and s_y^2.

$$\frac{s_x^2/\sigma_x^2}{s_y^2/\sigma_y^2} = F_{n_x, n_y} \qquad \begin{aligned} n_x &= N_x - 1 \\ n_y &= N_y - 1 \end{aligned} \qquad (4.41)$$

Here, F_{n_x, n_y} has an F distribution with $n_x = N_x - 1$ and $n_y = N_y - 1$ degrees of freedom, as defined in Section 4.2.4. It follows that a probability statement concerning the ratio of the sample variances s_x^2 and s_y^2 prior to collecting the sample may be made as follows.

$$\text{Prob}\left[\frac{s_x^2}{s_y^2} > \frac{\sigma_x^2}{\sigma_y^2} F_{n_x, n_y;\alpha}\right] = \alpha \qquad (4.42)$$

Note that if the two samples are obtained from the same random variable, $x(k) = y(k)$, then Eq. (4.41) reduces to

$$\frac{s_1^2}{s_2^2} = F_{n_1, n_2} \qquad \begin{aligned} n_1 &= N_1 - 1 \\ n_2 &= N_2 - 1 \end{aligned} \qquad (4.43)$$

Example 4.4. Assume a sample of $N_x = 25$ independent observations are to be collected from a normally distributed random variable $x(k)$ with a mean value of $\mu_x = 10$ and a variance of $\sigma_x^2 = 4$, and a sample of $N_y = 10$ dependent observations are to be collected from a second normally distributed random variable $y(k)$ with a mean value of $\mu_y = 100$ and a variance of $\sigma_y^2 = 8$. Determine an interval which will include the ratio of the sample variances with a probability of 95 per cent.

From Eq. (4.41), the following probability statement applies.

$$\text{Prob}\left[F_{24,9;1-\alpha/2} < \frac{s_x^2/4}{s_y^2/8} \le F_{24,9;\alpha/2}\right] = 1 - \alpha$$

From Table 4.9, for $\alpha = 0.05$, $F_{24,9;1-\alpha/2} = 1/F_{9,24;\alpha/2} = 1/F_{9,24;0.025} =$ $1/2.70 = 0.37$, and $F_{24,9;\alpha/2} = F_{24,9;0.025} = 3.61$. Hence

$$\text{Prob} \left[0.37 < \frac{s_x^2/4}{s_y^2/8} \leq 3.61 \right] = 0.95$$

By rearranging terms, the 95 per cent probability interval for the ratio s_x^2/s_y^2 is obtained as follows.

$$\text{Prob} \left[0.18 < \frac{s_x^2}{s_y^2} \leq 1.80 \right] = 0.95$$

4.4 Confidence Intervals

The use of sample values as estimators for parameters of random variables is discussed in Section 4.1. However, those procedures result only in point estimates for a parameter of interest; no indication is provided as to how closely a sample value estimates the parameter. A more complete and meaningful procedure for estimating parameters of random variables involves the estimation of an interval, as opposed to a single point value, which will include the parameter being estimated with a known degree of uncertainty. For example, consider the case where the mean value $\bar{x}$ for a sample of size N from a random variable $x(k)$ is being used as an estimator for the true mean value μ_x. It is far more meaningful if the true mean value μ_x is estimated in terms of some interval, such as $\bar{x} \pm d$, where there is some measure of the uncertainty that the true mean value μ_x falls within that interval. Such intervals can be estimated if the sampling distribution is known for the sample value being used as an estimator.

Continuing with the example of a mean value estimate, it is shown in Section 4.3 that probability statements can be made concerning the value of a sample mean $\bar{x}$ prior to collecting the sample. For the case of a normally distributed random variable with an unknown mean value and variance, a probability statement is obtained from Eq. (4.39) as follows.

$$\text{Prob} \left[t_{n;1-\alpha/2} < \frac{(\bar{x} - \mu_x)\sqrt{N}}{s} \leq t_{n;\alpha/2} \right] = 1 - \alpha \qquad n = N - 1$$

$$(4.44)$$

Now, *after* the sample has been collected, the values $\bar{x}$ and s are fixed numbers rather than random variables. Hence the above probability statement no longer applies since the quantity $(\bar{x} - \mu_x)\sqrt{N}/s$ either *does* or *does not* fall within the noted limits. In other words, after a sample has been collected, a technically correct probability statement would be as follows.

$$\text{Prob}\left[t_{n;1-\alpha/2} < \frac{(\bar{x} - \mu_x)\sqrt{N}}{s} \leq t_{n;\alpha/2}\right] = \begin{cases} 0 \\ 1 \end{cases} \tag{4.45}$$

Whether the correct probability is zero or unity is usually not known. However, as the value of α becomes small (as the interval between $t_{n;1-\alpha/2}$ and $t_{n;\alpha/2}$ becomes wide), one would tend to guess that the probability is more likely to be unity than zero. In slightly different terms, if many different samples were repeatedly collected and values for $\bar{x}$ and s were computed for each sample, one would tend to expect the quantity in Eq. (4.44) to fall within the noted interval for about $1 - \alpha$ of the samples.

In this context, a statement can be made about an interval within which one would expect to find the quantity $(\bar{x} - \mu_x)\sqrt{N}/s$ with a small degree of uncertainty. Such statements are called *confidence statements*. The interval associated with a confidence statement is called a *confidence interval*. The degree of trust associated with the confidence statement is called the *confidence coefficient*.

For the case of the mean value estimate, a confidence interval can be established for the mean value μ_x based upon sample values $\bar{x}$ and s by rearranging terms in Eq. (4.44) as follows.

$$\left[\left(\bar{x} - \frac{s t_{n;\alpha/2}}{\sqrt{N}} \leq \mu_x < \bar{x} + \frac{s t_{n;\alpha/2}}{\sqrt{N}}\right)\right] \qquad n = N - 1 \tag{4.46}$$

Equation (4.46) uses the fact that $t_{n;1-\alpha/2} = -t_{n;\alpha/2}$. The confidence coefficient associated with the above interval is $1 - \alpha$. Hence the confidence statement would be as follows: "The true mean value μ_x falls within the noted interval with a confidence coefficient of $1 - \alpha$," or, in more common terminology, "with a confidence of $100(1 - \alpha)$ per cent." Similar confidence statements can be established for any parameter estimates where proper sampling distributions are known. For example, from Eq. (4.37), a $1 - \alpha$ confidence interval for the variance σ_x^2 based upon a sample variance s^2 from a sample of size N is

$$\left[\frac{n s^2}{\chi_{n;\alpha/2}^2} \leq \sigma_x^2 < \frac{n s^2}{\chi_{n;1-\alpha/2}^2}\right] \qquad n = N - 1 \tag{4.47}$$

***Example* 4.5.**   Assume a sample of $N = 31$ independent observations are collected from a normally distributed random variable $x(k)$ with the following results:

$$\begin{array}{cccccc}
60 & 61 & 47 & 56 & 61 & 63 \\
65 & 69 & 54 & 59 & 43 & 61 \\
55 & 61 & 56 & 48 & 67 & 65 \\
60 & 58 & 57 & 62 & 57 & 58 \\
53 & 59 & 58 & 61 & 67 & 62 \\
54 & & & & &
\end{array}$$

Determine a 90 per cent confidence interval for the true mean value and variance of the random variable $x(k)$.

From Eq. (4.46), a $1 - \alpha$ confidence interval for the mean value μ_x based on the sample mean $\bar{x}$ and the sample variance s^2 for a sample size of $N = 31$ is given by

$$\left[\left(\bar{x} - \frac{s t_{30;\alpha/2}}{\sqrt{31}} \right) \leq \mu_x < \left(\bar{x} + \frac{s t_{30;\alpha/2}}{\sqrt{31}} \right) \right]$$

From Table 4.9, for $\alpha = 0.10$, $t_{30;\alpha/2} = t_{30;0.05} = 1.697$, so the interval reduces to

$$[(\bar{x} - 0.3048s) \leq \mu_x < (\bar{x} + 0.3048s)]$$

From Eq. (4.47), a $1 - \alpha$ confidence interval for the variance σ_x^2 based on the sample variance s^2 for a sample size of $N = 31$ is given by

$$\left[\frac{30s^2}{\chi_{30;\alpha/2}^2} \leq \sigma_x^2 < \frac{30s^2}{\chi_{30;1-\alpha/2}^2} \right]$$

From Table 4.8, for $\alpha = 0.10$, $\chi_{30;\alpha/2}^2 = \chi_{30;0.05}^2 = 43.77$ and $\chi_{30;1-\alpha/2}^2 = \chi_{30;0.95}^2 = 18.49$, so the interval reduces to

$$[0.6854s^2 \leq \sigma_x^2 < 1.622s^2]$$

It now remains to calculate the sample mean and variance, and substitute these values into the interval statements. From Eq. (4.3), the sample mean is

$$\bar{x} = \frac{1}{N} \sum_{i=1}^{N} x_i = 58.61$$

From Eq. (4.11), the sample variance is

$$s^2 = \frac{1}{N-1} \sum_{i=1}^{N} (x_i - \bar{x})^2 = \frac{1}{N-1} \left\{ \sum_{i=1}^{N} x_i^2 - N(\bar{x})^2 \right\} = 33.43$$

Hence the 90 per cent confidence intervals for the mean value and variance of the random variable $x(k)$ are as follows.

$$[56.85 \leq \mu_x < 60.37]$$
$$[22.91 \leq \sigma_x^2 < 54.22]$$

4.5 Hypothesis Tests

Consider the case where some estimator $\hat{\Phi}$ is computed from a sample of N independent observations of a random variable $x(k)$. Assume that there is reason to believe that the true parameter Φ being estimated has a specific value Φ_0. Now, even if $\Phi = \Phi_0$, the sample value $\hat{\Phi}$ will probably not come out exactly equal to Φ_0 because of the sampling variability associated with $\hat{\Phi}$. Hence the following question arises. If it is hypothesized that $\Phi = \Phi_0$, how much difference between $\hat{\Phi}$ and Φ_0 must occur before the hypothesis should be rejected as being invalid? This question can be

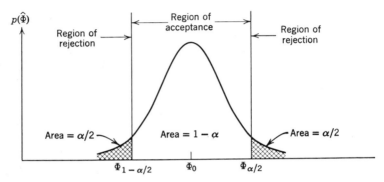

Figure 4.5 Acceptance and rejection regions for hypothesis tests.

answered in statistical terms by considering the probability of any noted difference between $\hat{\Phi}$ and Φ_0 based upon the sampling distribution for $\hat{\Phi}$. If the probability of a given difference is small, the difference would be considered significant and the hypothesis that $\Phi = \Phi_0$ would be rejected. If the probability of a given difference is not small, the difference would be accepted as normal statistical variability and the hypothesis that $\Phi = \Phi_0$ would be accepted.

The preceding discussion outlines the simplest form of a statistical procedure called hypothesis testing. To clarify the general technique, assume that a sample value $\hat{\Phi}$, which is an unbiased estimate for a parameter Φ, has a probability density function of $p(\hat{\Phi})$. Now, if a hypothesis that $\Phi = \Phi_0$ is true, then $p(\hat{\Phi})$ would have a mean value of Φ_0 as illustrated in Figure 4.5. The probability that $\hat{\Phi}$ would fall below the lower level $\Phi_{1-\alpha/2}$ is

$$\text{Prob}\,[\hat{\Phi} \leq \Phi_{1-\alpha/2}] = \int_{-\infty}^{\Phi_{1-\alpha/2}} p(\hat{\Phi})\,d\hat{\Phi} = \frac{\alpha}{2} \tag{4.48a}$$

The probability that $\hat{\Phi}$ would fall above the upper value $\Phi_{\alpha/2}$ is

$$\text{Prob}\,[\hat{\Phi} > \Phi_{\alpha/2}] = \int_{\Phi_{\alpha/2}}^{\infty} p(\hat{\Phi})\,d\hat{\Phi} = \frac{\alpha}{2} \qquad (4.48b)$$

Hence the probability that $\hat{\Phi}$ would be outside the range between $\Phi_{1-\alpha/2}$ and $\Phi_{\alpha/2}$ is α. Now let α be small so that it is very unlikely that $\hat{\Phi}$ would fall outside the range between $\Phi_{1-\alpha/2}$ and $\Phi_{\alpha/2}$. If a sample were collected and a value of $\hat{\Phi}$ were computed which in fact fell outside the range between $\Phi_{1-\alpha/2}$ and $\Phi_{\alpha/2}$, there would be strong reason to question the original hypothesis that $\Phi = \Phi_0$ since such a value for $\hat{\Phi}$ would be very unlikely if the hypothesis were true. Hence the hypothesis that $\Phi = \Phi_0$ would be rejected. On the other hand, if the value for $\hat{\Phi}$ fell within the range between $\Phi_{1-\alpha/2}$ and $\Phi_{\alpha/2}$, there would be no strong reason to question the original hypothesis. Hence the hypothesis that $\Phi = \Phi_0$ would be accepted.

The small probability α used for the hypothesis test is called the *level of significance* for the test. The range of values of $\hat{\Phi}$ for which the hypothesis will be rejected is called the *region of rejection* or *critical region*. The range of values of $\hat{\Phi}$ for which the hypothesis will be accepted is called the *region of acceptance*. The simple hypothesis test outlined above is called a *two-sided test* because, if the hypothesis is not true, the value of Φ could be either greater or less than Φ_0. Hence it is necessary to test for significant differences between Φ and Φ_0 in both directions. In other cases a *one-sided test* might be sufficient. For example, let it be hypothesized that $\Phi \geq \Phi_0$. For this case, the hypothesis would be false only if Φ were less than Φ_0. Thus the test would be performed using the lower side of the probability density function for $p(\hat{\Phi})$.

Two possible errors can occur when a hypothesis test is performed. First, the hypothesis might be rejected when in fact it is true. This possible error is called a *Type I Error*. Second, the hypothesis might be accepted when in fact it is false. This possible error is called a *Type II Error*. From Figure 4.5, a Type I Error would occur if the hypothesis were true and $\hat{\Phi}$ fell in the region of rejection. It follows that the probability of a Type I Error is simply equal to α, the level of significance for the test.

In order to establish the probability of a Type II Error, it is necessary to specify some deviation of the true parameter Φ from the hypothesized parameter Φ_0 which one desires to detect. For example, assume that the true parameter actually has a value of either $\Phi = \Phi_0 + d$ or $\Phi = \Phi_0 - d$, as illustrated in Figure 4.6. If it is hypothesized that $\Phi = \Phi_0$ when in fact $\Phi = \Phi_0 \pm d$, the probability that $\hat{\Phi}$ would fall inside the acceptance region between $\Phi_{1-\alpha/2}$ and $\Phi_{\alpha/2}$ is β. Hence the probability of a Type II Error is β for detecting a difference of $\pm d$ from the hypothesized value Φ_0.

The probability $1 - \beta$ is called the *power of the test*. Clearly, for any given sample size N, the probability of a Type I Error can be reduced by reducing the level of significance α. However, this will increase the probability β of a Type II Error (reduce the power of the test). The only way to reduce both α and β is to increase the sample size N for the estimate $\hat{\Phi}$.

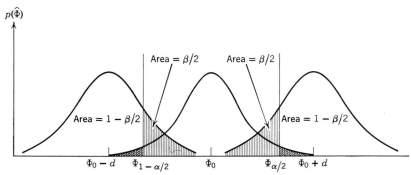

Figure 4.6   Type II Error regions for hypothesis tests.

These ideas form the basis for selecting the necessary sample sizes for statistical experiments.

***Example* 4.6.**   Assume there is reason to believe that the mean value of a random variable $x(k)$ is $\mu_x = 10$. Further assume that the variance for $x(k)$ is known to be $\sigma_x^2 = 4$. Determine the proper sample size to test the hypothesis that $\mu_x = 10$ at the 5 per cent level of significance, where the probability of a Type II Error is to be 5 per cent for detecting a difference of 10 per cent from the hypothesized value. Determine the region of acceptance to be used for the test.

An unbiased estimate for μ_x is given by the sample mean value $\bar{x}$ as defined in Eq. (4.3). The appropriate sampling distribution for $\bar{x}$ is given by Eq. (4.34) as

$$\bar{x} = \frac{\sigma_x}{\sqrt{N}} z(k) + \mu_x$$

where $z(k)$ is normally distributed with zero mean and unit variance. Note that this sampling distribution for $\bar{x}$ is precise if $x(k)$ is normally distributed and is still a good approximation if $x(k)$ is not normally distributed.

The upper and lower limits of the acceptance region for the hypothesis test are as follows:

$$\text{upper limit} = \frac{\sigma_x}{\sqrt{N}} z_{\alpha/2} + \mu_x$$

$$\text{lower limit} = \frac{\sigma_x}{\sqrt{N}} z_{1-\alpha/2} + \mu_x$$

Now if the true mean value were in fact $\mu_x' = \mu_x \pm d$, a Type II Error would occur with probability β if the sample value $\bar{x}$ fell below the upper limit or above the lower limit. In terms of the sampling distributions for $\mu_x' = \mu_x + d$ and $\mu_x' = \mu_x - d$,

$$\text{upper limit} = \frac{\sigma_x}{\sqrt{N}} z_{1-\beta/2} + \mu_x + d$$

$$\text{lower limit} = \frac{\sigma_x}{\sqrt{N}} z_{\beta/2} + \mu_x - d$$

Hence the following equalities apply.

$$\frac{\sigma_x}{\sqrt{N}} z_{\alpha/2} + \mu_x = \frac{\sigma_x}{\sqrt{N}} z_{1-\beta/2} + \mu_x + d$$

$$\frac{\sigma_x}{\sqrt{N}} z_{1-\alpha/2} + \mu_x = \frac{\sigma_x}{\sqrt{N}} z_{\beta/2} + \mu_x - d$$

Noting that $\alpha = \beta$ for this example, these relationships both reduce to

$$z_{\alpha/2} = z_{1-\alpha/2} + \frac{\sqrt{N}}{\sigma_x} d = -z_{\alpha/2} + \frac{\sqrt{N}}{\sigma_x} d$$

It follows that the required sample size is given by

$$N = 4\left(\frac{\sigma_x z_{\alpha/2}}{d}\right)^2$$

For the specific values in this example ($\sigma_x = 2$, $z_{\alpha/2} = 1.96$, $d = 0.1(10) = 1$), the required sample size is

$$N = 62$$

The region of acceptance for the hypothesis test will be

$$\text{upper limit} = \frac{\sigma_x}{\sqrt{N}} z_{\alpha/2} + \mu_x = 10.50$$

$$\text{lower limit} = \frac{\sigma_x}{\sqrt{N}} z_{1-\alpha/2} + \mu_x = 9.50$$

Now, a sample of $N = 62$ independent sample values should be collected and a sample mean $\bar{x}$ computed. If $\bar{x}$ falls in the interval between 9.50 and 10.50, the hypothesis that $\mu_x = 10$ would be accepted with the knowledge that there is a 5 per cent risk that the true mean value is actually less than 9 or greater than 11. If $\bar{x}$ falls above 10.5 or below 9.50, the hypothesis that $\bar{x} = 10$ would be rejected with a knowledge that there is a 5 per cent risk that the hypothesis is actually true.

4.6 Chi-Square Goodness-of-Fit Test

A special type of hypothesis test which is often used to test the equivalence of a probability density function for sampled data to some theoretical density function is called the chi-square goodness-of-fit test. The general procedure involves the use of a statistic with an approximate chi-square distribution as a measure of the discrepancy between an observed probability density function and the theoretical density function. A hypothesis of equivalence is then tested by studying the sampling distribution of this statistic.

To be more specific, consider a sample of N independent observations from a random variable $x(k)$ with a probability density function of $p(x)$. Let the observations be grouped into K intervals, called *class intervals*, which together form a *frequency histogram*. The number of observations falling within the ith class interval is called the *observed frequency* in the ith class, and will be denoted by f_i. The number of observations which would be expected to fall within the ith class interval if the true probability density function for $x(k)$ were $p_0(x)$ is called the *expected frequency* in the ith class interval, and will be denoted by F_i. Now, the discrepancy between the observed frequency and the expected frequency within each class interval is given by $f_i - F_i$. To measure the total discrepancy for all class intervals, the squares of the discrepancies in each interval are summed to obtain the sample statistic

$$X^2 = \sum_{i=1}^{K} \frac{(f_i - F_i)^2}{F_i} \qquad (4.49)$$

The distribution for X^2 is approximately the same as for χ_n^2 discussed in Section 4.2.2. The number of degrees of freedom, n, in this case is equal to K minus the number of different independent linear restrictions imposed on the observations. There is one such restriction due to the fact that the frequency in the last class interval is determined once the frequencies in the first $K - 1$ class intervals are known. There is at least one additional restriction owing to fitting the expected theoretical density function to the frequency histogram for the observed data. For the common case where the expected theoretical density function is the normal density function, two additional restrictions are imposed because a mean and variance must be computed to fit a normal density function. Hence, for the common case where the chi-square goodness-of-fit test is used as a test for normality, the number of degrees of freedom for X^2 in Eq. (4.49) is $n = K - 3$.

Having established the proper degrees of freedom for X^2, a hypothesis test may be performed as follows. Let it be hypothesized that the variable $x(k)$ has a probability density function $p(x) = p_0(x)$. After grouping the sampled observations into K class intervals and computing the expected frequency for each interval assuming $p(x) = p_0(x)$, compute X^2 as indicated in Eq. (4.49). Since any deviation of $p(x)$ from $p_0(x)$ will cause X^2 to increase, a one-sided (upper tail) test is used. The region of acceptance is

$$X^2 \leq \chi^2_{n;\alpha} \tag{4.50}$$

where the value of $\chi^2_{n;\alpha}$ is available from Table 4.8. If the sample value of X^2 is greater than $\chi^2_{n;\alpha}$, the hypothesis that $p(x) = p_0(x)$ is rejected at the α level of significance. If X^2 is less than or equal to $\chi^2_{n;\alpha}$, the hypothesis is accepted. The probability of a Type I Error is α. The probability of a Type II Error cannot easily be defined in meaningful terms because there are an infinite number of different ways in which $p(x)$ might deviate from $p_0(x)$.

The power of a chi-square goodness-of-fit test is influenced by the choice of the class intervals. Various theoretical and practical guidelines are available concerning this choice. For the case where the test will be performed at the $\alpha = 0.05$ level of significance, Reference 32 suggests that the minimum number of class intervals should be as given in Table 4.1.

Table 4.1 **Minimum Optimum Number (K) of Class Intervals for Sample Size N and $\alpha = 0.05$**

N	200	400	600	800	1000	1500	2000
K	16	20	24	27	30	35	39

The most convenient way to apply the test is to select class intervals of equal width. Excluding a uniform distribution hypothesis, this procedure will produce different expected frequencies from one class interval to another. It is often suggested that the interval widths be selected to produce equal expected frequencies in the class intervals. Again, except for a test of a uniform distribution this procedure will result in different widths from one class interval to another. The equal frequency procedure is more difficult to apply but will generally produce a more powerful test. In any case, it is desirable to have an expected frequency of at least five in each class interval, although frequencies as low as two are acceptable in the end intervals.

***Example* 4.7.** Assume that a random variable $x(k)$ is to be tested for normality at the $\alpha = 0.05$ level of significance, using a chi-square goodness-of-fit test on a sample of $N = 200$ independent observations. Assume that the numerical values for the observations, when arranged in increasing order, are as presented in Table 4.2. From Table 4.1, the test will be performed using $K = 16$ class intervals. For simplicity, class intervals of equal width will be selected. By visual inspection of the data in Table

Table 4.2   **Sample Observations Arranged in Increasing Order**

−7.6	−3.8	−2.5	−1.6	−0.7	0.2	1.1	2.0	3.4	4.6
−6.9	−3.8	−2.5	−1.6	−0.7	0.2	1.1	2.1	3.5	4.8
−6.6	−3.7	−2.4	−1.6	−0.6	0.2	1.2	2.3	3.5	4.8
−6.4	−3.6	−2.3	−1.5	−0.6	0.3	1.2	2.3	3.6	4.9
−6.4	−3.5	−2.3	−1.5	−0.5	0.3	1.3	2.3	3.6	5.0
−6.1	−3.4	−2.3	−1.4	−0.5	0.3	1.3	2.4	3.6	5.2
−6.0	−3.4	−2.2	−1.4	−0.4	0.4	1.3	2.4	3.7	5.3
−5.7	−3.4	−2.2	−1.2	−0.4	0.4	1.4	2.5	3.7	5.4
−5.6	−3.3	−2.1	−1.2	−0.4	0.5	1.5	2.5	3.7	5.6
−5.5	−3.2	−2.1	−1.2	−0.3	0.5	1.5	2.6	3.7	5.9
−5.1	−3.2	−2.0	−1.1	−0.3	0.6	1.6	2.6	3.8	6.1
−4.8	−3.1	−2.0	−1.1	−0.2	0.6	1.6	2.6	3.8	6.3
−4.8	−3.0	−1.9	−1.0	−0.2	0.7	1.6	2.7	3.9	6.3
−4.6	−3.0	−1.9	−1.0	−0.2	0.8	1.7	2.8	4.0	6.5
−4.4	−2.9	−1.8	−1.0	−0.1	0.9	1.8	2.8	4.2	6.9
−4.4	−2.9	−1.8	−0.9	−0.0	0.9	1.8	2.9	4.2	7.1
−4.3	−2.9	−1.8	−0.9	0.0	1.0	1.8	3.1	4.3	7.2
−4.1	−2.7	−1.7	−0.8	0.1	1.0	1.9	3.2	4.3	7.4
−4.0	−2.6	−1.7	−0.8	0.1	1.1	1.9	3.2	4.4	7.9
−3.8	−2.6	−1.6	−0.7	0.2	1.1	2.0	3.3	4.4	9.0

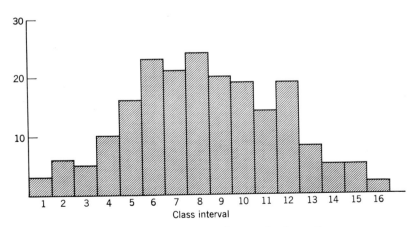

Figure 4.7   Frequency histogram for sample observations.

Table 4.3 Calculations for Goodness-of-Fit Test

Class Number	Interval x_i	x_{i+1}	Midpoint x	f	fx	x^2	fx^2	$z_{i+1} = \dfrac{x_{i+1} - \bar{x}}{s}$	A^*	$F = NA$	$|F - f|$	$\dfrac{(F-f)^2}{F}$
1	$-\infty$	-6.5	-7	3	-21	49	147	-2.06	0.0197	3.9	0.9	0.2
2	-6.5	-5.5	-6	6	-36	36	216	-1.76	0.0195	3.9	2.1	1.1
3	-5.5	-4.5	-5	5	-25	25	125	-1.45	0.0343	6.9	1.9	0.5
4	-4.5	-3.5	-4	10	-40	16	160	-1.15	0.0516	10.3	0.3	0.0
5	-3.5	-2.5	-3	16	-48	9	144	-0.85	0.0726	14.5	1.5	0.2
6	-2.5	-1.5	-2	23	-46	4	92	-0.54	0.0969	19.4	3.6	0.7
7	-1.5	-0.5	-1	21	-21	1	21	-0.24	0.1106	22.1	1.1	0.1
8	-0.5	0.5	0	24	0	0	0	0.06	0.1187	23.7	0.3	0.0
9	0.5	1.5	1	20	20	1	20	0.36	0.1167	23.3	3.3	0.5
10	1.5	2.5	2	19	38	4	76	0.67	0.1080	21.6	2.6	0.3
11	2.5	3.5	3	14	42	9	126	0.97	0.0854	17.1	3.1	0.6
12	3.5	4.5	4	19	76	16	304	1.27	0.0640	12.8	6.2	3.0
13	4.5	5.5	5	8	40	25	200	1.58	0.0449	9.0	1.0	0.1
14	5.5	6.5	6	5	30	36	180	1.88	0.0270	5.4	0.4	0.0
15	6.5	7.5	7	5	35	49	245	2.18	0.0155	3.1	1.9	1.2
16	7.5	∞	8	2	16	64	128	∞	0.0146	2.9	0.9	0.3
				200	60		2184					8.8

$$N = 200 \qquad \bar{x} = \frac{1}{N}\sum fx = 0.30 \qquad s = \left(\frac{\sum fx^2 - N(\bar{x})^2}{N-1}\right)^{1/2} = 3.30 \qquad n = K - 3 = 13 \qquad X^2 = 8.8$$

* A is the area under a standardized normal density function $p(z)$ between the limits z_i and z_{i+1}.

4.2, it appears that 16 class intervals of unit width will cover the range of values reasonably well. Let the class intervals be selected with borders at $-6.5, -5.5, \ldots, 6.5$, and 7.5, where values on the border are placed in the next highest class interval, as indicated in Table 4.2. By pooling values less than -6.5 into the first class interval and values greater than 7.5 into the last class interval, a frequency histogram is obtained (Figure 4.7). The various calculations required to perform the test are summarized in Table 4.3. Now, from Table 4.8, the value of $\chi^2_{n;\alpha}$ for $n = 13$ and $\alpha = 0.05$ is $\chi_{13;0.05} = 22.36$. The calculated sample value is $X^2 = 8.8$. Hence, the hypothesis of normality for the random variable $x(k)$ is accepted.

4.7 Analysis of Variance Procedures

Statistical techniques for testing the hypothesis that the mean value of a random variable is equal to a specific value μ_0 are discussed in Section 4.5. These techniques can be easily extended to include two random variables. For example, assume a sequence of N independent observations are collected from each of two normally distributed random variables, $x_1(k)$ and $x_2(k)$, with mean values of μ_1 and μ_2, respectively. Suppose the sample means are $\bar{x}_1$ and $\bar{x}_2$, and the sample variances are s_1^2 and s_2^2. If the two random variables have a common mean value μ and a common variance σ^2, the following sampling distribution applies.

$$\sqrt{N} \frac{\bar{x}_1 - \bar{x}_2}{\sqrt{s_1^2 + s_2^2}} = t_n \qquad n = 2(N - 1) \qquad (4.51)$$

Here, t_n has a Student t distribution as defined in Section 4.2.3, with $n = 2(N - 1)$ degrees of freedom. Using Eq. (4.51), a hypothesis of equality for the two mean values ($\mu_1 = \mu_2 = \mu$) can be tested as indicated in Section 4.5.

Consider the case where one wishes to test the hypothesis that a collection of c random variables $x_i(k)$, $i = 1, 2, \ldots, c$, have a common mean value. The situation now becomes more complex. All possible combinations of the sample means could be tested individually, but the level of significance becomes open to question if any one combination fails the test. Analysis of variance procedures offer a solution to this problem. These procedures will now be discussed.

4.7.1 One-Way Fixed-Effects Model

Assume that a sequence of N independent observations are collected from each of c normally distributed random variables which have true mean values of μ_i, $i = 1, 2, \ldots, c$. Let it be hypothesized that the random variables have a common mean, that is,

$$\mu_1 = \mu_2 = \cdots = \mu_c = \mu \qquad (4.52)$$

This hypothesis may be cast in a slightly different but equivalent form, as follows. Consider each observation to be of the form

$$x_{ij} = \mu + \phi_i + \epsilon_{ij} \qquad \begin{aligned} j &= 1, 2, \ldots, N \\ i &= 1, 2, \ldots, c \end{aligned} \qquad (4.53)$$

where μ is the overall true mean value, ϕ_i is an effect due to the ith variable, and ϵ_{ij} is an "error" term assumed to be normally distributed with zero mean and variance σ^2. In this model, the hypothesis becomes

$$\phi_1 = \phi_2 = \cdots = \phi_c = 0 \qquad (4.54)$$

The basis for the test of the hypothesis arises from the fact that the two independent estimates of the variance σ^2 may be calculated from the data if the hypothesis is true. The first of these estimates is obtained from the "within-group" variation given by the mean square value

$$MS_1 = \frac{1}{c} \sum_{i=1}^{c} s_i^2 \qquad (4.55)$$

which is simply the average of the c sample variances. The mean square MS_1 is an unbiased estimate of σ^2 whether or not the hypothesis of equal means is true. Now, using the relation $\sigma^2 = N\sigma_{\bar{x}}^2$, a second estimate is obtained from the "between-group" variation given by the mean square value

$$MS_2 = N \frac{\sum\limits_{i=1}^{c} (\bar{x}_i - \bar{x})^2}{c - 1} \qquad (4.56)$$

In words, MS_2 is equal to N times the variance of the sample means where $\bar{x}$ is the mean of the c sample means. That is,

$$\bar{x} = \frac{1}{c} \sum_{i=1}^{c} \bar{x}_i \qquad (4.57)$$

The mean square given by Eq. (4.56) will be an estimate of σ^2 if the hypothesis in Eq. (4.54) is true. However, if there is a contribution due to nonzero values of ϕ_i, then this mean square will be enlarged. It can be shown that the mean square ratio

$$F = \frac{MS_2}{MS_1} \qquad (4.58)$$

has an F distribution with $n_1 = c - 1$ and $n_2 = c(N - 1)$ degrees of freedom. Note that MS_2 will have a higher expectation than MS_1 if the hypothesis is not true. Hence a one-sided test at the α level of significance may be performed by comparing F from Eq. (4.58) with $F_{n_1, n_2; \alpha}$, where the region of acceptance for the hypothesis of equal means is

$$F \leq F_{n_1, n_2; \alpha} \qquad \begin{aligned} n_1 &= (c - 1) \\ n_2 &= c(N - 1) \end{aligned} \qquad (4.59)$$

The preceding development represents an analysis of variance procedure in its simplest form, called a one-way model. The term "fixed effects" means it is assumed that only the effects of c specific random variables are of interest.

4.7.2 One-Way Random-Effects Model

In contrast to the fixed-effects model, it may be desired to test the hypothesis that a collection of M random variables have a common mean based upon observations from only $c < M$ variables selected at random. This is called a random-effects model. The model is basically the same, that is,

$$x_{ij} = \mu + \phi_i + \epsilon_{ij} \qquad (4.60)$$

but in this case the ϕ_i are assumed to be c observations of a random variable with zero mean and variance σ_ϕ^2. The hypothesis now is slightly altered. Specifically, the hypothesis is

$$\sigma_\phi^2 = 0 \qquad (4.61)$$

However, the computing procedures and the F ratio remain identical.

4.7.3 Two-Way Mixed-Effects Model

Consider the case where the random variables in question are sampled under various different conditions. For example, the random variables might represent the results of a set of experiments performed during a specific time period or at a specific location. There might be reason to suspect that the results would be different if the experiments were performed at a different time or in a different location. Hence one might collect N independent observations for each of c random variables under certain given conditions (a given time, place, or other specific condition which might affect the variables). The sequence of observations for each variable might then be repeated for each of r different conditions, as illustrated in Table 4.4.

For clarity, a slightly modified notation for mean values will be adopted. The symbol $\bar{x}_{ij.}$ will represent an average taken over the observations represented by the subscript replaced with a dot. That is,

$$\bar{x}_{ij.} = \frac{1}{N} \sum_{v=1}^{N} x_{ijv} \qquad (4.62)$$

Assume that each cell represents a sample of size N from rc separate random variables where each is normally distributed about a mean value μ_{ij} and with a common variance σ^2. The model becomes

$$x_{ijv} = \mu_{ij} + \epsilon_{ijv} \tag{4.63}$$

The mean value μ_{ij}, however, is postulated to consist of a row effect g_i, a column effect h_j, and a possible interaction effect θ_{ij}. The interaction may

Table 4.4   Two-Way Analysis of Variance Format

	Variable			
	1	2	$\cdots$	c
Condition 1	x_{11v}	x_{12v}	$\cdots$	x_{1cv}
2	x_{21v}	x_{22v}	$\cdots$	x_{2cv}
.				
.		$\cdots$		
.				
r	x_{r1v}	x_{r2v}	$\cdots$	x_{rcv}

$v = 1, 2, \ldots, N$ $N =$ No. of observations
$r =$ No. of conditions (rows) $c =$ No. of variables (columns)

arise since the joint effect of the two variables taken together may differ from the sum of their separate effects. The column effects h_j are assumed to be due only to the c specific variables (fixed-effect model), and the row effects g_i are assumed to be due to r randomly selected conditions (random-effects model). Substituting these terms for μ_{ij}, Eq. (4.63) becomes

$$x_{ijv} = \mu + g_i + h_j + \theta_{ij} + \epsilon_{ijv} \tag{4.64}$$

where all the factors are considered as deviations from the common mean value μ.

The method for constructing the test of the hypothesis for the one-way analysis of variance still applies in principle to the two-way analysis. One obtains a variance estimate for the between-columns variation, an estimate from the between-rows variation, an estimate for interaction, and finally an estimate for the within-group (or *within-cell*) variation. Various F tests may then be devised to check for statistically significant interaction effects, column effects, and row effects. The F ratios are constructed by choosing variance estimate ratios where the numerator will have a larger expectation than the denominator if the effect being tested for exists.

The within-group variance estimate is given by the average of all the cell sample variances as follows.

$$MS_1 = \frac{1}{rc} \sum_{i=1}^{r} \sum_{j=1}^{c} s_{ij}^2 \tag{4.65}$$

where

$$s_{ij}^2 = \frac{1}{N-1} \sum_{v=1}^{N} (x_{ijv} - \bar{x}_{ij.})^2 \tag{4.66}$$

This mean square value gives an unbiased estimate of σ^2, that is, its expected value is σ^2 whether or not any of the effects are nonzero.

The between-columns variance estimate is given by the mean square value

$$MS_4 = \frac{rN}{c-1} \sum_{j=1}^{c} (\bar{x}_{.j.} - \bar{x}_{...})^2 \tag{4.67}$$

where the factor rN is needed because the variance of the underlying random variable is equal to rN times the variance of mean values $\bar{x}_{.j.}$ based on rN observations. This mean square value will have an expected value of σ^2 if no column effect exists, but otherwise it will have an expected value given by

$$E[MS_4] = \sigma^2 + N\sigma_\theta^2 + \frac{rN}{c-1} \sum_{j=1}^{c} h_j^2 \tag{4.68}$$

In Eq. (4.68), the term σ_θ^2 is the variance attributed to interaction if it exists, and the h_j are the fixed column effects if any exist.

The expression for the between-rows variance estimate is entirely analogous. Thus

$$MS_3 = \frac{cN}{r-1} \sum_{i=1}^{r} (\bar{x}_{i..} - \bar{x}_{...})^2 \tag{4.69}$$

The expected value of the between-rows mean square value is given by

$$E[MS_3] = \sigma^2 + Nc\sigma_g^2 \tag{4.70}$$

The interaction sum of squares is obtained by considering the identity

$$x_{ijv} - \bar{x} = (\bar{x}_{ij.} - \bar{x}_{i..} - \bar{x}_{.j.} + \bar{x}_{...}) + (\bar{x}_{i..} - \bar{x}_{...})$$
$$+ (\bar{x}_{.j.} - \bar{x}_{...}) + (x_{ijv} - \bar{x}_{ij.}) \tag{4.71}$$

where $\bar{x} = \bar{x}_{...}$, the average of all rcN values of x_{ijv}.

The sum of squares corresponding to each of the last three terms in Eq. (4.71) has already been accounted for by Eqs. (4.65), (4.67), and (4.69). The interaction mean square value is, therefore,

$$MS_2 = \frac{N}{(r-1)(c-1)} \sum_{i=1}^{r} \sum_{j=1}^{c} (\bar{x}_{ij.} - \bar{x}_{i..} - \bar{x}_{.j.} + \bar{x}_{...})^2 \tag{4.72}$$

This expression can be shown to have an expected value of σ^2 if there is no interaction effect, but otherwise will be increased by the factor $N\sigma_\theta^2$, that is,

$$E[MS_2] = \sigma^2 + N\sigma_\theta^2 \tag{4.73}$$

By examining the expected mean square values, the various F tests are seen to be as follows:

	Variance Ratio	Degrees of Freedom for F
(a) Interaction:	$F = \dfrac{MS_2}{MS_1}$	$([r-1][c-1], rc[N-1])$
(b) Columns:	$F = \dfrac{MS_4}{MS_2}$	$(c-1, [r-1][c-1])$
(c) Rows:	$F = \dfrac{MS_3}{MS_1}$	$(r-1, rc[N-1])$

The various hypotheses are accepted at the α level of significance if the computed F is less than the appropriate tabulated value of $F_{n_1 \cdot n_2; \; \alpha}$. Note that the test for interaction must be performed first since the presence of interaction requires different testing procedures which are not discussed here.

Example 4.8. Assume $N = 3$ observations are collected from each of $c = 10$ random variables, as shown in Table 4.5. Test the hypothesis that

Table 4.5   Sample Data for Analysis of Variance Test

		Variable									
		1	2	3	4	5	6	7	8	9	10
Observation	1	2.51	1.97	2.39	1.82	3.27	1.64	2.19	1.70	3.04	2.43
	2	2.29	2.09	3.48	2.02	2.87	1.70	2.45	1.52	2.20	2.49
	3	3.54	1.68	1.95	2.22	2.86	2.20	1.88	2.00	1.97	2.47
Sample means, $\bar{x}_i$		2.78	1.91	2.61	2.02	3.00	1.85	2.17	1.74	2.40	2.46
Sample variances, s_i^2		0.445	0.044	0.620	0.040	0.055	0.095	0.081	0.059	0.317	0.001

$$c = 10, \quad N = 3 \qquad MS_1 = \frac{1}{c}\sum s_i^2 = 0.176$$

$$\bar{x} = \frac{1}{c}\sum \bar{x}_i = 2.29 \qquad MS_2 = \frac{N}{c-1}\sum (\bar{x}_i - \bar{x})^2 = 0.538$$

$$F_{n_1, n_2} = \frac{MS_2}{MS_1} = 3.00 \text{ where } n_1 = c - 1 = 9 \text{ and } n_2 = c(N-1) = 20$$

the mean values for the variables are equal. Perform the test at the $\alpha = 0.05$ level of significance using a one-way analysis of variance test.

The various calculations required to perform the test are summarized in Table 4.5. The variance ratio is seen to be $F = 3.00$. From Table 4.10(a), the value of $F_{n_1, n_2; \alpha}$ for $n_1 = 9$, $n_2 = 20$, and $\alpha = 0.05$ is $F_{9,20;0.05} = 2.39$. Hence the hypothesis of equal means is rejected since $F = 3.00 > 2.39$.

4.8 Distribution-Free (Nonparametric) Procedures

The various procedures for establishing confidence intervals and performing hypothesis tests using sample data, as discussed in Sections 4.4, 4.5, and 4.7, all assume that the original random variables being sampled are normally distributed. In practice, the procedures are probably usable with reasonable accuracy for many random variables which are not normally distributed. However, there is no clear measure as to how much a random variable may deviate from normality before the sampling distributions discussed in Section 4.4 are no longer valid. This problem can often be avoided by using statistical procedures which do not assume a specific distribution function for the original random variable of interest. Such procedures are called distribution-free or nonparametric procedures.

One of the best-known distribution-free procedures used for data evaluation is the chi-square goodness-of-fit test, which is discussed in Section 4.6. Two other interesting distribution-free tests are valuable for the data evaluation techniques discussed in Chapter 5: the *run test* and the *trend test*. Each of these procedures will now be outlined.

4.8.1 Run Test

Consider a sequence of N observations of a random variable $x(k)$ where each observation is classified into one of two mutually exclusive categories, which may be identified simply by plus $(+)$ or minus $(-)$. The simplest example would be a sequence of flips of a coin where each observation is either a head $(+)$ or a tail $(-)$. A second example might be a sequence of measured values x_i, $i = 1, 2, 3, \ldots, N$, with a mean value $\bar{x}$, where each observation is $x_i \geq \bar{x}$ $(+)$ or $x_i < \bar{x}$ $(-)$. A third example might be a simultaneous sequence of two sets of measured values x_i and y_i, $i = 1, 2, 3, \ldots, N$, where each observation is $x_i \geq y_i$ $(+)$ or $x_i < y_i$ $(-)$. In any case, the sequence of plus and minus observations might be as follows.

$$
\underbrace{++}_{1} \quad \underbrace{-}_{2} \quad \underbrace{++}_{3} \quad \underbrace{-}_{4} \quad \underbrace{+++}_{5} \quad \underbrace{-}_{6} \quad \underbrace{+}_{7} \quad \underbrace{--}_{8} \quad \underbrace{+}_{9} \quad \underbrace{--}_{10} \quad \underbrace{+}_{11} \quad \underbrace{---}_{12}
$$

A run is defined as a sequence of identical observations that are followed or preceded by a different observation or no observation at all. In this example there are $r = 12$ runs in the sequence of $N = 20$ observations.

The number of runs which occur in a sequence of observations gives an indication as to whether or not results are independent random observations of the same random variable. Specifically, if a sequence of N observations are independent observations of the same random variable, that is, the probability of a $(+)$ or $(-)$ result does not change from one observation to the next, then the sampling distribution for the number of runs in the sequence is a random variable $r(k)$ with a mean value and variance as follows.

$$\mu_r = \frac{2N_1N_2}{N} + 1 \qquad (4.74)$$

$$\sigma_r^2 = \frac{2N_1N_2(2N_1N_2 - N)}{N^2(N - 1)} \qquad (4.75)$$

Here, N_1 is the number of $(+)$ observations and N_2 is the number of $(-)$ observations. For the special case where $N_1 = N_2 = N/2$, Eqs. (4.74) and (4.75) reduce to

$$\mu_r = \frac{N}{2} + 1 \qquad (4.76)$$

$$\sigma_r^2 = \frac{N(N - 2)}{4(N - 1)} \qquad (4.77)$$

A limited tabulation of 100α percentage points for the distribution function of $r(k)$ is presented in Table 4.11 at the end of this chapter.

Perhaps the most direct application of runs to data evaluation problems involves the testing of a single sequence of observations for independence. Assume there is reason to believe that there is an underlying trend in a sequence of observations; that is, there is reason to believe that the probability of a $(+)$ or $(-)$ is changing from one observation to the next. The existence of a trend can be tested for as follows. Let it be hypothesized that there is no trend by assuming that the sequence of N observations are independent observations of the same random variable. Then, assuming the number of $(+)$ observations equals the number of $(-)$ observations, the number of runs in the sequence will have a sampling distribution as given in Table 4.11. The hypothesis can be tested at any desired level of significance α by comparing the observed runs to the interval between $r_{n;1-\alpha/2}$ and $r_{n;\alpha/2}$ where $n = N/2$. If the observed runs fall outside the interval, the hypothesis would be rejected at the α level of significance. Otherwise, the hypothesis would be accepted.

Example **4.9.**   Assume a sequence of $N = 20$ observations of a random variable produces results as noted below.

(1) 5.5	(6) 5.7	(11) 6.8	(16) 5.4
(2) 5.1	(7) 5.0	(12) 6.6	(17) 6.8
(3) 5.7	(8) 6.5	(13) 4.9	(18) 5.8
(4) 5.2	(9) 5.4	(14) 5.4	(19) 6.9
(5) 4.8	(10) 5.8	(15) 5.9	(20) 5.5

Determine if the observations are independent by testing the runs which occur in the variation of the observations about their median value. Perform the test at the $\alpha = 0.05$ level of significance.

By visual inspection of the data, it is seen that $x = 5.6$ is the median value of the 20 observations. Let all observations with a value greater than 5.6 be identified by $(+)$ and all with a value less than 5.6 be identified by $(-)$. The result is

$$\underbrace{--}_{1} \; \underset{2}{+} \; \underbrace{--}_{3} \; \underset{4}{+} \; \underset{5}{-} \; \underset{6}{+} \; \underset{7}{-} \; \underbrace{+++}_{8} \; \underbrace{--}_{9} \; \underset{10\ 11}{+} \; \underset{}{-} \; \underbrace{+++}_{12} \; \underset{13}{-}$$

Hence there are 13 runs represented by the sequence of 20 observations. Let it be hypothesized that the observations are independent. The acceptance region for this hypothesis is

$$r_{10;1-\alpha/2} < r \leq r_{10;\alpha/2}$$

From Table 4.11, for $\alpha = 0.05$, $r_{10;1-\alpha/2} = r_{10;0.975} = 6$ and $r_{10;\alpha/2} = r_{10;0.025} = 15$. The hypothesis is accepted since $r = 13$ falls within the range between 6 and 15. That is, there is no reason to question that the observations are independent, which means there is no evidence of an underlying trend.

4.8.2 Trend Test

Consider a sequence of N observations of a random variable $x(k)$, where the observations are denoted by x_i, $i = 1, 2, 3, \ldots, N$. Now, count the number of times that $x_i > x_j$ for $i < j$. Each such inequality is called a reverse arrangement. The total number of reverse arrangements is denoted by A.

A general definition for A is as follows. From the set of observations $x_1, x_2, \ldots, x_N$, define

$$h_{ij} = \begin{cases} 1 & \text{if } x_i > x_j \\ 0 & \text{otherwise} \end{cases} \tag{4.78}$$

Then

$$A = \sum_{i=1}^{N-1} A_i \tag{4.79}$$

where

$$A_i = \sum_{j=i+1}^{N} h_{ij} \tag{4.80}$$

For example,

$$A_1 = \sum_{j=2}^{N} h_{1j} \qquad A_2 = \sum_{j=3}^{N} h_{2j} \qquad A_3 = \sum_{j=4}^{N} h_{3j} \qquad \text{etc.}$$

To help clarify the meaning of reverse arrangements, consider the following sequence of $N = 8$ observations.

$$x_1 = 5, \quad x_2 = 3, \quad x_3 = 8, \quad x_4 = 9, \quad x_5 = 4, \quad x_6 = 1, \quad x_7 = 7, \quad x_8 = 5$$

In the above sequence $x_1 > x_2$, $x_1 > x_5$, and $x_1 > x_6$ which gives $A_1 = 3$ reverse arrangements for x_1. Now, choosing x_2 and comparing it against subsequent observations (that is, for $i = 2$ and $i < j = 3, 4, \ldots, 8$), one notes $x_2 > x_6$ only, so that the number of reverse arrangements for x_2 is $A_2 = 1$. Continuing on, it is seen that $A_3 = 4$, $A_4 = 4$, $A_5 = 1$, $A_6 = 0$, and $A_7 = 1$. The total number of reverse arrangements is, therefore,

$$A = A_1 + A_2 + \cdots + A_7 = 3 + 1 + 4 + 4 + 1 + 0 + 1 = 14$$

If the sequence of N observations are independent observations of the same random variable, then the number of reverse arrangements is a random variable $A(k)$ with a mean variable and variance as follows.

$$\mu_A = \frac{N(N-1)}{4} \tag{4.81}$$

$$\sigma_A{}^2 = \frac{2N^3 + 3N^2 - 5N}{72} = \frac{N(2N+5)(N-1)}{72} \tag{4.82}$$

A limited tabulation of 100α percentage points for the distribution function of $A(k)$ is presented in Table 4.12 at the end of this chapter.

The trend test may be applied in basically the same way as the run test. Generally speaking, it is more powerful than the run test for detecting monotonic trends in a sequence of observations. The trend test is not powerful, however, for detecting fluctuating trends.

Example 4.10.   Test the sequence of $N = 20$ observations in Example 4.9 for a trend at the $\alpha = 0.05$ level of significance. The number of reverse arrangements in the observations is as follows.

$A_1 = 8$	$A_6 = 6$	$A_{11} = 7$	$A_{16} = 0$
$A_2 = 3$	$A_7 = 1$	$A_{12} = 6$	$A_{17} = 2$
$A_3 = 8$	$A_8 = 8$	$A_{13} = 0$	$A_{18} = 1$
$A_4 = 3$	$A_9 = 1$	$A_{14} = 0$	$A_{19} = 1$
$A_5 = 0$	$A_{10} = 4$	$A_{15} = 3$	

The total number of reverse arrangements is $A = 62$.

Let it be hypothesized that the observations are independent observations of a random variable $x(k)$ where there is no trend. The acceptance region for this hypothesis is

$$A_{20;1-\alpha/2} < A \le A_{20;\alpha/2}$$

From Table 4.12, for $\alpha = 0.05$, $A_{20;1-\alpha/2} = A_{20;0.975} = 64$ and $A_{20;\alpha/2} = A_{20;0.025} = 125$. Hence the hypothesis is rejected at the 5 per cent level of significance since $A = 62$ does not fall within the range between 64 and 125. Note that a hypothesis of independence for this same sequence of observations was accepted by the run test in Example 4.9. This illustrates the difference in sensitivity between the two testing procedures.

Table 4.6   **Ordinates of the Standardized Normal Density Function**

$$p(z) = \frac{1}{\sqrt{2\pi}} e^{-z^2/2}$$

z	0.00	0.01	0.02	0.03	0.04	0.05	0.06	0.07	0.08	0.09
0.0	0.3989	0.3989	0.3989	0.3988	0.3986	0.3984	0.3982	0.3980	0.3977	0.3973
0.1	0.3970	0.3956	0.3961	0.3956	0.3951	0.3945	0.3939	0.3932	0.3925	0.3918
0.2	0.3910	0.3902	0.3894	0.3884	0.3876	0.3967	0.3857	0.3847	0.3836	0.3825
0.3	0.3814	0.3802	0.3790	0.3778	0.3765	0.3752	0.3739	0.3725	0.3712	0.3697
0.4	0.3683	0.3668	0.3653	0.3637	0.3621	0.3605	0.3589	0.3572	0.3555	0.3538
0.5	0.3521	0.3503	0.3485	0.3467	0.3448	0.3429	0.3410	0.3391	0.3372	0.3352
0.6	0.3332	0.3312	0.3292	0.3271	·0.3251	0.3230	0.3209	0.3187	0.3166	0.3144
0.7	0.3123	0.3101	0.3079	0.3056	0.3034	0.3011	0.2989	0.2966	0.2943	0.2920
0.8	0.2897	0.2874	0.2850	0.2827	0.2803	0.2780	0.2756	0.2732	0.2709	0.2685
0.9	0.2661	0.2637	0.2613	0.2589	0.2565	0.2541	0.2516	0.2492	0.2468	0.2444
1.0	0.2420	0.2396	0.2371	0.2347	0.2323	0.2299	0.2275	0.2251	0.2227	0.2203
1.1	0.2179	0.2155	0.2131	0.2107	0.2083	0.2059	0.2036	0.2012	0.1989	0.1965
1.2	0.1942	0.1919	0.1895	0.1872	0.1849	0.1826	0.1804	0.1781	0.1758	0.1736
1.3	0.1714	0.1691	0.1669	0.1647	0.1626	0.1605	0.1582	0.1561	0.1539	0.1518
1.4	0.1497	0.1476	0.1456	0.1435	0.1415	0.1394	0.1374	0.1354	0.1334	0.1315
1.5	0.1295	0.1276	0.1257	0.1238	0.1219	0.1200	0.1282	0.1163	0.1145	0.1127
1.6	0.1109	0.1092	0.1074	0.1057	0.1040	0.1023	0.1006	0.0989	0.0973	0.0957
1.7	0.0940	0.0925	0.0909	0.0893	0.0878	0.0863	0.0848	0.0833	0.0818	0.0804
1.8	0.0790	0.0775	0.0761	0.0748	0.0734	0.0721	0.0707	0.0694	0.0681	0.0669
1.9	0.0656	0.0644	0.0632	0.0620	0.0608	0.0596	0.0584	0.0573	0.0562	0.0051
2.0	0.0540	0.0529	0.0519	0.0508	0.0498	0.0488	0.0478	0.0468	0.0459	0.0449
2.1	0.0440	0.0431	0.0422	0.0413	0.0404	0.0396	0.0387	0.0379	0.0371	0.0363
2.2	0.0355	0.0347	0.0339	0.0332	0.0325	0.0317	0.0310	0.0303	0.0297	0.0290
2.3	0.0283	0.0277	0.0270	0.0264	0.0258	0.0252	0.0246	0.0241	0.0235	0.0229
2.4	0.0224	0.0219	0.0213	0.0208	0.0203	0.0198	0.0194	0.0189	0.0184	0.0180
2.5	0.0175	0.0171	0.0167	0.0163	0.0158	0.0154	0.0151	0.0147	0.0143	0.0139
2.6	0.0136	0.0132	0.0129	0.0126	0.0122	0.0119	0.0116	0.0113	0.0110	0.0107
2.7	0.0104	0.0101	0.0099	0.0096	0.0093	0.0091	0.0088	0.0086	0.0084	0.0081
2.8	0.0079	0.0077	0.0075	0.0073	0.0071	0.0069	0.0067	0.0065	0.0063	0.0061
2.9	0.0060	0.0058	0.0056	0.0055	0.0053	0.0051	0.0050	0.0048	0.0047	0.0046
3.0	0.0044	0.0043	0.0042	0.0040	0.0039	0.0038	0.0037	0.0036	0.0035	0.0034
3.1	0.0033	0.0032	0.0031	0.0030	0.0029	0.0028	0.0027	0.0026	0.0025	0.0025
3.2	0.0024	0.0023	0.0022	0.0022	0.0021	0.0020	0.0020	0.0019	0.0018	0.0018
3.3	0.0017	0.0017	0.0016	0.0016	0.0015	0.0015	0.0014	0.0014	0.0013	0.0013
3.4	0.0012	0.0012	0.0012	0.0011	0.0011	0.0010	0.0010	0.0010	0.0009	0.0009
3.5	0.0009	0.0008	0.0008	0.0008	0.0008	0.0007	0.0007	0.0007	0.0007	0.0006
3.6	0.0006	0.0006	0.0006	0.0005	0.0005	0.0005	0.0005	0.0005	0.0005	0.0004
3.7	0.0004	0.0004	0.0004	0.0004	0.0004	0.0004	0.0003	0.0003	0.0003	0.0003
3.8	0.0003	0.0003	0.0003	0.0003	0.0003	0.0002	0.0002	0.0002	0.0002	0.0002
3.9	0.0002	0.0002	0.0002	0.0002	0.0002	0.0002	0.0002	0.0002	0.0001	0.0001

Table 4.7   **Areas under Standardized Normal Density Function**

$$\text{Value of } \alpha = \int_{z_\alpha}^{\infty} \frac{1}{\sqrt{2\pi}} e^{-z^2/2} = \text{Prob}[z > z_\alpha]$$

z_α	0.00	0.01	0.02	0.03	0.04	0.05	0.06	0.07	0.08	0.09
0.0	0.5000	0.4960	0.4920	0.4880	0.4840	0.4801	0.4761	0.4721	0.4681	0.4641
0.1	0.4602	0.4562	0.4522	0.4483	0.4443	0.4404	0.4364	0.4325	0.4286	0.4247
0.2	0.4207	0.4168	0.4129	0.4090	0.4052	0.4013	0.3974	0.3936	0.3897	0.3859
0.3	0.3821	0.3783	0.3745	0.3707	0.3669	0.3632	0.3594	0.3557	0.3520	0.3483
0.4	0.3446	0.3409	0.3372	0.3336	0.3300	0.3264	0.3228	0.3192	0.3156	0.3121
0.5	0.3085	0.3050	0.3015	0.2981	0.2946	0.2912	0.2877	0.2843	0.2810	0.2776
0.6	0.2743	0.2709	0.2676	0.2643	0.2611	0.2578	0.2546	0.2514	0.2483	0.2451
0.7	0.2420	0.2389	0.2358	0.2327	0.2296	0.2266	0.2236	0.2206	0.2177	0.2148
0.8	0.2119	0.2090	0.2061	0.2033	0.2005	0.1977	0.1949	0.1922	0.1894	0.1867
0.9	0.1841	0.1814	0.1788	0.1762	0.1736	0.1711	0.1685	0.1660	0.1635	0.1611
1.0	0.1587	0.1562	0.1539	0.1515	0.1492	0.1469	0.1446	0.1423	0.1401	0.1379
1.1	0.1357	0.1335	0.1314	0.1292	0.1271	0.1251	0.1230	0.1210	0.1190	0.1170
1.2	0.1151	0.1131	0.1112	0.1093	0.1075	0.1056	0.1038	0.1020	0.1003	0.0985
1.3	0.0968	0.0951	0.0934	0.0918	0.0901	0.0885	0.0869	0.0853	0.0838	0.0823
1.4	0.0808	0.0793	0.0778	0.0764	0.0749	0.0735	0.0721	0.0708	0.0694	0.0681
1.5	0.0668	0.0655	0.0643	0.0630	0.0618	0.0606	0.0594	0.0582	0.0571	0.0559
1.6	0.0548	0.0537	0.0526	0.0516	0.0505	0.0495	0.0485	0.0475	0.0465	0.0455
1.7	0.0446	0.0436	0.0427	0.0418	0.0409	0.0401	0.0392	0.0384	0.0375	0.0367
1.8	0.0359	0.0351	0.0344	0.0336	0.0329	0.0322	0.0314	0.0307	0.0301	0.0294
1.9	0.0287	0.0281	0.0274	0.0268	0.0262	0.0256	0.0250	0.0244	0.0239	0.0233
2.0	0.0228	0.0222	0.0217	0.0212	0.0207	0.0202	0.0197	0.0192	0.0188	0.0183
2.1	0.0179	0.0174	0.0170	0.0166	0.0162	0.0158	0.0154	0.0150	0.0146	0.0143
2.2	0.0139	0.0136	0.0132	0.0129	0.0125	0.0122	0.0119	0.0116	0.0113	0.0110
2.3	0.0107	0.0104	0.0102	0.00990	0.00964	0.00939	0.00914	0.00889	0.00866	0.00842
2.4	0.00820	0.00798	0.00776	0.00755	0.00734	0.00714	0.00695	0.00676	0.00657	0.00639
2.5	0.00621	0.00604	0.00587	0.00570	0.00554	0.00539	0.00523	0.00508	0.00494	0.00480
2.6	0.00466	0.00453	0.00440	0.00427	0.00415	0.00402	0.00391	0.00379	0.00368	0.00357
2.7	0.00347	0.00336	0.00326	0.00317	0.00307	0.00298	0.00289	0.00280	0.00272	0.00264
2.8	0.00256	0.00248	0.00240	0.00233	0.00226	0.00219	0.00212	0.00205	0.00199	0.00193
2.9	0.00187	0.00181	0.00175	0.00169	0.00164	0.00159	0.00154	0.00149	0.00144	0.00139

The data in Tables 4.7, 4.8, 4.9, 4.10, and 4.11 are extracted from *Handbook of Statistical Tables* by Donald B. Owen with the permission of the publisher, Addison-Wesley Publishing Company, Reading, Mass.

Table 4.8 Percentage Points of Chi-Square Distribution

Value of $\chi^2_{n;\alpha}$ such that $\text{Prob}[\chi_n{}^2 > \chi^2_{n;\alpha}] = \alpha$

					α					
n	0.995	0.990	0.975	0.950	0.900	0.10	0.05	0.025	0.010	0.005
1	0.000039	0.00016	0.00098	0.0039	0.0158	2.71	3.84	5.02	6.63	7.88
2	0.0100	0.0201	0.0506	0.103	0.211	4.61	5.99	7.38	9.21	10.60
3	0.0717	0.115	0.216	0.352	0.584	6.25	7.81	9.35	11.34	12.84
4	0.207	0.297	0.484	0.711	1.06	7.78	9.49	11.14	13.28	14.86
5	0.412	0.554	0.831	1.15	1.61	9.24	11.07	12.83	15.09	16.75
6	0.676	0.872	1.24	1.64	2.20	10.64	12.59	14.45	16.81	18.55
7	0.989	1.24	1.69	2.17	2.83	12.02	14.07	16.01	18.48	20.28
8	1.34	1.65	2.18	2.73	3.49	13.36	15.51	17.53	20.09	21.96
9	1.73	2.09	2.70	3.33	4.17	14.68	16.92	19.02	21.67	23.59
10	2.16	2.56	3.25	3.94	4.87	15.99	18.31	20.48	23.21	25.19
11	2.60	3.05	3.82	4.57	5.58	17.28	19.68	21.92	24.73	26.76
12	3.07	3.57	4.40	5.23	6.30	18.55	21.03	23.34	26.22	28.30
13	3.57	4.11	5.01	5.89	7.04	19.81	22.36	24.74	27.69	29.82
14	4.07	4.66	5.63	6.57	7.79	21.06	23.68	26.12	29.14	31.32
15	4.60	5.23	6.26	7.26	8.55	22.31	25.00	27.49	30.58	32.80
16	5.14	5.81	6.91	7.96	9.31	23.54	26.30	28.85	32.00	34.27
17	5.70	6.41	7.56	8.67	10.08	24.77	27.59	30.19	33.41	35.72
18	6.26	7.01	8.23	9.39	10.86	25.99	28.87	31.53	34.81	37.16
19	6.84	7.63	8.91	10.12	11.65	27.20	30.14	32.85	36.19	38.58
20	7.43	8.26	9.59	10.85	12.44	28.41	31.41	34.17	37.57	40.00
21	8.03	8.90	10.28	11.59	13.24	29.62	32.67	35.48	38.93	41.40
22	8.64	9.54	10.98	12.34	14.04	30.81	33.92	36.78	40.29	42.80
23	9.26	10.20	11.69	13.09	14.85	32.01	35.17	38.08	41.64	44.18
24	9.89	10.86	12.40	13.85	15.66	33.20	36.42	39.36	42.98	45.56
25	10.52	11.52	13.12	14.61	16.47	34.38	37.65	40.65	44.31	46.93
26	11.16	12.20	13.84	15.38	17.29	35.56	38.88	41.92	45.64	48.29
27	11.81	12.88	14.57	16.15	18.11	36.74	40.11	43.19	46.96	49.64
28	12.46	13.56	15.31	16.93	18.94	37.92	41.34	44.46	48.28	50.99
29	13.12	14.26	16.05	17.71	19.77	39.09	42.56	45.72	49.59	52.34
30	13.79	14.95	16.79	18.49	20.60	40.26	43.77	46.98	50.89	53.67
40	20.71	22.16	24.43	26.51	29.05	51.81	55.76	59.34	63.69	66.77
60	35.53	37.48	40.48	43.19	46.46	74.40	79.08	83.30	88.38	91.95
120	83.85	86.92	91.58	95.70	100.62	140.23	146.57	152.21	158.95	163.65

For $n > 120$, $\chi^2_{n;\alpha} \approx n \left[1 - \dfrac{2}{9n} + z_\alpha \sqrt{\dfrac{2}{9n}} \right]^3$ where z_α is the desired percentage point for a standardized normal distribution.

Table 4.9   Percentage Points of Student t Distribution

Value of $t_{n;\alpha}$ such that $\text{Prob}[t_n > t_{n;\alpha}] = \alpha$

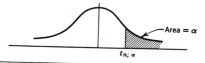

| | | | α | | |
n	0.10	0.050	0.025	0.010	0.005
1	3.078	6.314	12.706	31.821	63.657
2	1.886	2.920	4.303	6.965	9.925
3	1.638	2.353	3.182	4.541	5.841
4	1.533	2.132	2.776	3.747	4.604
5	1.476	2.015	2.571	3.365	4.032
6	1.440	1.943	2.447	3.143	3.707
7	1.415	1.895	2.365	2.998	3.499
8	1.397	1.860	2.306	2.896	3.355
9	1.383	1.833	2.262	2.821	3.250
10	1.372	1.812	2.228	2.764	3.169
11	1.363	1.796	2.201	2.718	3.106
12	1.356	1.782	2.179	2.681	3.055
13	1.350	1.771	2.160	2.650	3.012
14	1.345	1.761	2.145	2.624	2.977
15	1.341	1.753	2.131	2.602	2.947
16	1.337	1.746	2.120	2.583	2.921
17	1.333	1.740	2.110	2.567	2.898
18	1.330	1.734	2.101	2.552	2.878
19	1.328	1.729	2.093	2.539	2.861
20	1.325	1.725	2.086	2.528	2.845
21	1.323	1.721	2.080	2.518	2.831
22	1.321	1.717	2.074	2.508	2.819
23	1.319	1.714	2.069	2.500	2.807
24	1.318	1.711	2.064	2.492	2.797
25	1.316	1.708	2.060	2.485	2.787
26	1.315	1.706	2.056	2.479	2.779
27	1.314	1.703	2.052	2.473	2.771
28	1.313	1.701	2.048	2.467	2.763
29	1.311	1.699	2.045	2.462	2.756
30	1.310	1.697	2.042	2.457	2.750
40	1.303	1.684	2.021	2.423	2.704
60	1.296	1.671	2.000	2.390	2.660
120	1.289	1.658	1.980	2.358	2.617

$\alpha = 0.995, 0.990, 0.975, 0.950,$ and 0.900 follow from $t_{n;1-\alpha} = -t_{n;\alpha}$

Table 4.10(a)   **Percentage Points of F Distribution**

Values of $F_{n_1,n_2;0.05}$ such that $\text{Prob}[F_{n_1,n_2} > F_{n_1,n_2;0.05}] = 0.05$

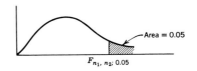

$F_{n_1,\ n_2;\ 0.05}$

n_2 \ n_1	1	2	3	4	5	6	7	8	9	10	11	12	13	14	16
1	161	200	216	225	230	234	237	239	241	242	243	244	245	245	246
2	18.5	19.0	19.2	19.2	19.3	19.3	19.4	19.4	19.4	19.4	19.4	19.4	19.4	19.4	19.4
3	10.1	9.55	9.28	9.12	9.01	8.94	8.89	8.85	8.81	8.79	8.76	8.74	8.73	8.71	8.69
4	7.71	6.94	6.59	6.39	6.26	6.16	6.09	6.04	6.00	5.96	5.94	5.91	5.89	5.87	5.84
5	6.61	5.79	5.41	5.19	5.05	4.95	4.88	4.82	4.77	4.73	4.70	4.68	4.66	4.64	4.60
6	5.99	5.14	4.76	4.53	4.39	4.28	4.21	4.15	4.10	4.06	4.03	4.00	3.98	3.96	3.92
7	5.59	4.74	4.35	4.12	3.97	3.87	3.79	3.73	3.68	3.64	3.60	3.57	3.55	3.53	3.49
8	5.32	4.46	4.07	3.84	3.69	3.58	3.50	3.44	3.39	3.35	3.31	3.28	3.26	3.24	3.20
9	5.12	4.26	3.86	3.63	3.48	3.37	3.29	3.23	3.18	3.14	3.14	3.10	3.05	3.03	2.99
10	4.96	4.10	3.71	3.48	3.33	3.22	3.14	3.07	3.02	2.98	2.94	2.91	2.89	2.86	2.83
11	4.84	3.98	3.59	3.36	3.20	3.09	3.01	2.95	2.90	2.85	2.82	2.79	2.76	2.74	2.70
12	4.75	3.89	3.49	3.25	3.11	3.00	2.91	2.85	2.80	2.75	2.72	2.69	2.66	2.64	2.60
13	4.67	3.81	3.41	3.18	3.03	2.92	2.83	2.77	2.71	2.67	2.63	2.60	2.58	2.55	2.51
14	4.60	3.74	3.35	3.11	2.96	2.85	2.76	2.70	2.65	2.60	2.57	2.53	2.51	2.48	2.44
16	4.49	3.63	3.24	3.01	2.85	2.74	2.66	2.59	2.54	2.49	2.46	2.42	2.40	2.37	2.33
18	4.41	3.55	3.16	2.93	2.77	2.66	2.58	2.51	2.46	2.41	2.37	2.34	2.31	2.29	2.25
20	4.35	3.49	3.10	2.87	2.71	2.60	2.51	2.45	2.39	2.35	2.31	2.28	2.25	2.22	2.18
22	4.30	3.44	3.05	2.82	2.66	2.55	2.46	2.40	2.34	2.30	2.26	2.23	2.20	2.17	2.13
24	4.26	3.40	3.01	2.78	2.62	2.51	2.42	2.36	2.30	2.25	2.21	2.18	2.15	2.13	2.09
26	4.23	3.37	2.98	2.74	2.59	2.47	2.39	2.32	2.27	2.22	2.18	2.15	2.12	2.09	2.05
28	4.20	3.34	2.95	2.71	2.56	2.45	2.36	2.29	2.24	2.19	2.15	2.12	2.09	2.06	2.02
30	4.17	3.32	2.92	2.69	2.53	2.42	2.33	2.27	2.21	2.16	2.13	2.09	2.06	2.04	1.99
40	4.08	3.23	2.84	2.61	2.45	2.34	2.25	2.18	2.12	2.08	2.04	2.00	1.97	1.95	1.90
50	4.03	3.18	2.79	2.56	2.40	2.29	2.20	2.13	2.07	2.03	1.99	1.95	1.92	1.89	1.85
60	4.00	3.15	2.76	2.53	2.37	2.25	2.17	2.10	2.04	1.99	1.95	1.92	1.89	1.86	1.82
80	3.96	3.11	2.72	2.49	2.33	2.21	2.13	2.06	2.00	1.95	1.91	1.88	1.84	1.82	1.77
100	3.94	3.09	2.70	2.46	2.31	2.19	2.10	2.03	1.97	1.93	1.89	1.85	1.82	1.79	1.75
200	3.89	3.04	2.65	2.42	2.26	2.14	2.06	1.98	1.93	1.88	1.84	1.80	1.77	1.74	1.69
500	3.86	3.01	2.62	2.39	2.23	2.12	2.03	1.96	1.90	1.85	1.81	1.77	1.74	1.71	1.66
∞	3.84	3.00	2.60	2.37	2.21	2.10	2.01	1.94	1.88	1.83	1.79	1.75	1.72	1.69	1.64

18	20	22	24	26	28	30	40	50	60	80	100	200	500	∞	n_1/n_2
247	248	249	249	249	250	250	251	252	252	252	253	254	254	254	1
19.4	19.5	19.5	19.5	19.5	19.5	19.5	19.5	19.5	19.5	19.5	19.5	19.5	19.5	19.5	2
8.67	8.66	8.65	8.64	8.63	8.62	8.62	8.59	8.59	8.57	8.56	8.55	8.54	8.53	8.53	3
5.82	5.80	5.79	5.77	5.76	5.75	5.75	5.72	5.70	5.69	5.67	5.66	5.65	5.64	5.63	4
4.58	3.56	4.54	4.53	4.52	4.50	4.50	4.46	4.44	4.43	4.41	4.41	4.39	4.37	4.37	5
3.90	3.87	3.86	3.84	3.83	3.82	3.81	3.77	3.75	3.74	3.72	3.71	3.69	3.68	3.67	6
3.47	3.44	3.43	3.41	3.40	3.39	3.38	3.34	3.32	3.30	3.29	3.27	3.25	3.24	3.23	7
3.17	3.15	3.13	3.12	3.10	3.09	3.08	3.04	3.02	3.01	2.99	2.97	2.95	2.94	2.93	8
2.96	2.94	2.92	2.90	2.89	2.87	2.86	2.83	2.80	2.79	2.77	2.76	2.73	2.72	2.71	9
2.80	2.77	2.75	2.74	2.72	2.71	2.70	2.66	2.64	2.62	2.60	2.59	2.56	2.55	2.54	10
2.67	2.65	2.63	2.61	2.59	2.58	2.57	2.53	2.51	2.49	2.47	2.46	2.43	2.42	2.40	11
2.57	2.54	2.52	2.51	2.49	2.48	2.47	2.43	2.40	2.38	2.36	2.35	2.32	2.31	2.30	12
2.48	2.46	2.44	2.42	2.41	2.39	2.38	2.34	2.31	2.30	2.27	2.26	2.23	2.22	2.21	13
2.41	2.38	2.37	2.35	2.33	2.32	2.31	2.27	2.24	2.22	2.20	2.19	2.16	2.14	2.13	14
2.30	2.28	2.25	2.24	2.22	2.21	2.19	2.15	2.12	2.11	2.08	2.07	2.04	2.02	2.01	16
2.22	2.19	2.17	2.15	2.13	2.12	2.11	2.06	2.04	2.02	1.99	1.98	1.95	1.93	1.92	18
2.15	2.12	2.10	2.08	2.07	2.05	2.04	1.99	1.97	1.95	1.92	1.91	1.88	1.86	1.84	20
2.10	2.07	2.05	2.03	2.01	2.00	1.98	1.94	1.91	1.89	1.86	1.85	1.82	1.80	1.78	22
2.05	2.03	2.00	1.98	1.97	1.95	1.94	1.89	1.86	1.84	1.82	1.80	1.77	1.75	1.73	24
2.02	1.99	1.97	1.95	1.93	1.91	1.90	1.84	1.82	1.80	1.78	1.76	1.73	1.71	1.69	26
1.99	1.96	1.93	1.91	1.90	1.88	1.87	1.82	1.79	1.77	1.74	1.73	1.69	1.67	1.65	28
1.96	1.93	1.91	1.89	1.87	1.85	1.84	1.79	1.76	1.74	1.71	1.70	1.66	1.64	1.62	30
1.87	1.84	1.81	1.79	1.77	1.76	1.74	1.69	1.66	1.64	1.61	1.59	1.55	1.53	1.51	40
1.81	1.78	1.76	1.74	1.72	1.70	1.69	1.63	1.60	1.58	1.54	1.52	1.48	1.46	1.44	50
1.78	1.75	1.72	1.70	1.68	1.66	1.65	1.59	1.56	1.53	1.50	1.48	1.44	1.41	1.39	60
1.73	1.70	1.68	1.65	1.63	1.62	1.60	1.54	1.51	1.48	1.45	1.43	1.38	1.35	1.32	80
1.71	1.68	1.65	1.63	1.61	1.59	1.57	1.52	1.48	1.45	1.41	1.39	1.34	1.31	1.28	100
1.66	1.62	1.60	1.57	1.55	1.53	1.52	1.46	1.41	1.39	1.35	1.32	1.26	1.22	1.19	200
1.62	1.59	1.56	1.54	1.52	1.50	1.48	1.42	1.38	1.34	1.30	1.28	1.21	1.16	1.11	500
1.60	1.57	1.54	1.52	1.50	1.48	1.46	1.39	1.35	1.32	1.27	1.24	1.17	1.11	1.00	∞

Table 4.10(b) Percentage Points of F Distribution

Values of $F_{n_1,n_2;0.025}$ such that Prob $[F_{n_1,n_2} > F_{n_1,n_2;0.025}] = 0.025$

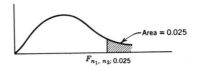

$F_{n_1,\,n_2;\,0.025}$

n_2 \ n_1	1	2	3	4	5	6	7	8	9	10	11	12	13	14	16
1	648	800	864	900	922	937	948	957	963	969	973	977	980	983	987
2	38.5	39.0	39.2	39.2	39.3	39.3	39.4	39.4	39.4	39.4	39.4	39.4	39.4	39.4	39.4
3	17.4	16.0	15.4	15.1	14.9	14.7	14.6	14.5	14.5	14.4	14.4	14.3	14.3	14.3	14.2
4	12.2	10.6	9.98	9.60	9.36	9.20	9.07	8.98	8.90	8.84	8.79	8.75	8.72	8.69	8.64
5	10.0	8.43	7.76	7.39	7.15	6.98	6.85	6.76	6.68	6.62	6.57	6.52	6.49	6.46	6.41
6	8.81	7.26	6.60	6.23	5.99	5.82	5.70	5.60	5.52	5.46	5.41	5.37	5.33	5.30	5.25
7	8.07	6.54	5.89	5.52	5.29	5.12	4.99	4.90	4.82	4.76	4.71	4.67	4.63	4.60	4.54
8	7.57	6.06	5.42	5.05	4.82	4.65	4.53	4.43	4.36	4.30	4.24	4.20	4.16	4.13	4.08
9	7.21	5.71	5.08	4.72	4.48	4.32	4.20	4.10	4.03	3.96	3.91	3.87	3.83	3.80	3.74
10	6.94	5.46	4.83	4.47	4.24	4.07	3.95	3.85	3.78	3.72	3.66	3.62	3.58	3.55	3.50
11	6.72	5.26	4.63	4.28	4.04	3.88	3.76	3.66	3.59	3.53	3.47	3.43	3.39	3.36	3.30
12	6.55	5.10	4.47	4.12	3.89	3.73	3.61	3.51	3.44	3.37	3.32	3.28	3.24	3.21	3.15
13	6.41	4.97	4.35	4.00	3.77	3.60	3.48	3.39	3.31	3.25	3.20	3.15	3.12	3.08	3.03
14	6.30	4.86	4.24	3.89	3.66	3.50	3.38	3.29	3.21	3.15	3.09	3.05	3.01	2.98	2.92
16	6.12	4.69	4.08	3.73	3.50	3.34	3.22	3.12	3.05	2.99	2.93	2.89	2.85	2.82	2.76
18	5.98	4.56	3.95	3.61	3.38	3.22	3.10	3.01	2.93	2.87	2.81	2.77	2.73	2.70	2.64
20	5.87	4.46	3.86	3.51	3.29	3.13	3.01	2.91	2.84	2.77	2.72	2.68	2.64	2.60	2.55
22	5.79	4.38	3.78	3.44	3.22	3.05	2.93	2.84	2.76	2.70	2.65	2.60	2.56	2.53	2.47
24	5.72	4.32	3.72	3.38	3.15	2.99	2.87	2.78	2.70	2.64	2.59	2.54	2.50	2.47	2.41
26	5.66	4.27	3.67	3.33	3.10	2.94	2.82	2.73	2.65	2.59	2.54	2.49	2.45	2.42	2.36
28	5.61	4.22	3.63	3.29	3.06	2.90	2.78	2.69	2.61	2.55	2.49	2.45	2.41	2.37	2.32
30	5.57	4.18	3.59	3.25	3.03	2.87	2.75	2.65	2.57	2.51	2.46	2.41	2.37	2.34	2.28
40	5.42	4.05	3.46	3.13	2.90	2.74	2.62	2.53	2.45	2.39	2.33	2.29	2.25	2.21	2.15
50	5.34	3.98	3.39	3.06	2.83	2.67	2.55	2.46	2.38	2.32	2.26	2.22	2.18	2.14	2.08
60	5.29	3.93	3.34	3.01	2.79	2.63	2.51	2.41	2.33	2.27	2.22	2.17	2.13	2.09	2.03
80	5.22	3.86	3.28	2.95	2.73	2.57	2.45	2.36	2.30	2.21	2.16	2.11	2.07	2.03	1.97
100	5.18	3.83	3.25	2.92	2.70	2.54	2.42	2.32	2.24	2.18	2.12	2.08	2.04	2.00	1.94
200	5.10	3.76	3.18	2.85	2.63	2.47	2.35	2.26	2.18	2.11	2.06	2.01	1.97	1.93	1.87
500	5.05	3.72	3.14	2.81	2.59	2.43	2.31	2.22	2.14	2.07	2.02	1.97	1.93	1.89	1.83
∞	5.02	3.69	3.12	2.79	2.57	2.41	2.29	2.19	2.11	2.05	1.99	1.94	1.90	1.87	1.80

18	20	22	24	26	28	30	40	50	60	80	100	200	500	∞	n_1/n_2
990	993	995	997	999	1000	1001	1006	1008	1010	1012	1013	1016	1017	1018	1
39.4	39.4	39.5	39.5	39.5	39.5	39.5	39.5	39.5	39.5	39.5	39.5	39.5	39.5	39.5	2
14.2	14.2	14.1	14.1	14.1	14.1	14.1	14.0	14.0	14.0	14.0	14.0	13.9	13.9	13.9	3
8.60	8.56	8.53	8.51	8.49	8.48	8.46	8.41	8.38	8.36	8.33	8.32	8.29	8.27	8.26	4
6.37	6.33	6.30	6.28	6.26	6.24	6.23	6.18	6.14	6.12	6.10	6.08	6.05	6.03	6.01	5
5.21	5.17	5.14	5.12	5.10	5.08	5.07	5.01	4.98	4.96	4.93	4.92	4.88	4.86	4.85	6
4.50	4.47	4.44	4.42	4.39	4.38	4.36	4.31	4.28	4.25	4.23	4.21	4.18	4.16	4.14	7
4.03	4.00	3.97	3.95	3.93	3.91	3.89	3.84	3.81	3.78	3.76	3.74	3.70	3.68	3.67	8
3.70	3.67	3.64	3.61	3.59	3.58	3.56	3.51	3.47	3.45	3.42	3.40	3.37	3.35	3.33	9
3.45	3.42	3.39	3.37	3.34	3.33	3.31	3.26	3.22	3.20	3.17	3.15	3.12	3.09	3.08	10
3.26	3.23	3.20	3.17	3.15	3.13	3.12	3.06	3.03	3.00	2.97	2.96	2.92	2.90	2.88	11
3.11	3.07	3.04	3.02	3.00	2.98	2.96	2.91	2.87	2.85	2.82	2.80	2.76	2.74	2.72	12
2.98	2.95	2.92	2.89	2.87	2.85	2.84	2.78	2.74	2.72	2.69	2.67	2.63	2.61	2.60	13
2.88	2.84	2.81	2.79	2.77	2.75	2.73	2.67	2.64	2.61	2.58	2.56	2.53	2.50	2.49	14
2.72	2.68	2.65	2.63	2.60	2.58	2.57	2.51	2.47	2.45	2.42	2.40	2.36	2.33	2.32	16
2.60	2.56	2.53	2.50	2.48	2.46	2.44	2.38	2.35	2.32	2.29	2.27	2.23	2.20	2.19	18
2.50	2.46	2.43	2.41	2.39	2.37	2.35	2.29	2.25	2.22	2.19	2.17	2.13	2.10	2.09	20
2.43	2.39	2.36	2.33	2.31	2.29	2.27	2.21	2.17	2.14	2.11	2.09	2.05	2.02	2.00	22
2.36	2.33	2.30	2.27	2.25	2.23	2.21	2.15	2.11	2.08	2.05	2.02	1.98	1.95	1.94	24
2.31	2.28	2.24	2.22	2.19	2.17	2.16	2.09	2.05	2.03	1.99	1.97	1.92	1.90	1.88	26
2.27	2.23	2.20	2.17	2.15	2.13	2.11	2.05	2.01	1.98	1.94	1.92	1.88	1.85	1.83	28
2.23	2.20	2.16	2.14	2.11	2.09	2.07	2.01	1.97	1.94	1.90	1.88	1.84	1.81	1.79	30
2.11	2.07	2.03	2.01	1.98	1.96	1.94	1.88	1.83	1.80	1.76	1.74	1.69	1.66	1.64	40
2.03	1.99	1.96	1.93	1.91	1.88	1.87	1.80	1.75	1.72	1.68	1.66	1.60	1.57	1.55	50
1.98	1.94	1.91	1.88	1.86	1.83	1.82	1.74	1.70	1.67	1.62	1.60	1.54	1.51	1.48	60
1.93	1.88	1.85	1.82	1.79	1.77	1.75	1.68	1.63	1.60	1.55	1.53	1.47	1.43	1.40	80
1.89	1.85	1.81	1.78	1.76	1.74	1.71	1.64	1.59	1.56	1.51	1.48	1.42	1.38	1.35	100
1.82	1.78	1.74	1.71	1.68	1.66	1.64	1.56	1.51	1.47	1.42	1.39	1.32	1.27	1.23	200
1.78	1.74	1.70	1.67	1.64	1.62	1.60	1.51	1.46	1.42	1.37	1.34	1.25	1.19	1.14	500
1.75	1.71	1.67	1.64	1.61	1.59	1.57	1.48	1.43	1.39	1.33	1.30	1.21	1.13	1.00	∞

Table 4.10(c) Percentage Points of F Distribution

Values of $F_{n_1,n_2;0.01}$ such that $\text{Prob}[F_{n_1,n_2} > F_{n_1,n_2;0.01}] = 0.01$

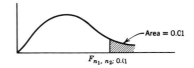

n_2 \ n_1	1	2	3	4	5	6	7	8	9	10	11	12	13	14	16
*1	405	500	540	563	576	586	593	598	602	606	608	611	613	614	617
2	98.5	99.0	99.2	99.2	99.3	99.3	99.4	99.4	99.4	99.4	99.4	99.4	99.4	99.4	99.4
3	34.1	30.8	29.5	28.7	28.2	27.9	27.7	27.5	27.3	27.2	27.1	27.1	27.0	26.9	26.8
4	21.2	18.0	16.7	16.0	15.5	15.2	15.0	14.8	14.7	14.5	14.4	14.4	14.3	14.2	14.2
5	16.3	13.3	12.1	11.4	11.0	10.7	10.5	10.3	10.2	10.1	9.96	9.89	9.82	9.77	9.68
6	13.7	10.9	9.78	9.15	8.75	8.47	8.26	8.10	7.98	7.87	7.79	7.72	7.66	7.60	7.52
7	12.2	9.55	8.45	7.85	7.46	7.19	6.99	6.84	6.72	6.62	6.54	6.47	6.41	6.36	6.27
8	11.3	8.65	7.59	7.01	6.63	6.37	6.18	6.03	5.91	5.81	5.73	5.67	5.61	5.56	5.48
9	10.6	8.02	6.99	6.42	6.06	5.80	5.61	5.47	5.35	5.26	5.18	5.11	5.05	5.00	4.92
10	10.0	7.56	6.55	5.99	5.64	5.39	5.20	5.06	4.94	4.85	4.77	4.71	4.65	4.60	4.52
11	9.65	7.21	6.22	5.67	5.32	5.07	4.89	4.74	4.63	4.54	4.46	4.40	4.34	4.29	4.21
12	9.33	6.93	5.95	5.41	5.06	4.82	4.64	4.50	4.39	4.30	4.22	4.16	4.10	4.05	3.97
13	9.07	6.70	5.74	5.21	4.86	4.62	4.44	4.30	4.19	4.10	4.02	3.96	3.91	3.86	3.78
14	8.86	6.51	5.56	5.04	4.70	4.46	4.28	4.14	4.03	3.94	3.86	3.80	3.75	3.70	3.62
16	8.53	6.23	5.29	4.77	4.44	4.20	4.03	3.89	3.78	3.69	3.62	3.55	3.50	3.45	3.37
18	8.29	6.01	5.09	4.58	4.25	4.01	3.84	3.71	3.60	3.51	3.43	3.37	3.32	3.27	3.19
20	8.10	5.85	4.94	4.43	4.10	3.87	3.70	3.56	3.46	3.37	3.29	3.23	3.18	3.13	3.05
22	7.95	5.72	4.82	4.31	3.99	3.76	3.59	3.45	3.35	3.26	3.18	3.12	3.07	3.02	2.94
24	7.82	5.61	4.72	4.22	3.90	3.67	3.50	3.36	3.26	3.17	3.09	3.03	2.98	2.93	2.85
26	7.72	5.53	4.64	4.14	3.82	3.59	3.42	3.29	3.18	3.09	3.02	2.96	2.90	2.86	2.78
28	7.64	5.45	4.57	4.07	3.75	3.53	3.36	3.23	3.12	3.03	2.96	2.90	2·84	2.79	2.72
30	7.56	5.39	4.51	4.02	3.70	3.47	3.30	3.17	3.07	2.98	2.91	2.84	2.79	2.74	7.66
40	7.31	5.18	4.31	3.83	3.51	3.29	3.12	2.99	2.89	2.80	2.73	2.66	2.61	2.56	2.48
50	7.17	5.06	4.20	3.72	3.41	3.19	3.02	2.89	2.79	2.70	2.63	2.56	2.51	2.46	2.38
60	7.08	4.98	4.13	3.65	3.34	3.12	2.95	2.82	2.72	2.63	2.56	2.50	2.44	2.39	2.31
80	6.96	4.88	4.04	3.56	3.26	3.04	2.87	2.74	2.64	2.55	2.48	2.42	2.36	2.31	2.23
100	6.90	4.82	3.98	3.51	3.21	2.99	2.82	2.69	2.59	2.50	2.43	2.37	2.31	2.26	2.19
200	6.76	4.71	3.88	3.41	3.11	2.89	2.73	2.60	2.50	2 41	2.34	2.27	2.22	2.17	2.09
500	6.69	4.65	3.82	3.36	3.05	2.84	2.68	2.55	2.44	2.36	2.28	2.22	2.17	2.12	2.04
∞	6.63	4.61	3.78	3.32	3.02	2.80	2.64	2.51	2.41	2.32	2.25	2.18	2.13	2.08	2.00

18	20	22	24	26	28	30	40	50	60	80	100	200	500	∞	n_1/n_2
619	621	622	623	624	625	626	629	630	631	633	633	635	636	637	1
99.4	99.4	99.5	99.5	99.5	99.5	99.5	99.5	99.5	99.5	99.5	99.5	99.5	99.5	99.5	2
26.8	26.7	26.6	26.6	26.6	26.5	26.5	26.4	26.4	26.3	26.3	26.2	26.2	26.1	26.1	3
14.1	14.0	14.0	13.9	13.9	13.9	13.8	13.7	13.7	13.7	13.6	13.6	13.5	13.5	13.5	4
9.61	9.55	9.51	9.47	9.43	9.40	9.38	9.29	9.24	9.20	9.16	9.13	9.08	9.04	9.02	5
7.45	7.40	7.35	7.31	7.28	7.25	7.23	7.14	7.09	7.06	7.01	6.99	6.93	6.90	6.88	6
6.21	6.16	6.11	6.07	6.04	6.02	5.99	5.91	5.86	5.82	5.78	5.75	5.70	5.67	5.65	7
5.41	5.36	5.32	5.28	5.25	5.22	5.20	5.12	5.07	5.03	4.99	4.96	4.91	4.88	4.85	8
4.86	4.81	4.77	4.73	4.70	4.67	4.65	4.57	4.52	4.48	4.44	4.42	4.36	4.33	4.31	9
4.46	4.41	4.36	4.33	4.30	4.27	4.25	4.17	4.12	4.08	4.04	4.01	3.96	3.93	3.91	10
4.15	4.10	4.06	4.02	3.99	3.96	3.94	3.86	3.81	3.78	3.73	3.71	3.66	3.62	3.60	11
3.91	3.86	3.82	3.78	3.75	3.72	3.70	3.62	3.57	3.54	3.49	3.47	3.41	3.38	3.36	12
3.72	3.66	3.62	3.59	3.56	3.53	3.51	3.43	3.38	3.34	3.30	3.27	3.22	3.19	3.16	13
3.56	3.51	3.46	3.43	3.40	3.37	3.35	3.27	3.22	3.18	3.14	3.11	3.06	3.03	3.00	14
3.31	3.26	3.22	3.18	3.15	3.12	3.10	3.02	2.97	2.93	2.89	2.86	2.81	2.78	2.75	16
3.13	3.08	3.03	3.00	2.97	2.94	2.92	2.84	2.78	2.75	2.70	2.68	2.62	2.59	2.57	18
2.99	2.94	2.90	2.86	2.83	2.80	2.78	2.69	2.64	2.61	2.56	2.54	2.48	2.44	2.42	20
2.88	2.83	2.78	2.75	2.72	2.69	2.67	2.58	2.53	2.50	2.45	2.42	2.36	2.33	2.31	22
2.79	2.74	2.70	2.66	2.63	2.60	2.58	2.49	2.44	2.40	2.36	2.33	2.27	2.24	2.21	24
2.72	2.66	2.62	2.58	2.55	2.53	2.50	2.42	2.36	2.33	2.28	2.25	2.19	2.16	2.13	26
2.65	2.60	2.56	2.52	2.49	2.46	2.44	2.35	2.30	2.26	2.22	2.19	2.13	2.09	2.06	28
2.60	2.55	2.51	2.47	2.44	2.41	2.39	2.30	2.25	2.21	2.16	2.13	2.07	2.03	2.01	30
2.42	2.37	2.33	2.29	2.26	2.23	2.20	2.11	2.06	2.02	1.97	1.94	1.87	1.83	1.80	40
2.32	2.27	2.22	2.18	2.15	2.12	2.10	2.01	1.95	1.91	1.86	1.82	1.76	1.71	1.68	50
2.25	2.20	2.15	2.12	2.08	2.05	2.03	1.94	1.88	1.84	1.78	1.75	1.68	1.63	1.60	60
2.17	2.12	2.07	2.03	2.00	1.97	1.94	1.85	1.79	1.75	1.69	1.66	1.58	1.53	1.49	80
2.12	2.07	2.02	1.98	1.94	1.92	1.89	1.80	1.73	1.69	1.63	1.60	1.52	1.47	1.43	100
2.02	1.97	1.93	1.89	1.85	1.82	1.79	1.69	1.63	1.58	1.52	1.48	1.39	1.33	1.28	200
1.97	1.92	1.87	1.83	1.79	1.76	1.74	1.63	1.56	1.52	1.45	1.41	1.31	1.23	1.16	500
1.93	1.88	1.83	1.79	1.76	1.72	1.70	1.59	1.52	1.47	1.40	1.36	1.25	1.15	1.00	∞

* Multiply the number of the first row ($v_2 = 1$) by 10.

Table 4.11   Percentage Points of Run Distribution

Values of $r_{n:\alpha}$ such that Prob $[r_n > r_{n:\alpha}] = \alpha$, where $n = N_1 = N_2 = N/2$

$n = N/2$	α					
	0.99	0.975	0.95	0.05	0.025	0.01
5	2	2	3	8	9	9
6	2	3	3	10	10	11
7	3	3	4	11	12	12
8	4	4	5	12	13	13
9	4	5	6	13	14	15
10	5	6	6	15	15	16
11	6	7	7	16	16	17
12	7	7	8	17	18	18
13	7	8	9	18	19	20
14	8	9	10	19	20	21
15	9	10	11	20	21	22
16	10	11	11	22	22	23
18	11	12	13	24	25	26
20	13	14	15	26	27	28
25	17	18	19	32	33	34
30	21	22	24	37	39	40
35	25	27	28	43	44	46
40	30	31	33	48	50	51
45	34	36	37	54	55	57
50	38	40	42	59	61	63
55	43	45	46	65	66	68
60	47	49	51	70	72	74
65	52	54	56	75	77	79
70	56	58	60	81	83	85
75	61	63	65	86	88	90
80	65	68	70	91	93	96
85	70	72	74	97	99	101
90	74	77	79	102	104	107
95	79	82	84	107	109	112
100	84	86	88	113	115	117

Table 4.12   Percentage Points of Reverse Arrangement Distribution

Values of $A_{N;\alpha}$ such that Prob $[A_N > A_{N;\alpha}] = \alpha$ where $N =$ total number of measurements

N	α					
	0.99	0.975	0.95	0.05	0.025	0.01
10	9	11	13	31	33	35
12	16	18	21	44	47	49
14	24	27	30	60	63	66
16	34	38	41	78	81	85
18	45	50	54	98	102	107
20	59	64	69	120	125	130
30	152	162	171	263	272	282
40	290	305	319	460	474	489
50	473	495	514	710	729	751
60	702	731	756	1013	1038	1067
70	977	1014	1045	1369	1400	1437
80	1299	1344	1382	1777	1815	1860
90	1668	1721	1766	2238	2283	2336
100	2083	2145	2198	2751	2804	2866

5

DATA PROCESSING PROCEDURES
AND ERRORS

The procedures for determining the properties of random data may be divided logically into two parts: Part 1. The procedure for analyzing the pertinent statistical properties of a single sample record. Part 2. The procedure for establishing the overall properties given the statistical properties of each of a collection of sample records.

Section 5.1 describes a procedure for Part 1; Section 5.2 describes a procedure for Part 2. These procedures represent systematic methods of acquiring, establishing basic properties of, and analyzing desired parameters for individual records and for collections of records. Of course, all the steps listed may not apply to a particular problem. Moreover, special parallel processing techniques may be useful to speed up some of the analysis.

Theoretical material on statistical errors for parameter estimates appears in Section 5.3. The discussion includes the derivation of estimation errors for mean values, mean square values, probability density functions, correlation functions, and spectral density functions. This material is then utilized in Section 5.4 to determine sample size and record length requirements to measure these various parameters. A discussion is given also of requirements for determining the accuracy of frequency response function and coherence function measurements for establishing linear relationships between data.

Section 5.5 develops theoretical ideas for the extraction of a maximum amount of information from a minimum amount of data by using appropriate random or periodic sampling procedures. Formulas are presented which will predict the probability of detecting an unexpected event, and the probability of covering a range of expected events. Section 5.6 is concerned with statistical tests for the basic assumptions of randomness, stationarity, normality, and equivalence. Section 5.7 presents relationships

172

for the accuracy of frequency response function measurements of multiple-input linear systems based upon sampled data.

5.1 Procedure for Analyzing Single Records

An overall procedure for analyzing the pertinent statistical properties of a single sample time history record is presented in Figure 5.1. Each block in Figure 5.1 will be discussed in this section. Note that any of the recommended steps may be accomplished by either analog or digital techniques. Analog measurement techniques are discussed in Chapter 6; digital computer techniques are discussed in Chapter 7. Furthermore, many of the steps can often be omitted depending upon the specific requirements and desired end use of the data.

Figure 5.1 indicates that certain critical assumptions which are often made concerning random data should be verified before proceeding with a detailed analysis. More specifically, it is desirable to establish whether or not the sampled data is (*a*) random, (*b*) stationary, and/or (*c*) normal. It should be emphasized, however, that these various determinations do not necessarily have to be accomplished by the formal procedures indicated in Figure 5.1. For example, an experienced analyst can often detect the presence of a periodicity, a lack of stationarity, and/or a significant deviation from normality by simple observation of the time history data or other data which might be available. These matters are developed further in Section 5.6.

Data Acquisition. The first step in the procedure is obviously to convert the physical parameter of interest into either an analog voltage signal or a digital format, as noted by Block *A* in Figure 5.1. For example, if the physical parameter of interest were air temperature versus time, the data could be converted into an analog signal by using a simple thermocouple, or into a digital format by simply reading the temperature indicated by a mercury thermometer at regular time intervals.

Data Sampling. Samples of the data from the transducer must be obtained by some sampling procedure, as noted by Block *B*. The length of each time history sample obtained is of direct importance to the statistical accuracy of the analyses to follow. The desired sample record length T_r will be discussed in Sections 5.3 and 5.4 for each type of analysis.

On the other hand, the number of samples obtained and the manner in which they are selected is of direct importance to establishing the overall statistical properties of a collection of records. In general, samples should be obtained in the form of either one long continuous record or a set of short records of predetermined length selected randomly or periodically. This subject is discussed in Section 5.5.

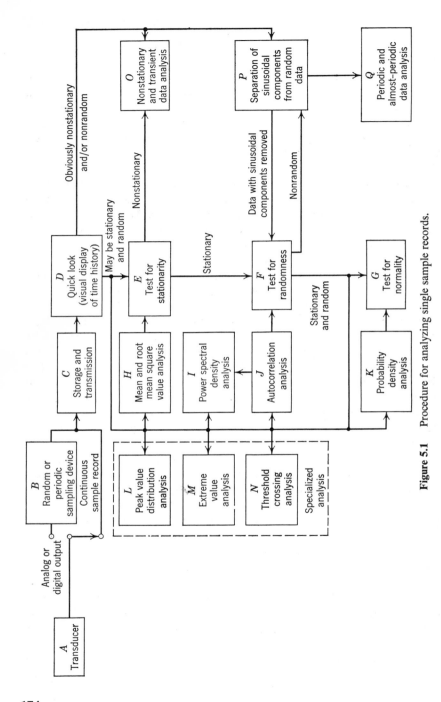

Figure 5.1 Procedure for analyzing single sample records.

Storage and Transmission. After the individual sample records are obtained, the samples must either be analyzed directly, or recorded and stored in some suitable way for later analysis. As is seen in Chapters 6 and 7, the analysis techniques may require a repeated investigation of each time history sample. Hence the recording and storage of the time history data are desired. Magnetic tape recording is probably the most convenient means for storing analog data. Numerous techniques, including magnetic tape, punched cards, and even simple tabulations, can be used to store digital data.

The time history samples might be recorded on magnetic tape at the source. In some cases, however, it may be necessary to transfer the data from the source to a more convenient location for recording and/or analysis. For example, environmental data collected in flight vehicles are often transmitted to the ground using telemetry equipment, and recorded and/or analyzed by ground equipment.

"Quick Look" Analysis. The procedure at this point requires that sample records be divided into two categories: records which are stationary and random, and records which are nonstationary and/or nonrandom. Explicit statistical procedures for establishing whether or not a sample time history record is stationary or random are discussed in Sections 5.6.1 and 5.6.2, and are indicated by Blocks *E* and *F*. Before proceeding with a detailed analysis, however, it would be desirable to take a "quick look" at the time history to see if the sample record is obviously nonstationary or nonrandom, as indicated by Block *D*. This may be done for analog data records by displaying the record on a cathode ray oscilloscope or a galvanometer oscillograph. If time trends or strong sinusoidal components are obviously present, the sample record should be rejected immediately as being nonstationary or nonrandom without wasting time on more detailed tests. Nonstationary data should be transferred to Block *O*, and nonrandom data should be transferred to Block *P*.

Test for Stationarity. Those samples data records accepted as possibly being stationary by the "quick look" analysis should now be investigated more rigorously, as indicated by Block *E*. This is an important step because, if a sample record is stationary, certain analysis procedures will be greatly simplified. Note that deterministic data of the transient form defined in Section 1.1.4 will generally appear nonstationary and should be classified as such. The distinction between transient deterministic data and nonstationary random data is not discernible by investigating single sample records. A collection of records is needed to identify deterministic transient data or nonstationary random data.

Techniques for determining whether sample data are stationary or nonstationary are detailed in Section 5.6.1. Sample records which are nonstationary (or transient) should be transferred to Block *P*.

Test for Randomness. Sample records which have been confirmed to be stationary should now be tested for the presence of sinusoidal components due either to periodic or almost-periodic contributions in the data, as indicated by Block *F*. This is necessary because some analysis procedures to follow will require that periodic components be removed or at least identified if the results are to be completely meaningful. Note that nonrandomness due to deterministic factors other than periodic or almost-periodic components is of no concern, since transient types of nonrandomness would have been detected in Block *E* as nonstationary data.

Explicit statistical procedures to establish whether or not stationary time history data are random are discussed in Section 5.6.2. Sample records which are nonrandom should be transferred to Block *P* for separation or identification of sinusoidal components.

Test for Normality. Random data are often assumed to have a normal (Gaussian) probability density function without specific evidence. This is assumed because of the practical implications of the Central Limit Theorem, which, in effect, implies that any physical phenomenon produced by the sum of numerous random effects will tend to be normally distributed. This is generally true in actual practice as long as the physical operations associated with creating the phenomenon are relatively linear. However, the presence of strong nonlinear operations will often produce deviations from the ideal Gaussian form. Hence it is desirable that an assumption of normality be tested to verify that it is justified, as indicated by Block *G*. Tests for normality are discussed in Section 5.6.3.

Mean and Root Mean Square Level Analysis. The next step indicated by Block *H* is a mean value and rms value measurement. This step will not actually supply any new or particularly significant information over other analyses to follow. That is, an estimate of the mean and rms values of the sample record will automatically result from a probability density function, a power spectral density function, or an autocorrelation function of the sample data, as discussed in the next three sections. It is indicated as a cardinal step in the analysis procedure in Figure 5.1 because, in some cases, mean and rms values may be the only data properties of interest for a given application. If this is true, it is much simpler to measure them directly rather than to bother with more detailed analyses.

Analog procedures for measuring mean values and rms values are discussed in Section 6.1. Digital computation techniques are discussed in Section 7.2.1. The statistical accuracy of mean value and mean square value measurements is developed in Sections 5.3.1 and 5.3.2.

Power Spectral Density Analysis. Perhaps the most important single descriptive characteristic of stationary random data is the power spectral density function, which defines the frequency composition of the data. For linear physical systems, the output power spectrum is equal to the input power spectrum multiplied by the square of the gain factor for the system. Thus power spectra measurements can yield information concerning the dynamic characteristics of the system. The total area under a power spectrum is equal to the mean square value Ψ'^2. To be more general, the mean square value of the data in any frequency range of concern is determined by the area under the power spectrum bounded by the limits of that frequency range. Obviously, the measurement of power spectra data, as indicated by Block I, will be valuable for most analysis objectives.

The physical significance of the power spectral density function for input-output random data is shown clearly in Chapter 3. Analog procedures for measuring power spectra are detailed in Section 6.4, and digital techniques are discussed in Section 7.3.3. The statistical accuracy of power spectral density measurements is discussed in Section 5.3.5.

Autocorrelation Analysis.   The next suggested analysis is autocorrelation, as indicated by Block J. The autocorrelation function of stationary data is the inverse Fourier transform of the power spectral density function. Thus the determination of the autocorrelation function will technically not yield any new information over the power spectrum. There are situations, however, when the autocorrelation function will present the desired information in a more convenient format than will the power spectral density function. An example is the case of detecting sinusoid components in otherwise random data. Autocorrelation analysis will quickly identify sinusoids that might be misinterpreted in the power spectrum. As a result, autocorrelation analysis is very valuable in support of Blocks F and P, as indicated. Note that the peak value of the autocorrelogram, which occurs at zero time displacement, is equal to the mean square value Ψ'^2.

Analog procedures for measuring autocorrelation functions are detailed in Section 6.3, and digital techniques are discussed in Section 7.3.2. The statistical accuracy of autocorrelation measurements is discussed in Section 5.3.4.

Probability Density Analysis.   The last fundamental analysis included in the procedure is probability density analysis, as indicated by Block K. Probability density analysis is often omitted from a data analysis procedure because of the tendency to assume that all random phenomena are normally distributed, as discussed before. In some cases, however, random data may deviate substantially from normality. If such deviations are detected by a test for normality, then the probability density function for the data must be measured to establish the actual probabilistic characteristics of the data, as indicated by Block K. Note that the mean square value of the data is given by $\Psi'^2 = \sigma^2 + \mu^2$, where σ is the standard deviation of the probability density function and μ is the mean value.

Analog procedures for measuring probability density functions are detailed in Section 6.2, and digital techniques are discussed in Section 7.2.2. The statistical accuracy of probability density measurements is discussed in Section 5.3.3.

Specialized Analysis. Other analyses remaining in the procedure are often useful for specialized applications. Three of the most prominent specialized types of analysis are the following.

Peak Value Distribution Analysis. The first specialized analysis, indicated by Block *L*, is peak value distribution analysis. For some applications the statistics of peak values is more useful than the ordinary probability density function for instantaneous values determined in Block *G* or *K*. Pertinent material for this topic is discussed in Refs. 3, 7, 9.

Extreme Value Analysis. Another specialized analysis that might be of interest for some problems is extreme values, indicated by Block *M*. Some of the techniques that exist for defining and estimating extreme values are discussed in Refs. 14, 28.

Threshold Crossing Analysis. An investigation of threshold crossings (or zero crossings), as indicated by Block *N*, may be desired for various problems where the mean time between arbitrary level crossings is of interest. Some references for this subject are Refs. 1, 19, 26.

Nonstationary Data Analysis. Referring back to Blocks *D* and *E*, those sample records which are found to be nonstationary are transferred to Block *O* for special consideration. Chapter 9 is entirely devoted to the analysis of random time history records which are nonstationary.

Separation of Sinusoidal Components. Those sample records that are found to be nonrandom in either Block *D* or Block *F* are transferred to Block *P*. If the data appear to be stationary, the most likely reason for its being nonrandom would be the presence of sinusoidal components due either to periodic or almost-periodic data, as defined in Section 1.1. If sinusoidal components are present, it may often be possible to separate them from the random components and then return the record, with sinusoids removed, to the procedure for random data.

The first problem is detection. The presence of reasonably intense sinusoidal components in otherwise random data will often be obvious by visual inspection of a sample time history. Less intense sinusoidal components will often still be obvious from commonly analyzed properties such as power spectra or probability density plots. The most powerful detection procedure is autocorrelation analysis, as covered by Block *J*. The various detection procedures are discussed in more detail in Section 5.6.2.

The next problem is separation. The required separation can be accomplished with narrow-band rejection filters. Of course, when a sine wave is filtered out of the record by a rejection filter, a narrow frequency band of the random component will also be removed. However, if the rejection filter is very narrow, the random data removed will usually be incidental in terms of the total broad-band random energy represented in the data. For some applications, it may be sufficient simply to identify sinusoidal components without actually removing them. If this is done, however, the random portions of the data cannot be effectively tested for normality.

If all sinusoidal components are removed, the sample record should be returned to the procedure at Block *F*, the test for randomness. If the record is again rejected as nonrandom, it should be transferred to Block *O* for analysis as aperiodic deterministic (transient) data.

Periodic Data Analysis. Periodic and almost periodic portions separated from otherwise random records in Block *P* may be analyzed separately, as indicated by Block *Q*. Procedures and techniques associated with periodic data analysis are thoroughly covered in the literature, and are reviewed in Chapter 1. Digital techniques for analyzing periodic data are discussed in Section 7.2.3.

5.2 Procedure for Analyzing a Collection of Records

The preceding section presented methods for analyzing each individual random record from an experiment. A procedure for analyzing further pertinent statistical properties of a collection of sample records is presented in Figure 5.2. As for the analysis of individual records outlined in Figure 5.1, many of the recommended steps in Figure 5.2 may be accomplished either by analog or digital techniques.

Collection and Analysis of Individual Records. The first step in the procedure is to collect the individual sample records for the collective analysis, and to analyze the individual records as outlined in Figure 5.1. Hence, the applicable portions of Figure 5.1 constitute Block *A* in Figure 5.2.

Tests for Equivalence. The next step, indicated by Block *B*, is to test any or all of the sample records for equivalence. For example, several sample records of the data of interest might have been obtained under identical conditions but at different times or from simultaneous but different experiments. Explicit procedures for establishing whether or not a collection of sample time history records represent equivalent data are discussed in Section 5.6.4.

Pool Equivalent Data. If it can be established that two or more records in a collection are effectively samples of the same random process, then the measurements for the individual records can be pooled together to obtain one set of measurements which are applicable to the two or more equivalent sample records. This pooling operation is indicated by Block *C*.

The result is fewer and more accurate descriptive characteristics for the entire collection of sample records.

Cross-Spectral Density Analysis. The most important joint measurement of any two random records is a cross-spectral density measurement, as indicated by Block *D*. If two sample records represent completely independent random data, the cross-spectral density function will be zero at all frequencies. In this case, no information is yielded by the cross-spectrum

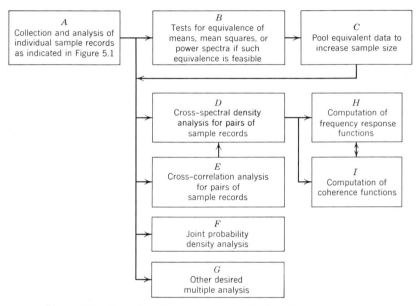

Figure 5.2   Procedure for analyzing a collection of sample records.

other than the fact that the two records are of independent data. However, if the cross-spectral density measurement is not zero at all frequencies, then important information concerning the linear relationships between the data represented by the two sample records is obtained, as indicated by Blocks *H* and *I*. These ideas are developed in detail in Section 3.4.

Analog procedures for measuring cross-spectral density functions are covered in Section 6.7, and digital techniques are discussed in Section 7.4.3. The statistical accuracy of cross-spectral density measurements is discussed in Section 5.3.5.

Cross-Correlation Analysis. As for the case of autocorrelation and power spectral density functions, the cross-correlation and cross-spectral density functions are Fourier transform pairs. Hence the measurement of a cross-correlogram will technically not yield any new information over the cross-spectrum. However, it is generally simpler to measure than a cross-spectrum and may present desired information in a more convenient format. An example is the simple detection of a linear relationship between two measurement points. Therefore, cross-correlation analysis is included in the procedure as Block *E*.

Analog procedures for measuring cross-correlation functions are detailed in Section 6.6, and digital techniques are discussed in Section 7.4.2. The statistical accuracy of cross-correlation measurements is discussed in Section 5.3.4.

Joint Probability Density Analysis. Block *F* indicates a joint probability density analysis of two or more sample records simultaneously. Such analysis is not required for sample records of independent data since the joint probability density function in this case is simply the product of the first-order probability density functions for the records of interest. This is not true, however, for correlated data.

Analog procedures for measuring joint probability density functions are detailed in Section 6.5, and digital techniques are discussed in Section 7.4.1. The statistical accuracy of joint probability density measurements is discussed in Section 5.3.3.

Other Desired Multiple Analysis. Other desired analysis might be performed on two or more records as indicated by Block *G*. Included might be joint peak value probability density measurements and conditional probability density measurements, as discussed in Section 3.1.

Computation of Frequency Response Functions. For analyses of collections of sample records, the ultimate goal is often the establishment of linear relationships between the data from various sample records. The existence of such linear relationships can be detected from cross-spectral density, cross-correlation, or joint probability density measurements. However, a meaningful description of the linear relationship is perhaps best afforded by computing the frequency response function for the relationship, as indicated in Block *H*. This important subject is developed in Sections 3.4, 3.5, and 7.5. The statistical accuracy of frequency response function calculations based on power spectra and cross-spectra measurements is discussed in Sections 5.4.6, 5.7.4, and 5.7.5.

Computation of Coherence Functions. An important practical quantity which is valuable for interpreting cross-spectra data is the coherence function, as indicated by Block *I*. The computation of coherence functions and their applications are detailed in Sections 3.5.2, 3.5.6, and 7.5. The statistical accuracy of coherence function measurements is discussed in Sections 5.4.7 and 5.7.1.

5.3 Statistical Errors for Parameter Estimates

Errors associated with the analysis of sample records of random data may be divided into three main categories: (*a*) estimation errors (sometimes called statistical errors), (*b*) instrument errors (sometimes called calibration errors), and (*c*) usage errors (sometimes called personnel errors).

Estimation errors associated with various sample values will now be discussed. It should be remembered that the predicted estimation errors are over and above the conventional instrument and usage errors to be expected. The instrument or calibration error for each analysis procedure is, of course, a function of the specific equipment employed. The usage error is, similarly, a function of the particular people involved.

Let $\{x(t)\}$ be a stationary random process where t is time or any other variable of interest which might take the place of time. Suppose that Φ is the true value of an unknown parameter of the random process $\{x(t)\}$. For example, Φ might represent the mean value or the power spectral density at a particular frequency. Assume that $\hat{\Phi}$ is an estimate of Φ obtained from a measurement made on a particular sample time history record $x(t)$ extending over a finite time interval T. Since the sample record $x(t)$ represents a unique set of circumstances which are never likely to be exactly repeated, the measured estimate $\hat{\Phi}$ is a random variable. That is, the values of $\hat{\Phi}$ computed for different sample records from $\{x(t)\}$ will vary randomly. Hence the following question arises. How closely will any one estimated value $\hat{\Phi}$ represent the true parameter value Φ?

First consider the expected value for the estimate $\hat{\Phi}$ based upon any finite sampling time T. It is obviously desirable that the expected value for $\hat{\Phi}$ should yield the true value Φ. In other words, if a set of estimates $\{\hat{\Phi}\}$ were measured from many different samples of $\{x(t)\}$, it is desirable that the expected value of this set of estimates give Φ without any error. From Section 4.1, a parameter estimate with this property is said to be *unbiased*. Specifically, an estimate is unbiased if

$$E[\hat{\Phi}] = \Phi \tag{5.1}$$

If $E[\hat{\Phi}] \neq \Phi$, then a bias error may be defined as the expected value about the true mean. That is,

$$b[\hat{\Phi}] = E[\hat{\Phi}] - \Phi = E[\hat{\Phi}] - E[\Phi] = E[\hat{\Phi} - \Phi] \tag{5.2}$$

where the notation $b[\ ]$ means the bias of the estimate in the brackets. For unbiased estimates, $b[\hat{\Phi}] = 0$. The derivation of Eq. (5.2) uses the properties that the expected value of a constant is the constant, and that the expectation operation is linear.

For a fixed T, the mere fact that $\hat{\Phi}$ may be unbiased does not imply that $\hat{\Phi}$ will lie close to the true value Φ. There may, in fact, be a significant deviation from the true value. Furthermore, it may happen that this deviation will not decrease as T is increased. To analyze these cases, let the *mean square error* be defined as the expected value of the square of the deviation of the estimate from the true value. That is,

$$\text{mean square error} = E[(\hat{\Phi} - \Phi)^2] \tag{5.3}$$

It appears highly desirable, from a physical point of view, to require that this mean square error should approach zero as T becomes large. Then, for large T, any particular estimate $\hat{\Phi}$ would necessarily tend to closely approximate the true value Φ. From Section 4.1, estimates having this desired property are said to be *consistent*. Specifically, an estimate is consistent if

$$\lim_{T \to \infty} E[(\hat{\Phi} - \Phi)^2] = 0 \tag{5.4}$$

Observe that the mean square error reduces to

$$
\begin{aligned}
E[(\hat{\Phi} - \Phi)^2] &= E[(\hat{\Phi} - E[\hat{\Phi}] + E[\hat{\Phi}] - \Phi)^2] \\
&= E[(\hat{\Phi} - E[\hat{\Phi}])^2] + 2E[(\hat{\Phi} - E[\hat{\Phi}])(E[\hat{\Phi}] - \Phi)] \\
&\quad + E[(E[\hat{\Phi}] - \Phi)^2] \\
&= E[(\hat{\Phi} - E[\hat{\Phi}])^2] + E[(E[\hat{\Phi}] - \Phi)^2] \tag{5.5}
\end{aligned}
$$

since the middle term has a factor equal to zero. That is,

$$E[\hat{\Phi} - E[\hat{\Phi}]] = E[\hat{\Phi}] - E[\hat{\Phi}] = 0 \tag{5.6}$$

In words, Eq. (5.5) states that the mean square value about the true value equals the sum of the mean square value about the expected value plus the square of the expected value about the true value. Thus the mean square error is the sum of two parts. The first part is the variance of the estimate as given by

$$\text{Var}[\hat{\Phi}] = \sigma_{\hat{\Phi}}^2 = E[(\hat{\Phi} - E[\hat{\Phi}])^2] = E[\hat{\Phi}^2] - E^2[\hat{\Phi}] \tag{5.7}$$

The second part is the square of the bias of the estimate as given by

$$b^2[\hat{\Phi}] = E[b^2[\hat{\Phi}]] = E[(E[\hat{\Phi}] - \Phi)^2] \tag{5.8}$$

In general, compromises may be required to insure that both the variance and the bias will approach zero as T becomes large. In terms of the variance and the square of the bias, the mean square error is

$$E[(\hat{\Phi} - \Phi)^2] = \text{Var}[\hat{\Phi}] + b^2[\hat{\Phi}] \tag{5.9}$$

5.3.1 Mean Value Estimates

Suppose that a single sample time history record $x(t)$ from a stationary (ergodic) random process $\{x(t)\}$ exists over a finite time T. The sample mean value can be estimated by

$$\hat{\mu}_x = \frac{1}{T} \int_0^T x(t)\, dt \tag{5.10}$$

The true mean value is

$$\mu_x = E[x(t)] \tag{5.11}$$

and is independent of t since $\{x(t)\}$ is stationary. The expected value of the estimate $\hat{\mu}_x$ is

$$E[\hat{\mu}_x] = E\left[\frac{1}{T} \int_0^T x(t)\, dt\right] = \frac{1}{T} \int_0^T E[x(t)]\, dt = \frac{1}{T} \int_0^T \mu_x\, dt = \mu_x \tag{5.12}$$

since expected values commute with linear operations, as given by Eqs. (3.116) and (3.127). Hence $\hat{\mu}_x$ is an *unbiased* estimate of μ_x, independent of T.

Since $\hat{\mu}_x$ is unbiased, the mean square error for the estimate $\hat{\mu}_x$ is equal to the variance,

$$\text{Var}\,[\hat{\mu}_x] = E[(\hat{\mu}_x - \mu_x)^2] = E[\hat{\mu}_x^2] - \mu_x^2 \tag{5.13}$$

where from Eq. (5.10),

$$E[\hat{\mu}_x^2] = \frac{1}{T^2} \int_0^T \int_0^T E[x(\xi)\, x(\eta)]\, d\eta\, d\xi \tag{5.14}$$

Now the autocorrelation function $R_x(\tau)$ for a stationary random process $\{x(t)\}$ is defined by Eq. (3.44) as

$$R_x(\tau) = E[x(t)\, x(t + \tau)] \tag{5.15}$$

From the stationary hypothesis, $R_x(\tau)$ is independent of t, and an even function of τ with a maximum at $\tau = 0$. It will be assumed that $R_x(\tau)$ is continuous and finite for all values of τ, and that all periodic components in $R_x(\tau)$ have been removed at the onset. The autocovariance function $C_x(\tau)$ is defined by Eq. (3.47) as

$$C_x(\tau) = R_x(\tau) - \mu_x^2 \tag{5.16}$$

It turns out that whenever $\mu_x \neq 0$, it is more convenient to work with $C_x(\tau)$ than with $R_x(\tau)$. It will be assumed that $C_x(\tau)$ satisfies the integrable properties of Eq. (3.96) so as to make $\{x(t)\}$ ergodic.

In terms of the autocovariance function $C_x(\tau)$, the variance (mean square error) from Eqs. (5.13) and (5.14) becomes

$$\text{Var}\,[\hat{\mu}_x] = \frac{1}{T^2}\int_0^T\int_0^T C_x(\eta-\xi)\,d\eta\,d\xi = \frac{1}{T^2}\int_0^T\int_{-\xi}^{T-\xi} C_x(\tau)\,d\tau\,d\xi \quad (5.17)$$

$$= \frac{1}{T}\int_{-T}^T\left(1-\frac{|\tau|}{T}\right)C_x(\tau)\,d\tau$$

The last expression occurs by reversing the orders of integration between τ and ξ and carrying out the ξ integration. Now,

$$\lim_{T\to\infty} T\,\text{Var}\,[\hat{\mu}_x] = \int_{-\infty}^{\infty} C_x(\tau)\,d\tau < \infty \quad (5.18)$$

where Eq. (3.96) is used, which provides that $C_x(\tau)$ and $\tau\,C_x(\tau)$ are absolutely integrable over $(-\infty, \infty)$ to justify passage to the limit inside the integral sign. In particular, Eq. (5.18) shows that for large T, where $|\tau| \ll T$, the variance

$$\text{Var}\,[\hat{\mu}_x] \approx \frac{1}{T}\int_{-\infty}^{\infty} C_x(\tau)\,d\tau \quad (5.19)$$

Hence when the integral is finite-valued, $\text{Var}[\hat{\mu}_x]$ approaches zero as T approaches infinity, proving that $\hat{\mu}_x$ is a *consistent* estimate of μ_x.

Example **5.1. Variance for Mean Value Estimates of Bandwidth Limited White Noise.** Consider the important special case where $\{x(t)\}$ is bandwidth limited white noise with a mean value $\mu_x \neq 0$. Assume the power spectral density function is

$$G_x(f) = \frac{1}{B} + \mu_x^2\,\delta(f) \qquad 0 \le f \le B$$
$$= 0 \qquad\qquad\qquad f > B \qquad (5.20)$$

where B is the bandwidth. The associated autocovariance function $C_x(\tau)$ is given by

$$C_x(\tau) = \int_0^{\infty} G_x(f)\cos 2\pi f\tau\,df - \mu_x^2$$
$$= \int_0^B \frac{1}{B}\cos 2\pi f\tau\,df = \frac{\sin 2\pi B\tau}{2\pi B\tau} \qquad (5.21)$$

Note that $C_x(0) = 1$ and that $C_x(\tau) = 0$ for $\tau = 1/2B$. Thus points $1/2B$ apart are uncorrelated. (They will be statistically independent if $\{x(t)\}$ is Gaussian.) For this case, Eq. (5.19) yields the result

$$\text{Var}\,[\hat{\mu}_x] \approx \frac{1}{T}\int_{-\infty}^{\infty}\left(\frac{\sin 2\pi B\tau}{2\pi B\tau}\right)d\tau = \frac{1}{2BT} \qquad (5.22)$$

This is the variance for mean value estimates of bandwidth limited white noise of bandwidth B and sampling time T. Equation (5.22) requires that T be sufficiently large so that Eq. (5.19) can replace Eq. (5.17). Satisfactory conditions in practice are $T \geq 10 \, |\tau|$ and $BT \geq 5$.

For $C_x(0) \neq 1$, Eq. (5.22) would be

$$\text{Var } [\hat{\mu}_x] \approx \frac{C_x(0)}{2BT} = \frac{\sigma_x^2}{2BT}$$

Hence, when $\mu_x \neq 0$, a normalized mean square error is given by

$$\epsilon^2 = \frac{\text{Var } [\hat{\mu}_x]}{\mu_x^2} \approx \frac{1}{2BT}\left(\frac{\sigma_x}{\mu_x}\right)^2 \tag{5.23}$$

The term ϵ, given by the square root of Eq. (5.23), is called the *normalized standard error* of the estimate.

5.3.2 Mean Square Value Estimates

As in Section 5.3.1, let $x(t)$ be a single sample time history record from a stationary (ergodic) random process $\{x(t)\}$. The mean square value for $\{x(t)\}$ can be estimated by time averaging over a finite time interval T as follows.

$$\hat{\Psi}_x^2 = \frac{1}{T}\int_0^T x^2(t) \, dt \tag{5.24}$$

The true mean square value is

$$\Psi_x^2 = E[x^2(t)] \tag{5.25}$$

and is independent of t since $\{x(t)\}$ is stationary. The expected value of the estimate $\hat{\Psi}_x^2$ is

$$E[\hat{\Psi}_x^2] = \frac{1}{T}\int_0^T E[x^2(t)] \, dt = \frac{1}{T}\int_0^T \Psi_x^2 \, dt = \Psi_x^2 \tag{5.26}$$

Hence $\hat{\Psi}_x^2$ is an *unbiased* estimate of Ψ_x^2, independent of T.

The mean square error here is given by the variance

$$\text{Var } [\hat{\Psi}_x^2] = E[(\hat{\Psi}_x^2 - \Psi_x^2)^2] = E[\hat{\Psi}_x^4] - \Psi_x^4$$
$$= \frac{1}{T^2}\int_0^T \int_0^T (E[x^2(\xi) \, x^2(\eta)] - \Psi_x^4) \, d\eta \, d\xi \tag{5.27}$$

Assume now that $\{x(t)\}$ is a Gaussian random process with mean value $\mu_x \neq 0$. Then, the expected value in Eq. (5.27) takes the special form, derived from Eq. (3.113),

$$E[x^2(\xi) \, x^2(\eta)] = 2(R_x^2(\eta - \xi) - \mu_x^4) + \Psi_x^4 \tag{5.28}$$

From the basic relation of Eq. (5.16),

$$R_x^2(\eta - \xi) - \mu_x^4 = C_x^2(\eta - \xi) + 2\mu_x^2 C_x(\eta - \xi) \tag{5.29}$$

Hence

$$\begin{aligned}
\text{Var}[\hat{\Psi}_x^2] &= \frac{2}{T^2} \int_0^T \int_0^T (R_x^2(\eta - \xi) - \mu_x^4) \, d\eta \, d\xi \\
&= \frac{2}{T} \int_{-T}^T \left(1 - \frac{|\tau|}{T}\right)(R_x^2(\tau) - \mu_x^4) \, d\tau \\
&= \frac{2}{T} \int_{-T}^T \left(1 - \frac{|\tau|}{T}\right)(C_x^2(\tau) + 2\mu_x^2 C_x(\tau)) \, d\tau \tag{5.30}
\end{aligned}$$

For large T, where $|\tau| \ll T$, the variance becomes

$$\text{Var}[\hat{\Psi}_x^2] \approx \frac{2}{T} \int_{-\infty}^{\infty} (C_x^2(\tau) + 2\mu_x^2 C_x(\tau)) \, d\tau \tag{5.31}$$

Thus, $\hat{\Psi}_x^2$ is a *consistent* estimate of Ψ_x^2 since $\text{Var}[\hat{\Psi}_x^2]$ will approach zero as T approaches infinity assuming $C_x^2(\tau)$ and $C_x(\tau)$ are absolutely integrable over $(-\infty, \infty)$ as stated in Eq. (3.96).

Example 5.2. **Variance for Mean Square Value Estimates of Bandwidth Limited White Noise.** Consider the important special case of bandwidth limited white noise where

$$C_x(\tau) = C_x(0)\left(\frac{\sin 2\pi B\tau}{2\pi B\tau}\right) \tag{5.32}$$

For this case, Eq. (5.31) shows that

$$\text{Var}[\hat{\Psi}_x^2] \approx \frac{C_x^2(0)}{BT} + \frac{2}{BT}\mu_x^2 C_x(0) \tag{5.33}$$

This is the variance for mean square value estimates of bandwidth limited white noise of bandwidth B and sampling time T. Equation (5.33) requires that T be sufficiently large so that Eq. (5.31) can replace Eq. (5.30). Satisfactory conditions in practice are $T \geq 10 |\tau|$ and $BT \geq 5$.

For $\mu_x = 0$ and $R_x(0) \neq 1$, Eq. (5.33) becomes

$$\text{Var}[\hat{\Psi}_x^2] \approx \frac{R_x^2(0)}{BT} = \frac{\Psi_x^4}{BT} \tag{5.34}$$

Hence, when $\mu_x = 0$, a normalized mean square error is given by

$$\epsilon^2 = \frac{\text{Var}[\hat{\Psi}_x^2]}{\Psi_x^4} \approx \frac{1}{BT} \tag{5.35}$$

The square root of Eq. (5.35) gives the normalized standard error ϵ.

5.3.3 Probability Density Estimates

Consider a probability density measurement of a single sample time history record $x(t)$ from a stationary (ergodic) random process $\{x(t)\}$. The probability that $x(t)$ assumes particular amplitude values between $x - (W/2)$ and $x + (W/2)$ during a time interval T may be estimated by

$$\hat{P}[x, W] = \text{Prob}\left[\left(x - \frac{W}{2}\right) \leq x(t) \leq \left(x + \frac{W}{2}\right)\right]$$

$$= \frac{1}{T}\sum_i \Delta t_i = \frac{T_x}{T} \tag{5.36}$$

where Δt_i is the time spent by $x(t)$ in this amplitude range during the ith entry into the range, and $T_x = \sum_i \Delta t_i$. The ratio T_x/T is the total fractional portion of the time spent by $x(t)$ in the range $[x - (W/2), x + (W/2)]$. It should be noted that T_x will usually be a function of the amplitude x.

This estimated probability $\hat{P}[x, W]$ will approach the true probability $P[x, W]$ as T approaches infinity. Moreover this estimated probability is an unbiased estimate for the true probability. Hence

$$P[x, W] = E[\hat{P}[x, W]] = \lim_{T \to \infty} \hat{P}[x, W] = \lim_{T \to \infty} \frac{T_x}{T} \tag{5.37}$$

The first-order probability density function $p(x)$ is defined by

$$p(x) = \lim_{W \to 0} \frac{P[x, W]}{W} = \lim_{\substack{T \to \infty \\ W \to 0}} \frac{\hat{P}[x, W]}{W} = \lim_{\substack{T \to \infty \\ W \to 0}} \hat{p}(x) \tag{5.38}$$

where

$$\hat{p}(x) = \frac{\hat{P}[x, W]}{W} = \frac{T_x}{TW} \tag{5.39}$$

is a sample estimate for $p(x)$.

In terms of the true probability density function $p(x)$, the probability of the time history $x(t)$ falling between any two values x_1 and x_2 is given by

$$\text{Prob}\,[x_1 \leq x \leq x_2] = \int_{x_1}^{x_2} p(x)\,dx \tag{5.40}$$

In particular

$$P[x, W] = \text{Prob}\left[x - \frac{W}{2} \leq x(t) \leq x + \frac{W}{2}\right] = \int_{x-(W/2)}^{x+(W/2)} p(\xi)\,d\xi \tag{5.41}$$

Then, from Eq. (5.39),

$$E[\hat{p}(x)] = \frac{E[\hat{P}[x, W]]}{W} = \frac{P[x, W]}{W} = \frac{1}{W}\int_{x-(W/2)}^{x+(W/2)} p(\xi)\,d\xi \tag{5.42}$$

Thus, for most $p(x)$,

$$E[\hat{p}(x)] \neq p(x) \tag{5.43}$$

proving that $\hat{p}(x)$ is generally a biased estimate for $p(x)$.

The mean square error for the estimate $\hat{p}(x)$ is calculated from Eq. (5.9) by

$$E[(\hat{p}(x) - p(x))^2] = \text{Var}[\hat{p}(x)] + b^2[\hat{p}(x)] \tag{5.44}$$

where $\text{Var}[\hat{p}(x)]$ is the variance of the estimate as defined by

$$\text{Var}[\hat{p}(x)] = E[(\hat{p}(x) - E[\hat{p}(x)])^2] \tag{5.45}$$

and $b[\hat{p}(x)]$ is the bias of the estimate as defined by

$$b[\hat{p}(x)] = E[\hat{p}(x) - p(x)] \tag{5.46}$$

Variance of the Estimate. To evaluate the variance of an estimate $\hat{p}(x)$, it is necessary to know the statistical properties of the time intervals Δt_i which comprise T_x. Unfortunately, such time statistics for a random process are very difficult, if not impossible, to obtain. However, the general form of an appropriate variance expression for $\hat{p}(x)$ can be established by the following heuristic argument.

As shown in Eq. (4.33), the variance of any sample mean is equal to the variance of the sampled random variable divided by the sample size. Then

$$\text{Var}\,[\hat{p}(x)] = \frac{\text{Var}\,[p_i(x)]}{N} \tag{5.47}$$

where $\text{Var}[p_i(x)]$ is effectively the variance of a probability density measurement having one degree of freedom (representing the equivalent of one discrete observation). The specific expression for this variance is unknown, but it appears likely that it would be of the general form

$$\text{Var}[p_i(x)] = 2A_1^2 p^2(x) \tag{5.48}$$

where A_1 is a constant. In other words, it is reasonable to expect that the standard deviation of $p_i(x)$ would be proportional to the probability density $p(x)$.

For example, assume the probability density function for $p_i(x)$ is uniform. Since $p_i(x)$ can never be negative, the limits of the uniform density function would be zero and $2p(x)$, and the density would be $1/2p(x)$. For this special case

$$\text{Var}\,[p_i(x)] = \int_0^{2p(x)} [\xi - p(x)]^2 \left[\frac{1}{2p(x)}\right] d\xi = \tfrac{1}{3}p^2(x)$$

The constant in Eq. (5.48) for this case would be $A \approx 0.41$.

Returning to Eq. (5.47), N represents the number of *independent* observations used to compute $\hat{p}(x)$. An appropriate expression for N can be arrived at by using the time domain sampling theorem derived in Section 5.4.1. Specifically a sample record $x(t)$ of bandwidth B and length T can be completely reproduced by $n = 2BT$ discrete values. For the case of probability density measurements, data are actually being viewed and analyzed only when the time history falls within the range between $x -$ $(W/2)$ and $x + (W/2)$. From Eq. (5.39), this time interval is equal to $T_x =$ $TW\,\hat{p}(x)$. Hence the number of discrete values that will reproduce the data is $n = 2BTW\,\hat{p}(x)$. For the special case where $x(t)$ is bandwidth limited (Gaussian) white noise, it is shown in Section 5.4.1 that these n values will be independent. For this special case, $n = N$ so that

$$N = 2BTW\,\hat{p}(x) \tag{5.49}$$

Substituting Eqs. (5.48) and (5.49) into Eq. (5.47) yields

$$\text{Var}\,[\hat{p}(x)] \approx \frac{A_1^2\,p^2(x)}{BTW\,\hat{p}(x)} \tag{5.50}$$

Bias of the Estimate.   An expression will now be derived for the bias term of Eq. (5.46). In terms of the true probability density function, Eq. (5.42) shows

$$E[\hat{p}(x)] = \frac{1}{W}\int_{x-(W/2)}^{x+(W/2)} p(\xi)\,d\xi \tag{5.51}$$

By expanding $p(\xi)$ in a Taylor series about the point $\xi = x$, and retaining only the first three terms,

$$p(\xi) \approx p(x) + (\xi - x)\,p'(x) + \frac{(\xi - x)^2}{2}\,p''(x) \tag{5.52}$$

From the two relations

$$\int_{x-(W/2)}^{x+(W/2)} (\xi - x)\,d\xi = 0$$

and

$$\int_{x-(W/2)}^{x+(W/2)} \frac{(\xi - x)^2}{2}\,d\xi = \frac{W^2}{24} \tag{5.53}$$

It follows that

$$E[\hat{p}(x)] \approx p(x) + \frac{W^2}{24}\,p''(x) \tag{5.54}$$

Thus the bias term is

$$b[\hat{p}(x)] \approx \frac{W^2}{24}\,p''(x) \tag{5.55}$$

where $p''(x)$ is the second derivative of $p(x)$ with respect to x.

Mean Square Error.   The total mean square error, Eq. (5.44), for the probability density estimate $\hat{p}(x)$ is given by the sum of Eq. (5.50) and the square of Eq. (5.55). That is

$$E[(\hat{p}(x) - p(x))^2] \approx \frac{A_1^2\, p^2(x)}{BTW\, \hat{p}(x)} + \left(\frac{W^2\, p''(x)}{24}\right)^2 \tag{5.56}$$

It is clear that the mean square error approaches zero as $T \to \infty$ if W is restricted so that $W \to 0$ and $WT \to \infty$.

Joint Probability Density Estimates.   Joint probability density estimates for a pair of sample time history records, $x(t)$ and $y(t)$, from two stationary (ergodic) random processes $\{x(t)\}$ and $\{y(t)\}$, may be defined as follows. Analogous to Eq. (5.36), let

$$\hat{P}[x, W_x;\ y, W_y] = \frac{T_{x,y}}{T} \tag{5.57}$$

estimate the joint probability that $x(t)$ is inside the amplitude interval W_x centered at x, when simultaneously $y(t)$ is inside the amplitude interval W_y centered at y. This is measured by the ratio $T_{x,y}/T$ where $T_{x,y}$ represents the amount of time that these two events coincide in time T. Clearly, $T_{x,y}$ will usually be a function of both x and y. This estimated joint probability will approach the true probability $P[x, W_x;\ y, W_y]$ as T approaches infinity, namely,

$$P[x, W_x;\ y, W_y] = \lim_{T \to \infty} \hat{P}[x, W_x;\ y, W_y] = \lim_{T \to \infty} \frac{T_{x,y}}{T} \tag{5.58}$$

The joint probability density function $p(x, y)$ is now defined by

$$p(x, y) = \lim_{\substack{W_x \to 0 \\ W_y \to 0}} \frac{P[x, W_x;\ y, W_y]}{W_x W_y} = \lim_{\substack{T \to \infty \\ W_x \to 0 \\ W_y \to 0}} \frac{\hat{P}[x, W_x;\ y, W_y]}{W_x W_y} = \lim_{\substack{T \to \infty \\ W_x \to 0 \\ W_y \to 0}} \hat{p}(x, y) \tag{5.59}$$

where

$$\hat{p}(x, y) = \frac{\hat{P}[x, W_x;\ y, W_y]}{W_x W_y} = \frac{T_{x,y}}{T W_x W_y} \tag{5.60}$$

Assume that W_x and W_y are sufficiently small so that the bias errors are negligible. Then the mean square error associated with the estimate $\hat{p}(x, y)$ will be given by the variance of the estimate. As for first-order probability density estimates, this quantity is difficult if not impossible to determine precisely by theoretical arguments alone. However, by using the same heuristic arguments which produced Eq. (5.50), a general form for the variance can be approximated. Specifically, for the special case where $x(t)$

and $y(t)$ are both bandwidth limited white noise with identical bandwidths B,

$$\text{Var}\,[\hat{p}(x, y)] \approx \frac{A_2^{\,2}\,p^2(x, y)}{BTW_xW_y\,\hat{p}(x, y)} \tag{5.61}$$

where A_2 is an unknown constant.

Normalized Error and Amplitude Resolution. Returning now to first-order probability density estimates, the normalized mean square error of an estimate $\hat{p}(x)$ is approximated by

$$\epsilon^2 = \frac{E[(\hat{p}(x) - p(x))^2]}{p^2(x)} \approx \frac{A_1^{\,2}}{BTW\,\hat{p}(x)} + \frac{W^4}{576}\left(\frac{p''(x)}{p(x)}\right)^2 \tag{5.62}$$

The square root of Eq. (5.62) gives the normalized standard error ϵ.

It is clear from Eq. (5.62) that the bias term on the right will be negligible if the $W^4[p''(x)]^2$ is small. This requirement is usually easy to meet in practice because probability density functions for common random data do not tend to display abrupt or sharp peaks, which are indicative of a large second derivative.

5.3.4 Correlation Function Estimates

Consider now two sample time history records $x(t)$ and $y(t)$, from two stationary (ergodic) random processes, $\{x(t)\}$ and $\{y(t)\}$. The next statistical quantities of interest are the stationary autocorrelation functions, $R_x(\tau)$ and $R_y(\tau)$, and the cross-correlation function $R_{xy}(\tau)$. To simplify the following derivation, the mean values μ_x and μ_y will be assumed to be zero. For continuous data, $x(t)$ and $y(t)$, which exist only over a time interval T, the sample cross-correlation estimate $\hat{R}_{xy}(\tau)$ can be defined by

$$\hat{R}_{xy}(\tau) = \frac{1}{T - \tau}\int_0^{T-\tau} x(t)\,y(t + \tau)\,dt \qquad 0 \le \tau < T$$
$$= \frac{1}{T - |\tau|}\int_{|\tau|}^{T} x(t)\,y(t + \tau)\,dt \qquad -T < \tau \le 0 \tag{5.63}$$

To avoid use of absolute value signs, τ will be considered positive henceforth since a similar proof applies for negative τ. The sample autocorrelation function estimates $\hat{R}_x(\tau)$ and $\hat{R}_y(\tau)$ are merely special cases when the two records coincide. That is,

$$\hat{R}_x(\tau) = \frac{1}{T - \tau}\int_0^{T-\tau} x(t)\,x(t + \tau)\,dt \qquad 0 \le \tau < T$$
$$\hat{R}_y(\tau) = \frac{1}{T - \tau}\int_0^{T-\tau} y(t)\,y(t + \tau)\,dt \qquad 0 \le \tau < T \tag{5.64}$$

Thus, by analyzing the cross-correlation function estimate, one derives results which are also applicable to the autocorrelation function estimates.

If the data exists for time $T + \tau$ instead of only for time T, then an alternative definition for $\hat{R}_{xy}(\tau)$ is

$$\hat{R}_{xy}(\tau) = \frac{1}{T} \int_0^T x(t)\, y(t + \tau)\, dt \qquad 0 \leq \tau < T \qquad (5.65)$$

This formula has a fixed integration time T instead of a variable integration time as in Eq. (5.63), and is the way the correlation functions have been defined previously. Note that for either Eq. (5.63) or Eq. (5.65), mean square estimates of $x(t)$ or $y(t)$ are merely special cases when $\tau = 0$.

For simplicity in notation, Eq. (5.65) will be used in the following development instead of Eq. (5.63). The same final results are obtained for both definitions, assuming the data exists for time $T + \tau$.

The expected value for the estimate $\hat{R}_{xy}(\tau)$ is given by

$$E[\hat{R}_{xy}(\tau)] = \frac{1}{T} \int_0^T E[x(t)\, y(t + \tau)]\, dt$$
$$= \frac{1}{T} \int_0^T R_{xy}(\tau)\, dt = R_{xy}(\tau) \qquad (5.66)$$

Hence $\hat{R}_{xy}(\tau)$ is an *unbiased* estimate of $R_{xy}(\tau)$, independent of T. The mean square error is given by the variance

$$\text{Var}\,[\hat{R}_{xy}(\tau)] = E([\hat{R}_{xy}(\tau) - R_{xy}(\tau))^2] = E[\hat{R}_{xy}^{\ 2}(\tau)] - R_{xy}^{\ 2}(\tau)$$
$$= \frac{1}{T^2} \int_0^T \int_0^T (E[x(u)\, y(u + \tau)\, x(v)\, y(v + \tau)] - R_{xy}^{\ 2}(\tau))\, dv\, du$$

$$(5.67)$$

At this point, in order to simplify the later mathematical analysis and to agree with many physical cases of interest, it will be assumed that the random processes $\{x(t)\}$ and $\{y(t)\}$ are jointly *Gaussian* for any set of fixed times. This restriction may be removed by substituting certain integrability conditions on the non-Gaussian parts of the random processes without altering in any essential way the results to be derived. When $\{x(t)\}$ and $\{y(t)\}$ are jointly Gaussian, it follows that $\{x(t)\}$ and $\{y(t)\}$ are separately Gaussian.

For Gaussian stationary random processes with zero mean values, the fourth-order statistical expression is obtained from Eq. (3.113) as follows.

$$E[x(u)\, y(u + \tau)\, x(v)\, y(v + \tau)]$$
$$= R_{xy}^{\ 2}(\tau) + R_x(v - u)\, R_y(v - u) + R_{xy}(v - u + \tau)\, R_{yx}(v - u - \tau)$$

$$(5.68)$$

Hence the variance

$$\begin{aligned}
\text{Var}\,[\hat{R}_{xy}(\tau)] &= \frac{1}{T^2}\int_0^T \int_0^T (R_x(v-u)\,R_y(v-u) \\
&\quad + R_{xy}(v-u+\tau)\,R_{yx}(v-u-\tau))\,dv\,du \\
&= \frac{1}{T}\int_{-T}^{T}\left(1 - \frac{|\xi|}{T}\right)(R_x(\xi)\,R_y(\xi) \\
&\quad + R_{xy}(\xi+\tau)\,R_{yx}(\xi-\tau))\,d\xi \quad (5.69)
\end{aligned}$$

The second expression occurs from the first by letting $\xi = v - u$, $d\xi = dv$, and then reversing the order of integration between ξ and u. Now,

$$\lim_{T\to\infty} T\,\text{Var}\,[\hat{R}_{xy}(\tau)] = \int_{-\infty}^{\infty} (R_x(\xi)\,R_y(\xi) + R_{xy}(\xi+\tau)\,R_{yx}(\xi-\tau))\,d\xi < \infty \quad (5.70)$$

assuming $R_x(\xi)\,R_y(\xi)$ and $R_{xy}(\xi)\,R_{yx}(\xi)$ are absolutely integrable over $(-\infty, \infty)$. This proves that $\hat{R}_{xy}(\tau)$ is a *consistent* estimate of $R_{xy}(\tau)$, which for large T has a variance given by

$$\text{Var}\,[\hat{R}_{xy}(\tau)] \approx \frac{1}{T}\int_{-\infty}^{\infty} (R_x(\xi)\,R_y(\xi) + R_{xy}(\xi+\tau)\,R_{yx}(\xi-\tau))\,d\xi \quad (5.71)$$

Several special cases of Eq. (5.71) are worthy of note. For autocorrelation estimates, Eq. (5.71) becomes

$$\text{Var}\,[\hat{R}_x(\tau)] \approx \frac{1}{T}\int_{-\infty}^{\infty} (R_x{}^2(\xi) + R_x(\xi+\tau)\,R_x(\xi-\tau))\,d\xi \quad (5.72)$$

At the zero displacement point $\tau = 0$,

$$\text{Var}\,[\hat{R}_x(0)] \approx \frac{2}{T}\int_{-\infty}^{\infty} R_x{}^2(\xi)\,d\xi \quad (5.73)$$

The assumption that $R_x(\tau)$ approaches zero for large τ shows that for large τ

$$R_x{}^2(\xi) \gg R_x(\xi+\tau)\,R_x(\xi-\tau) \quad (5.74)$$

Hence, for large τ,

$$\text{Var}\,[\hat{R}_x(\tau)] \approx \frac{1}{T}\int_{-\infty}^{\infty} R_x{}^2(\xi)\,d\xi \quad (5.75)$$

which is one-half the value of Eq. (5.73).

***Example* 5.3. Variance for Correlation Estimates of Bandwidth Limited White Noise.** For bandwidth limited white noise with a mean value $\mu_x = 0$, a bandwidth B, and covering a time interval T, the variance for all τ is conservatively given by

$$\text{Var} \left[\hat{R}_x(\tau) \right] \approx \frac{1}{2BT} \left(R_x^2(0) + R_x^2(\tau) \right) \tag{5.76}$$

This reduces to Eq. (5.34) at the point $\tau = 0$.

Similarly, when both $x(t)$ and $y(t)$ are samples of length T from bandwidth limited white noise with mean values $\mu_x = \mu_y = 0$ and identical bandwidths B, it follows that

$$\text{Var} \left[\hat{R}_{xy}(\tau) \right] \approx \frac{1}{2BT} \left(R_x(0) R_y(0) + R_{xy}^2(\tau) \right) \tag{5.77}$$

Equation (5.77) requires that T be sufficiently large that Eq. (5.71) can replace Eq. (5.69). Satisfactory conditions in practice are $T \geq 10 \, |\tau|$ and $BT \geq 5$.

For $\mu_x = \mu_y = 0$ and $R_{xy} \neq 0$, a normalized mean square error is given by

$$\epsilon^2 = \frac{\text{Var} \left[\hat{R}_{xy}(\tau) \right]}{R_{xy}^2(\tau)} \approx \frac{1}{2BT} \left(1 + \frac{R_x(0) R_y(0)}{R_{xy}^2(\tau)} \right) \tag{5.78}$$

The square root of Eq. (5.78) gives the normalized standard error ϵ.

5.3.5 Spectral Density Estimates

A schematic diagram of a general filter device for estimating the power spectral density function associated with a sample time history record $x(t)$, is displayed in Figure 5.3. The input sample record $x(t)$ is assumed to be averaged over a time interval T, and to be drawn from a stationary (ergodic) random process with zero mean value. The tunable narrow-band resolution filter is assumed to have a finite nonzero constant bandwidth B_e centered at a frequency f which may be varied over the frequency range of interest. This resolution bandwidth B_e should not be confused with the full bandwidth occupied by the record $x(t)$. It turns out that in order to obtain a consistent estimate of $G_x(f)$, one must introduce a filtering procedure which averages over a band of frequencies. The final estimate $\hat{G}_x(f)$ describes the time average of $x^2(t)$ in terms of its frequency components lying inside the frequency band $f - (B_e/2)$ to $f + (B_e/2)$, divided by the bandwidth B_e. Note that because a nonzero mean value corresponds to a discrete frequency component at zero frequency, the zero mean value assumption in the following developments is critical only when B_e includes $f = 0$. For all other cases where B_e does not include $f = 0$, the results to follow apply to data with arbitrary nonzero mean values.

The mean square value of $x(t)$ within the bandwidth B_e centered at f is estimated by

$$\hat{\Psi}_x^2(f, B_e) = \frac{1}{T} \int_0^T x^2(t, f, B_e) \, dt \tag{5.79}$$

where $x(t, f, B_e)$ represents the narrow-band filter output and T is the averaging time. It is shown in Section 5.3.2 that this estimated value will be an unbiased and consistent estimate of the true mean square value as T approaches infinity. Hence

$$E[\hat{\Psi}_x^2(f, B_e)] = \lim_{T \to \infty} \frac{1}{T} \int_0^T x^2(t, f, B_e)\, dt \tag{5.80}$$

where $\Psi_x^2(f, B_e)$ is the mean square value of $x(t)$ associated with the filter bandwidth B_e centered at f.

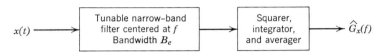

Figure 5.3   Constant bandwidth filter device for measuring power spectrum.

The power spectral density function is defined by

$$G_x(f) = \lim_{B_e \to 0} \frac{\Psi_x^2(f, B_e)}{B_e} = \lim_{\substack{T \to \infty \\ B_e \to 0}} \frac{1}{BT} \int_0^T x^2(t, f, B_e)\, dt = \lim_{\substack{T \to \infty \\ B_e \to 0}} \hat{G}_x(f) \tag{5.81}$$

where

$$\hat{G}_x(f) = \frac{1}{B_e T} \int_0^T x^2(t, f, B_e)\, dt = \frac{\hat{\Psi}_x^2(f, B_e)}{B_e} \tag{5.82}$$

is the sample estimate for $G_x(f)$ determined by the procedure of Figure 5.3. The limiting operations specified in Eq. (5.81) must be carried out to obtain the true value $G_x(f)$.

In terms of the true power spectral density function $G_x(f)$, the mean square value of $x(t)$ between any two frequency limits f_1 and f_2 is given by

$$\Psi_x^2(f_1, f_2) = \int_{f_1}^{f_2} G_x(f)\, df \tag{5.83}$$

In particular

$$\Psi_x^2(f, B_e) = \int_{f-(B_e/2)}^{f+(B_e/2)} G_x(\xi)\, d\xi \tag{5.84}$$

Equations (5.82) and (5.84) show that

$$E[\hat{G}_x(f)] = \frac{\Psi_x^2(f, B_e)}{B_e} = \frac{1}{B_e} \int_{f-(B_e/2)}^{f+(B_e/2)} G_x(\xi)\, d\xi \tag{5.85}$$

Thus, for most $G_x(f)$,

$$E[\hat{G}_x(f)] \neq G_x(f) \tag{5.86}$$

so that $\hat{G}_x(f)$ is generally a biased estimate of $G_x(f)$.

The mean square error for the estimate $\hat{G}_x(f)$ is calculated from Eq. (5.9) by

$$E[(\hat{G}_x(f) - G_x(f))^2] = \text{Var}[\hat{G}_x(f)] + b^2[\hat{G}_x(f)] \tag{5.87}$$

where $\text{Var}[\hat{G}_x(f)]$ is the variance of the estimate as defined by

$$\text{Var}[\hat{G}_x(f)] = E[(\hat{G}_x(f) - E[\hat{G}_x(f)])^2] \tag{5.88}$$

and $b[\hat{G}_x(f)]$ is the bias of the estimate as defined by

$$b[\hat{G}_x(f)] = E[\hat{G}_x(f) - G_x(f)] \tag{5.89}$$

Variance of the Estimate. From Eq. (5.82), the estimate

$$B_e \hat{G}_x(f) = \hat{\Psi}_x^2(f, B_e) \tag{5.90}$$

is an unbiased estimate of the mean square value of $x(t)$ within the bandwidth B_e centered at f. The true value is given by $\Psi_x^2(f, B_e) = B_e G_x(f)$, if $G_x(f)$ were constant over the bandwidth B_e. This will be approximately the case if B_e is sufficiently small. The result of Eq. (5.34) applies to these estimates with $R_x(0) = B_e G_x(f)$. Hence

$$\text{Var}[B_e \hat{G}_x(f)] \approx \frac{B_e^2 G_x^2(f)}{BT} \tag{5.91}$$

But, since B_e is a constant,

$$\text{Var}[B_e \hat{G}_x(f)] = B_e^2 \text{Var}[\hat{G}_x(f)] \tag{5.92}$$

This gives for the variance of the estimate

$$\text{Var}[\hat{G}_x(f)] \approx \frac{G_x^2(f)}{B_e T} \tag{5.93}$$

A satisfactory condition for using Eq. (5.93) in practice is $B_e T \geq 5$.

Bias of the Estimate. An expression for the bias term of Eq. (5.89) may be derived by the procedure used to derive the bias term for probability density estimates in Section 5.3.3. Specifically, by expanding $G_x(\xi)$ in a Taylor series about the point $\xi = f$, and retaining only the first three terms, it follows from Eq. (5.85) that

$$[E\hat{G}_x(f)] \approx G_x(f) + \frac{B_e^2}{24} G_x''(f) \tag{5.94}$$

Thus the bias term is

$$b[\hat{G}_x(f)] \approx \frac{B_e^2}{24} G_x''(f) \tag{5.95}$$

where $G_x''(f)$ is the second derivative of $G_x(f)$ with respect to f, and is related to $R_x(\tau)$ by the expression

$$G_x''(f) = -8\pi^2 \int_{-\infty}^{\infty} \tau^2 R_x(\tau) e^{-j2\pi f \tau} d\tau \tag{5.96}$$

Mean Square Error.   The total mean square error, Eq. (5.87), for the spectral density estimate $\hat{G}_x(f)$ is given by the sum of Eq. (5.93) and the square of Eq. (5.95). Hence

$$E[(\hat{G}_x(f) - G_x(f))^2] \approx \frac{G_x^{\,2}(f)}{B_e T} + \left(\frac{B_e^{\,2}\, G_x''(f)}{24}\right)^2 \qquad (5.97)$$

It is clear that the mean square error approaches zero as $T \to \infty$ if B_e is restricted so that $B_e \to 0$ and $B_e T \to \infty$. For example, one could choose

$$B_e = cT^{\alpha-1} \qquad c > 0, \quad 0 < \alpha < 1 \qquad (5.98)$$

Then $B_e \to 0$ as $T \to \infty$, and $B_e T \to \infty$ as $T \to \infty$.

Cross-Spectral Density Estimates.   Equation (5.97) is an important result and should be well understood since it states the mean square error to be expected in estimating $G_x(f)$ from continuous data using any given finite B_e and T. The same type of formula occurs for estimating the co-spectrum $C_{xy}(f)$ or the quadrature spectrum $Q_{xy}(f)$ of the cross-spectral density function of two stationary (ergodic) random processes $\{x(t)\}$ and $\{y(t)\}$, where

$$G_{xy}(f) = C_{xy}(f) - j\, Q_{xy}(f) \qquad (5.99)$$

Through an analysis similar to the derivation of Eq. (5.93), one can show that the variance terms for estimates $\hat{C}_{xy}(f)$ and $\hat{Q}_{xy}(f)$ are bounded by

$$\mathrm{Var}\,[\hat{C}_{xy}(f)] \leq \frac{G_x(f)\,G_y(f)}{B_e T}$$

$$\mathrm{Var}\,[\hat{Q}_{xy}(f)] \leq \frac{G_x(f)\,G_y(f)}{B_e T}$$

The bias terms for any frequency are bounded by

$$b[\hat{C}_{xy}(f)] \leq \frac{B_e^{\,2}}{24}\, G_{xy}''(f)$$

$$b[\hat{Q}_{xy}(f)] \leq \frac{B_e^{\,2}}{24}\, G_{xy}''(f)$$

where $G_{xy}''(f)$ is the second derivative of $G_{xy}(f)$ with respect to f. Thus one finds that a mean square error analysis for co-spectrum and quadrature spectrum estimates is closely analogous to a mean square error analysis for ordinary spectrum estimates. In particular, there are the same conflicting demands on B_e to be small for low bias and high resolution, and to be large for low variance and high statistical accuracy.

The cross-spectral density function $G_{xy}(f)$ may be presented in complex polar notation as

$$G_{xy}(f) = |G_{xy}(f)|\, e^{-j\theta_{xy}(f)} \qquad (5.100)$$

where the absolute value and phase angle are determined by

$$|G_{xy}(f)| = \sqrt{C_{xy}^{2}(f) + Q_{xy}^{2}(f)}$$

$$\theta_{xy}(f) = \tan^{-1}\frac{Q_{xy}(f)}{C_{xy}(f)}$$

(5.101)

The signs of the cross-spectral terms $C_{xy}(f)$ and $Q_{xy}(f)$ may be positive or negative and determine the quadrant for the phase angle. These signs determine also at each frequency f whether $x(t)$ leads $y(t)$, or $y(t)$ leads $x(t)$. This is illustrated in the diagram of Figure 5.4.

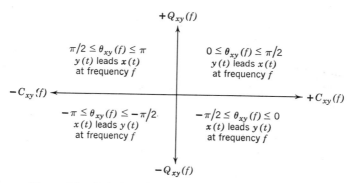

Figure 5.4 Relation of phase angle to cross-spectral terms.

Normalized Error and Spectral Resolution.   The normalized mean square error of the estimate $G_x(f)$, which will be taken as representative of $\hat{G}_x(f)$, $\hat{G}_y(f)$, $\hat{C}_{xy}(f)$, or $\hat{Q}_{xy}(f)$, is given by

$$\epsilon^2 = \frac{E[(\hat{G}_x(f) - G_x(f))^2]}{G_x^{2}(f)} \approx \frac{1}{B_e T} + \frac{B_e^{4}}{576}\left(\frac{G_x''(f)}{G_x(f)}\right)^2$$

(5.102)

It is convenient to define the inverse of the spectral term in Eq. (5.102) by

$$\lambda(f) = \left|\frac{G_x(f)}{G_x''(f)}\right|^{\frac{1}{2}}$$

(5.103)

Then $\lambda(f)$ has units of frequency, and is called the "*spectral bandwidth*" of the random process $\{x(t)\}$ under consideration. In terms of $\lambda(f)$, the normalized mean square error is

$$\epsilon^2 \approx \frac{1}{B_e T} + \frac{1}{576}\left(\frac{B_e}{\lambda(f)}\right)^4$$

(5.104)

The square root of Eq. (5.104) gives the normalized standard error ϵ.

Example **5.4.**   Suppose a random process of interest has a known "spectral bandwidth" function $\lambda(f)$. Further suppose the power spectral density function for the process is to be measured using a device as illustrated in Figure 5.3, where it is desired to limit the bias error in the measurement to no greater than 1 per cent.

To meet this requirement, it follows from Eq. (5.104) that

$$\epsilon_b^2 = (0.01)^2 = \frac{1}{576}\left(\frac{B_e}{\lambda_{max}}\right)^4$$

where ϵ_b^2 is the bias portion of the normalized mean square error. Hence

$$B_e \leq 0.49\lambda_{max}$$

Now, if the variance of the measurement is also to be limited to 1 per cent, it is necessary that

$$\epsilon_v^2 = (0.01)^2 = \frac{1}{B_e T} = \frac{1}{0.49 T \lambda_{max}}$$

where ϵ_v^2 is the variance portion of the normalized mean square error. Hence, if these error requirements are to be met, the required sampling time for the measurement is

$$T \geq \frac{10^4}{0.49\lambda_{max}}$$

5.4   Sample Size and Record Length Requirements

5.4.1   Sampling Theorems for Random Data

Suppose a sample random time history record $x(t)$ exists only for the time interval from 0 to T seconds, and is zero at all other times. Its Fourier transform is

$$X(f) = \int_0^T x(t)\, e^{-j2\pi ft}\, dt \tag{5.105}$$

Assume that $x(t)$ is continually repeated to obtain a periodic time function with a period of T seconds. The fundamental frequency increment is $f = 1/T$. By a Fourier series expansion

$$x(t) = \sum_{-\infty}^{\infty} A_n\, e^{j2\pi nt/T} \tag{5.106}$$

where

$$A_n = \frac{1}{T}\int_0^T x(t)\, e^{-j2\pi nt/T}\, dt \tag{5.107}$$

From Eq. (5.105),

$$X\left(\frac{n}{T}\right) = \int_0^T x(t)\, e^{-j2\pi nt/T}\, dt = TA_n \tag{5.108}$$

Thus $X(n/T)$ determines A_n and, therefore $x(t)$ at all t. This, in turn, determines $X(f)$ for all f. This result is the *sampling theorem* in the *frequency domain*. The fundamental frequency increment $1/T$ is called a *Nyquist co-interval*.

Suppose that a Fourier transform $X(f)$ of some sample random time history record $x(t)$ exists only over a frequency interval from $-B$ to B cps, and is zero at all other frequencies. The actual realizable frequency band ranges from 0 to B cps. The inverse Fourier transform yields

$$x(t) = \int_{-B}^{B} X(f)\, e^{j2\pi ft}\, df \tag{5.109}$$

Assume that $X(f)$ is continually repeated in frequency to obtain a periodic frequency function with a period of $2B$ cps. The fundamental time increment is $t = 1/2B$. Now

$$X(f) = \sum_{-\infty}^{\infty} C_n\, e^{-j\pi nf/B} \tag{5.110}$$

where

$$C_n = \frac{1}{2B} \int_{-B}^{B} X(f)\, e^{j\pi nf/B}\, df \tag{5.111}$$

From Eq. (5.109),

$$x\left(\frac{n}{2B}\right) = \int_{-B}^{B} X(f)\, e^{j\pi nf/B}\, df = 2BC_n \tag{5.112}$$

Thus $x(n/2B)$ determines C_n and, hence, $X(f)$ at all f. This, in turn, determines $x(t)$ for all t. This result is the *sampling theorem* in the *time domain*. The fundamental time increment $1/2B$ is called a *Nyquist interval*. Recall that for bandwidth limited white noise of bandwidth B, Eq. (5.21) shows that points $1/2B$ apart are uncorrelated.

Suppose that the sample record $x(t)$ exists only for the time interval from 0 to T seconds, and suppose also that its Fourier transform $X(f)$ exists only in a frequency interval from $-B$ to B cps. This dual assumption is not theoretically possible because of an *uncertainty principle*, Ref. 1, p. 52. In actual practice, however, it may be closely approximated with finite time intervals and band-pass filters. Assuming $x(t)$ and $X(f)$ are so restricted as to their time and frequency properties, it will now be shown how many distinct samples of $x(t)$ or $X(f)$ are required to describe $x(t)$ completely for all t.

From Eq. (5.108), by sampling $X(f)$ at Nyquist co-interval points $1/T$ apart on the frequency scale from $-B$ to B, the number of discrete samples required to describe $x(t)$ is

$$n = \frac{2B}{1/T} = 2BT \tag{5.113}$$

From Eq. (5.112), by sampling $x(t)$ at Nyquist interval points $1/2B$ apart on the time scale from 0 to T, it follows that

$$n = \frac{T}{1/2B} = 2BT \tag{5.114}$$

Thus the same number of discrete samples are required when sampling the Nyquist co-intervals on the frequency scale, or when sampling the Nyquist intervals on the time scale.

It should be noted that the $n = 2BT$ discrete samples will be _statistically independent_ samples for the special case of bandwidth limited Gaussian white noise. For actual random data, the bandwidth limited white noise requirement will generally not be satisfied. However, no matter what spectral composition the data may have, one can always think of the spectral characteristics in terms of an "equivalent bandwidth" which would produce an equivalent number of independent samples when used in Eq. (5.114). Such an "equivalent bandwidth" is, in fact, defined for certain types of parameter estimates, as shall be pointed out later. Hence, for the discussions to follow, it is assumed that one can define a bandwidth B which will produce $n = 2BT$ discrete samples which are statistically independent. This number n is called the _number of degrees of freedom_.

5.4.2 Mean and Mean Square Values

Mean Values.   From Eq. (5.23), the normalized standard error for a mean value estimate $\hat{\mu}_x$ from a sample record $x(t)$ with a true mean value $\mu_x \neq 0$ and standard deviation σ_x is

$$\epsilon = \frac{\text{s.d. } [\hat{\mu}_x]}{\mu_x} \approx \frac{1}{\sqrt{2BT}} \left(\frac{\sigma_x}{\mu_x} \right) \tag{5.115}$$

Thus

$$T_r = \frac{1}{2B\epsilon^2} \left(\frac{\sigma_x}{\mu_x} \right)^2 \tag{5.116}$$

gives the minimum sample record length in seconds required to achieve a desired error ϵ when B is the bandwidth in cps occupied by $x(t)$, assuming a uniform power spectrum within B. Where $x(t)$ does not have a uniform power spectrum within B, an "equivalent bandwidth" can be established based upon the autocovariance function for $x(t)$, and evaluation of Eq. (5.17).

Since $\hat{\mu}_x$ is a sample mean, the sampling distribution for $\hat{\mu}_x$ is governed by the t distribution with $n = 2BT$ degrees of freedom, as discussed in Section 4.3.3. A plot of ϵ versus the BT product for various ratios of σ_x/μ_x is presented in Figure 5.5.

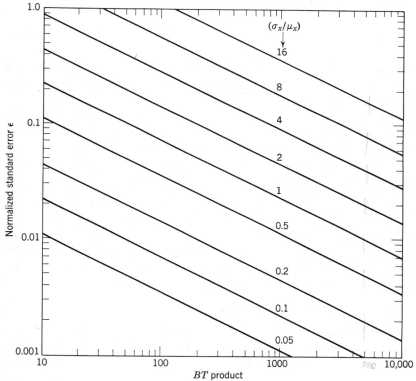

Figure 5.5 Statistical error versus BT product for mean value estimates.

It is clear from Eq. (5.116) that an unreasonably long sample record would be required to measure mean values near zero with a fixed error ϵ. Hence, when selecting a sampling time for a mean value estimate, it is necessary to specify not only an error ϵ, but also a minimum value of μ_x to which the error applies. For example, it may be desired to obtain an estimate to within $\epsilon = 0.10$ for values down to $\mu_x = 0.1\sigma_x$. For this case, the quantity $\epsilon(\mu_x/\sigma_x) = 0.01$ and the required record length T_r is $5000/B$ seconds. If μ_x is less than $0.1\sigma_x$, the estimate will be less accurate than given by $\epsilon = 0.10$.

Mean Square Values. From Eq. (5.35), the normalized standard error for a mean square value estimate $\hat{\Psi}_x^2$ from a sample record $x(t)$ with a true mean value of $\mu_x = 0$ and a true rms value of Ψ_x is

$$\epsilon = \frac{\text{s.d.} [\hat{\Psi}_x^2]}{\Psi_x^2} \approx \frac{1}{\sqrt{BT}} \tag{5.117}$$

Thus

$$T_r = \frac{1}{B\epsilon^2} \tag{5.118}$$

gives the minimum sample record length in seconds required to achieve a desired error ϵ when B is the bandwidth in cps occupied by $x(t)$, assuming a uniform power spectrum within B. For the case where $x(t)$ does not have a uniform power spectrum within B, an "equivalent bandwidth" can be established based upon the autocovariance function for $x(t)$, and evaluation of Eq. (5.30).

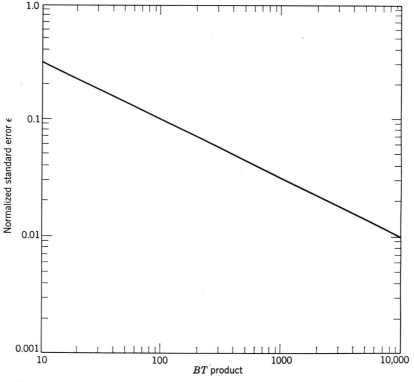

Figure 5.6 Statistical error versus BT product for mean square value estimates.

Since $\hat{\Psi}_x^2$ is a variance estimate when $\mu_x = 0$, the sampling distribution for $\hat{\Psi}_x^2$ is governed by a χ^2 distribution with $n = 2BT$ degrees of freedom, as discussed in Section 4.3.2. A plot of ϵ versus the BT product is presented in Figure 5.6.

5.4.3 Probability Density Functions

First-Order Probability Density Functions. From Eq. (5.62), a reasonable approximation of the normalized standard error for a "highly resolved" first-order probability density estimate $\hat{p}(x)$ from a sample record $x(t)$ with a true probability density of $p(x)$ is

$$\epsilon = \frac{\text{s.d. } [\hat{p}(x)]}{p(x)} \approx \frac{A_1}{\sqrt{BTW \, \hat{p}(x)}} \qquad (5.119)$$

Note that it is being assumed here that the bias term in Eq. (5.62) is negligible, as is implied by the restriction that the estimate is "highly resolved." Thus

$$T_r = \frac{A_1^2}{\epsilon^2 WB \, \hat{p}(x)} \qquad (5.120)$$

gives the minimum sample record length in seconds required to achieve a desired error ϵ when B is the bandwidth in cps occupied by $x(t)$ assuming a uniform power spectrum within B. The term W is the amplitude resolution width and A_1 is a constant.

From Ref. 29, an appropriate value for A_1 when computing $\hat{p}(x)$ from $2BT$ discrete independent sample values is $A_1 = 1/\sqrt{2}$. However, Ref. 5 indicates that this value is conservative when measuring $\hat{p}(x)$ with an analog instrument that more exactly performs the operations in Eq. (5.39). Furthermore, the value for A_1 will be different when $x(t)$ does not have a uniform power spectrum within B. The sampling distribution for $\hat{p}(x)$ is unknown, although a Gaussian assumption for the sampling distribution is acceptable when ϵ is small, say $\epsilon < 0.2$. A plot of ϵ versus the WBT product for various values of $p(x)$ is presented for $A_1 = 1/\sqrt{2}$ in Figure 5.7.

Joint Probability Density Functions. The normalized standard error for a joint probability density estimate is not known, although it appears plausible that it has the form given from Eq. (5.61) as

$$\epsilon = \frac{\text{s.d. } [\hat{p}(x, y)]}{p(x, y)} \frac{A_2}{\sqrt{BTW_x W_y \, \hat{p}(x, y)}} \qquad (5.121)$$

where it is assumed that all bias terms are negligible. Thus

$$T_r = \frac{A_2^2}{\epsilon^2 W_x W_y B \, \hat{p}(x, y)} \qquad (5.122)$$

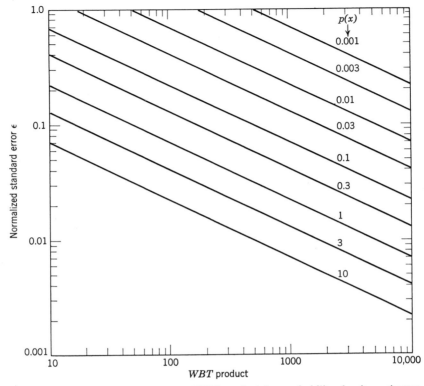

Figure 5.7 Statistical error versus WBT product for probability density estimates.

gives the minimum sample record length in seconds required to achieve a desired error ϵ when B is the bandwidth in cps occupied by $x(t)$ and $y(t)$, assuming a uniform power spectrum for both within B. The terms W_x and W_y are the amplitude resolution widths and A_2 is an unknown constant. The result in Eq. (5.122) is offered only as a guideline, and not for specific evaluation purposes.

5.4.4 Correlation Functions

Autocorrelation Functions. From Eq. (5.78), for $x(t) = y(t)$, the normalized standard error for an autocorrelation function estimate $\hat{R}_x(\tau)$ from a sample record $x(t)$ with a mean value of $\mu_x = 0$ and a true autocorrelation function $R_x(\tau)$ is

$$\epsilon = \frac{\text{s.d. } [\hat{R}_x(\tau)]}{R_x(\tau)} \approx \frac{1}{\sqrt{2BT}}\left(1 + \frac{R_x^2(0)}{R_x^2(\tau)}\right)^{\frac{1}{2}} \tag{5.123}$$

Thus

$$T_r = \frac{1}{2B\epsilon^2}\left[1 + \frac{R_x^2(0)}{R_x^2(\tau)}\right] \tag{5.124}$$

gives the minimum sample record length in seconds required to achieve a desired error ϵ when B is the bandwidth in cps occupied by $x(t)$, assuming a uniform power spectrum within B. A plot of ϵ versus the BT product for various ratios of $R_x(0)/R_x(\tau)$ is presented in Figure 5.8.

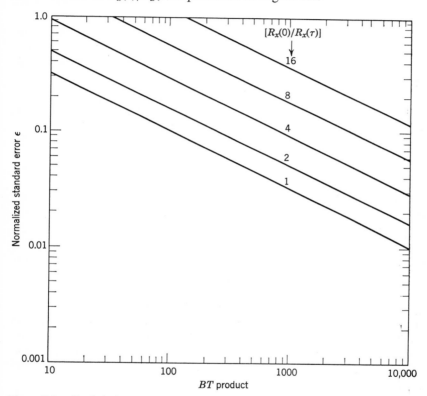

Figure 5.8 Statistical error versus BT product for autocorrelation function estimates.

It is clear from Eqs. (5.124) that an unreasonably long sample record would be required to measure autocorrelation values near zero with a fixed error ϵ, just as was true for mean value estimates in Section 5.4.2. Hence, when selecting a record length for an autocorrelation function estimate, it is necessary to specify a minimum value to be estimated with an error ϵ.

For the case where $\tau = 0$, Eq. (5.124) reduces to

$$T_r = 1/B\epsilon^2 \tag{5.125}$$

This is the same result that was obtained for mean square value estimates in Eq. (5.118), as it should be since $R_x(0) = \Psi_x^2$.

For mean square value estimates, a general expression for the error ϵ when $x(t)$ is a sample record from a nonstationary random process is developed in Section 9.2.2. The error expression is a function of the correlation between adjacent discrete samples, and is directly applicable to correlation function estimates which are calculated using a digital computer. This general expression may be applied to situations where $x(t)$ does not have a uniform power spectrum within B.

Cross-Correlation Functions.   Returning to Eq. (5.78), the normalized standard error for a cross-correlation function estimate $\hat{R}_{xy}(\tau)$ from two sample records $x(t)$ and $y(t)$ with mean values of $\mu_x = \mu_y = 0$, and a true cross-correlation function $R_{xy}(\tau)$ is

$$\epsilon = \frac{\text{s.d. } [\hat{R}_{xy}(\tau)]}{R_{xy}(\tau)} \approx \frac{1}{\sqrt{2BT}}\left[1 + \frac{R_x(0)\,R_y(0)}{R_{xy}^2(\tau)}\right]^{\frac{1}{2}} \qquad (5.126)$$

Thus

$$T_r = \frac{1}{2B\epsilon^2}\left[1 + \frac{R_x(0)\,R_y(0)}{R_{xy}^2(\tau)}\right] \qquad (5.127)$$

gives the minimum sample record length in seconds required to achieve the desired error ϵ when B is the bandwidth in cps occupied by $x(t)$ and $y(t)$, assuming a uniform power spectrum for both within B. Accurate application of Eq. (5.127) requires that these assumptions be reasonably satisfied. Otherwise, Eq. (5.127) acts only as a guideline for selecting sample sizes.

5.4.5   Spectral Density Functions

A.   Power Spectral Density Functions.   From Eq. (5.104), the normalized standard error for a "highly resolved" power spectral density function estimate $\hat{G}_x(f)$ from a sample record $x(t)$ with a true power spectral density function $G_x(f)$ is

$$\epsilon = \frac{\text{s.d. } [\hat{G}_x(f)]}{G_x(f)} \approx \frac{1}{\sqrt{B_e T}} \qquad (5.128)$$

Note that it is being assumed here that the bias term in Eq. (5.104) is negligible, as is implied by the restriction that the estimate is "highly resolved." Thus

$$T_r = 1/B_e\epsilon^2 \qquad (5.129)$$

gives the minimum sample record length in seconds required to achieve a desired error ϵ when B_e is the equivalent ideal bandwidth in cps of the narrow bandwidth resolution filter. The derivation of B_e for a narrow band-pass filter with any given frequency response function is given in Section 6.4.6.

Noting that $\hat{G}_x(f)$ is a variance estimate when B_e does not include $f = 0$, or when $\mu_x = 0$, the sampling distribution for $\hat{G}_x(f)$ is governed by a χ^2 distribution with $n = 2B_eT$ degrees of freedom as discussed in Section 4.3.2. A plot of Eq. (5.129) is the same as presented in Figure 5.6, except that B_e replaces B.

Cross-Spectral Density Functions.   Returning to Eq. (5.104), the normalized standard error for the co-spectral density function and the quad-spectral density function is bounded by the error value developed for the power spectral density function. Hence Eq. (5.129) applies conservatively to sample selections for cospectral density as well as quadspectral density estimates.

5.4.6   Frequency Response Functions

The sampling distribution for frequency response function estimates is generally difficult to analyze. However, statistical error formulas have been developed for certain important special cases. Specifically, consider the case where an *unbiased* estimate of the frequency response function for a linear system can be calculated from an observed input $x(t)$ and an observed output $y(t)$ by the relationship of Eq. (3.140). This yields

$$\hat{H}(f) = \frac{\hat{G}_{xy}(f)}{\hat{G}_x(f)} \tag{5.130}$$

This estimate will be unbiased when there are no contributions to $y(t)$ which are correlated with $x(t)$. In other words, Eq. (5.130) gives a valid unbiased estimate for the single input-single output case where $y(t)$ may include extraneous noise, and the multiple input-single output case where the inputs are uncorrelated (incoherent). For these problems, the statistical accuracy of the estimate $\hat{H}(f)$ has been studied in Refs. 12, 16.

As defined in Chapter 2, the frequency response function for a constant parameter linear system is a complex-valued quantity which can be described in terms of a gain factor $|H(f)|$ and a phase factor $\phi(f)$, as follows.

$$H(f) = |H(f)|\, e^{-j\phi(f)} \tag{5.131}$$

For the type of problem being considered here, the statistical errors associated with the estimates for $|H(f)|$ and $\phi(f)$ are a function of n, the number of degrees of freedom available for the measurements of the spectral quantities, and $\gamma_{xy}^2(f)$, the true coherence function between the observed input and output. As defined in Eq. (3.148), the true coherence function is

$$\gamma_{xy}^2(f) = \frac{|G_{xy}(f)|^2}{G_x(f)\, G_y(f)} \tag{5.132}$$

The probability error formula for the gain factor and phase factor estimates is

$$P = \text{Prob} \left[\left| \frac{\hat{H}(f) - H(f)}{H(f)} \right| < \sin \epsilon \quad \text{and} \quad |\hat{\phi}(f) - \phi(f)| < \epsilon \right]$$

$$\approx 1 - \left[\frac{1 - \gamma_{xy}^{2}(f)}{1 - \gamma_{xy}^{2}(f) \cos^{2} \epsilon} \right]^{n/2} \tag{5.133}$$

For small values of ϵ, both inequalities hold for the same numerical values since $\sin \epsilon \approx \epsilon$. From Eq. (5.133), the required number n of degrees of freedom is

$$n = \frac{2 \ln (1 - P)}{\ln \left[\dfrac{1 - \gamma_{xy}^{2}(f)}{1 - \gamma_{xy}^{2}(f) \cos^{2} \epsilon} \right]} = 2B_e T \tag{5.134}$$

where B_e is the bandwidth in cps of the resolution filter used for the spectral estimates, and T is the averaging time in seconds. If desired, Eq. (5.134) may be solved for the minimum sample record length T_r.

To illustrate Eq. (5.134), if $\gamma_{xy}^{2}(f) = 0.90$, then choosing $\epsilon = 0.10$ and $P = 0.90$ requires that $n = 44$. This value for n will maintain the sample gain factor $|\hat{H}(f)|$ within 10 per cent of the true gain factor, and the sample phase factor $\hat{\phi}(f)$ within 0.10 radian of the true phase factor, for approximately 90 out of 100 experiments.

Equation (5.134) is plotted in Figures 5.9. There are three sets of curves in groups of three, one set of three curves for $P = 0.90$, $P = 0.85$, and $P = 0.80$ when $\epsilon = 0.05$ radian; one set when $\epsilon = 0.10$ radian; and one set when $\epsilon = 0.15$ radian. Since $\sin \epsilon \approx \epsilon$ for these small values of ϵ, the curves are satisfactory for a gain factor accuracy of 5, 10, and 15 per cent, and a phase angle accuracy of 0.05, 0.10, and 0.15 radian, which are approximately 2.9, 5.7, and 8.6 degrees.

The application of these curves to determine a sample size necessary to measure a frequency response function with a desired accuracy is somewhat limited at times. This is due primarily to the fact that Eq. (5.130) may not be an unbiased estimate. Moreover, the coherence function is not known in advance, and therefore must be estimated. A conservative choice is usually in order so that the above relations can be practical guidelines. Thus Eq. (5.134) can be used for planning purposes before making desired measurements, but Eq. (5.133) cannot be used for precise evaluation purposes after the actual measurements. After data are gathered, the more advanced procedures developed in Section 5.7 must be used to establish confidence intervals for the estimated frequency response functions.

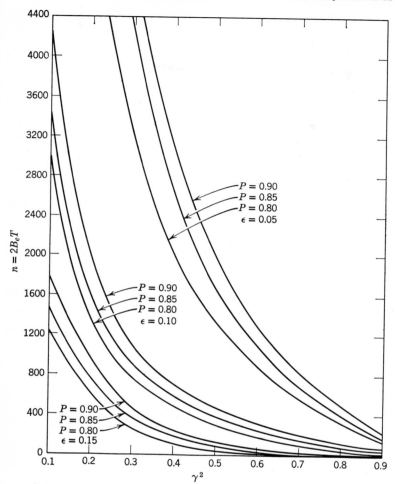

Figure 5.9   Probability errors for frequency response function measurements.
ϵ = Allowable measurement error.
P = Probability of error not greater than ϵ.
γ^2 = Value of coherence function.
n = Number of degrees-of-freedom of estimate.

Example **5.5.**   Suppose the frequency response function for a linear system is to be measured from random input-output data where there are other uncorrelated noise sources contributing to the measured output. Further assume that, based upon estimates for this extraneous noise and the spectra for the input and output, the coherence function for the measurements is expected to be about $\gamma^2 = 0.8$. Now assume that a maximum

5 per cent error in the gain factor measurement with a corresponding maximum 3-degree error in the phase is considered acceptable when there is a probability of 90 per cent of measuring these quantities that accurately. That is, $\gamma_{xy}^2(f) = 0.8$, $\epsilon = 0.05$, and $P = 0.90$. How many degrees of freedom are needed for the measurements?

From Figure 5.9, for the $\gamma^2 = 0.8$ value, the intersection with the top curve corresponding to $P = 0.90$ and $\epsilon = 0.05$ occurs when the value of n is 480. Therefore, about 480 degrees of freedom are needed to measure the frequency response function under these given conditions. When the resolution filter bandwidth for the analyzer used for the measurements is B_e cps, the minimum required sample record length is $T_r = 240/B_e$ seconds. This concludes Example 5.5.

An alternative way to interpret Eq. (5.133) is to solve for sin ϵ. For given values of P, n, and $\gamma_{xy}^2(f)$, the result is

$$\sin \epsilon \approx [\gamma_{xy}(f)]^{-1}\sqrt{[1 - \gamma_{xy}^2(f)][(1 - P)^{-2/n} - 1]} \qquad (5.135)$$

Then, Eq. (5.133) states that the true gain factor $|H(f)|$ and the true phase factor $\phi(f)$ lie between the lower limits $L(|H|)$, $l(\phi)$, and the upper limits $U(|H|)$, $u(\phi)$ with probability P. That is,

$$P = \text{Prob}[L(|H|) \leq |H(f)| \leq U(|H|) \quad \text{and} \quad l(\phi) \leq \phi(f) \leq u(\phi)] \qquad (5.136)$$

where

$$L(|H|) = \frac{|\hat{H}(f)|}{1 + \sin \epsilon} \qquad U(|H|) = \frac{|\hat{H}(f)|}{1 - \sin \epsilon}$$

$$l(\phi) = \hat{\phi}(f) - \epsilon \qquad u(\phi) = \hat{\phi}(f) + \epsilon \qquad (5.137)$$

These limits provide a polar fan region for any given f which contains the true gain and true phase factors with probability P, as illustrated in Figure 5.10.

Another procedure sometimes employed to compute the gain factor $|H(f)|$ alone for a linear system with input $x(t)$ and output $y(t)$ is based upon Eq. (3.139). This relationship yields

$$|\hat{H}(f)| = \left|\frac{\hat{G}_y(f)}{\hat{G}_x(f)}\right|^{1/2} \qquad (5.138)$$

where $\hat{G}_x(f)$ and $\hat{G}_y(f)$ are estimates for the input and output power spectral density functions. Equation (5.138) will give an unbiased estimate of $|H(f)|$ only for the special case where there is a single input producing the output and no extraneous noise is present in the measurement at either the input or output. For this case, the coherence function between $x(t)$ and $y(t)$ will theoretically be unity, and the variance of $|\hat{H}(f)|$ will be near zero independent of the degrees of freedom for the estimate, assuming $\hat{G}_x(f)$ and $\hat{G}_y(f)$ are measured simultaneously. Unfortunately, these ideal conditions are rarely satisfied in practice. Hence the estimation procedure given by Eq. (5.138) is of little value except for results obtained from controlled

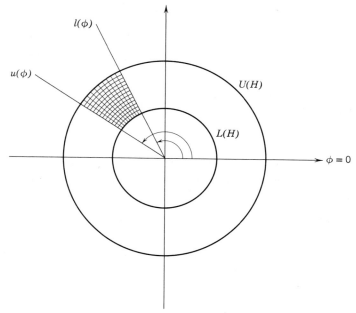

Figure 5.10   Polar fan region for any given f containing true gain factor and true phase factor with probability P.

laboratory experiments. Even for the case of controlled experiments, it is usually simpler and more effective to measure frequency response functions using a contrived sinusoidal input, as discussed in Section 2.5.

5.4.7   Coherence Function Measurements

As mentioned in the preceding section, probability limits for frequency response function measurements are based upon knowing the true coherence function. From actual data, however, only sample estimates of the coherence function will be available. The sampling distribution for these sample coherence functions has been studied in Ref. 13. For practical situations where the number of degrees of freedom, n, is of moderate size, say $n \geq 20$, and where the true coherence function $\gamma^2(f)$ is in the range

(0.35, 0.95), it has been determined empirically in Ref. 13 that the transformed function $z(f)$ defined by

$$z(f) = \tanh^{-1} \hat{\gamma}(f) = \tfrac{1}{2} \ln \frac{1 + \hat{\gamma}(f)}{1 - \hat{\gamma}(f)} \tag{5.139}$$

will follow to a very close approximation a normal distribution with a mean value $\mu(f)$ and a variance σ^2 as follows.

$$\mu(f) = (n - 2)^{-1} + \tanh^{-1} \gamma(f)$$
$$\sigma^2 = (n - 2)^{-1} \qquad n = 2B_e T \tag{5.140}$$

In these equations, $\gamma(f)$ is the positive square root of $\gamma^2(f)$, and $\hat{\gamma}(f)$ is a sample estimate for $\gamma(f)$.

From the preceding equations, for given values of n and $\hat{\gamma}^2(f)$, one can determine confidence limits for the true value $\gamma^2(f)$ as follows. First, since $z(f)$ is normally distributed, Eq. (4.15) applies to yield

$$\text{Prob} \left[z_{1-\alpha/2} < \frac{z(f) - \mu(f)}{\sigma} \le z_{\alpha/2} \right] = 1 - \alpha \tag{5.141}$$

where z_α is the 100α percentage point of the normal distribution. In Eq. (5.141), $\mu(f)$ can now be replaced by Eq. (5.140), and then rearranged in terms of $\gamma(f)$ to yield

$$[\tanh (z(f) - (n - 2)^{-1} - \sigma z_{\alpha/2}) \le \gamma(f)$$
$$\le \tanh (z(f) - (n - 2)^{-1} + \sigma z_{\alpha/2})] \tag{5.142}$$

where one uses the fact that $z_{1-\alpha/2} = -z_{\alpha/2}$. This result gives the two confidence limits within which $\gamma(f)$ will lie with $1 - \alpha$ confidence as a function of n, $\hat{\gamma}(f)$, and α. The confidence limits for $\gamma^2(f)$ are the squares of the corresponding confidence limits for $\gamma(f)$.

***Example* 5.6.** Suppose a coherence function is measured from two sample records of length $T_r = 10$ seconds using a resolution bandwidth of $B_e = 5$ cps so that the resulting coherence estimate $\hat{\gamma}^2(f)$ has $n = 100$ degrees of freedom. What are the 99 per cent confidence limits for $\gamma^2(f)$ if the measured values of $\hat{\gamma}^2(f)$ are 0.40, 0.50, 0.60, 0.70, 0.80, or 0.90?

From Table 4.7, for $\alpha/2 = 0.005$, $z_{\alpha/2} = 2.58$; from Eq. (5.140), $\sigma = 0.10$. Hence, Eq. (5.142) becomes

$$[\tanh (z(f) - 0.268) \le \gamma(f) \le \tanh(z(f) + 0.248)]$$

with $z(f)$ determined by Eq. (5.139). Table 5.1 shows the 99 per cent confidence limits for $\gamma^2(f)$ as a function of $\hat{\gamma}^2(f)$ for this example. Similar results may be obtained for other values of n and α. This table concludes Example 5.6.

Table 5.1   **99 Per Cent Confidence Limits when $n = 100$ for True Coherence Function $\gamma^2(f)$**

$\hat{\gamma}^2(f)$	0.4	0.5	0.6	0.7	0.8	0.9
Lower limit	0.19	0.29	0.41	0.54	0.68	0.83
Upper limit	0.58	0.66	0.74	0.81	0.88	0.94

The effect of additive noise on coherence function measurements will now be indicated. Assume a measured input $x(t)$ and a measured output $y(t)$ are composed of true signals $u(t)$ and $v(t)$ and uncorrelated noise components $n(t)$ and $m(t)$, respectively, as shown below.

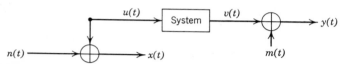

The measured input and output are given by

$$x(t) = u(t) + n(t)$$
$$y(t) = v(t) + m(t)$$

(5.143)

The measured spectral density relations are, under ideal conditions,

$$G_x(f) = G_u(f) + G_n(f)$$
$$G_y(f) = G_v(f) + G_m(f)$$
$$G_{xy}(f) = G_{uv}(f)$$

(5.144)

For this problem, the desired coherence function is

$$\gamma_{uv}^2(f) = \frac{|G_{uv}(f)|^2}{G_u(f) \, G_v(f)}$$

(5.145)

The measured coherence function will be

$$\gamma_{xy}^2(f) = \frac{|G_{xy}(f)|^2}{G_x(f) \, G_y(f)} = \frac{|G_{uv}(f)|^2}{[G_u(f) + G_n(f)][G_v(f) + G_m(f)]}$$

$$= \frac{\gamma_{uv}^2(f)}{1 + (N_1/G_1) + (N_2/G_2) + (N_1/G_1)(N_2/G_2)} < \gamma_{uv}^2(f)$$

(5.146)

where

$$N_1 = G_n(f) \qquad G_1 = G_u(f)$$
$$N_2 = G_m(f) \qquad G_2 = G_v(f)$$

(5.147)

Equation (5.146) illustrates the behavior that would be expected when uncorrelated extraneous noise is present in both the input and output measurements. Observe that the measured coherence function will theoretically always be less than the desired coherence function whenever the ratios N_1/G_1 and N_2/G_2 are positive. Special cases of interest are when $N_1 = 0$ or when $N_2 = 0$. These results can also be interpreted to show the effect of additive noise on frequency response function measurements.

5.5 Data Sampling Techniques

5.5.1 Random Sampling

A major consideration in any data analysis is the extraction of the maximum amount of information from the minimum amount of data. Selection of an appropriate sampling scheme (random or periodic) can usually decrease the volume of data required to define the parameters of interest with the desired precision. With a knowledge of the mean time between samples, the distribution of these times, and the length of each sample record, quantitative results can be obtained for predicting the probability of detecting significant unexpected events and for determining the minimum number of sample records required to achieve this probability.

The required length of each sample record to be collected is generally established by the statistical error considerations outlined in Section 5.4. Hence, in a random sampling scheme, only the time interval between samples will be random. On the practical side, instrumentation problems of recording such data will be simplified if it is decided in advance that each sample record length should be of a specific duration.

The principal difficulty in a random sampling plan is the likelihood of missing certain important unexpected events which might occur between sample records. It is of interest to know the probability of missing such events for a given sample record length and a given mean time between samples. For the subsequent discussion, let

$$e = \text{length of unexpected event in seconds}$$
$$T_r = \text{length of each sample record in seconds}$$
$$l = \text{mean time between samples in seconds}$$
$$\text{(measured from center to center)}$$

The sketch below shows a possible sequence, given that e will occur once during l, and that $T_r + e \leq l$.

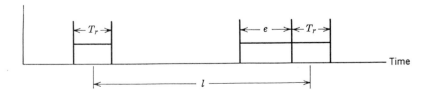

Assuming that the probability density function for the random sampling is uniform, the average probability $\bar{P}$ of *missing all parts* of e is

$$\bar{P}\,(\text{missing } e) = \frac{l - (T_r + e)}{l} = 1 - \frac{T_r + e}{l} \qquad (5.148)$$

This equation does not apply to situations of a predetermined fixed time between samples. For predetermined fixed sampling times,

$$\bar{P}\,(\text{missing } e) = \begin{cases} 0 & \text{if } e \text{ occurs inside the sample record length} \\ 1 & \text{if } e \text{ occurs outside the sample record length} \end{cases}$$

The average probability of *recording any part* of e for random sampling is

$$\bar{P}\,(\text{recording } e) = \frac{T_r + e}{l} \qquad (5.149)$$

Suppose that the time history information of interest is sampled in a random manner. If $l = 100$ seconds, $T_r. = 5$ seconds, and $e = 10$ seconds, then

$$\bar{P}\,(\text{recording } e) = \frac{5 + 10}{100} = 0.15$$

This might appear to be quite low, but if e occurs only once, it might not be of too great interest. If e occurs, for example, ten times during a 1000-second interval, a much higher probability would be desired and, in fact, does exist. Using the same values for e, T_r, and l, the average recording probability is now

$$\bar{P}\,(\text{recording } e) = 1 - \left(1 - \frac{T_r + e}{l}\right)^{10} = 0.84$$

The preceding ideas can assist in determining an appropriate mean time l between samples based on a desired sample record length T_r. Of course, judgment is necessary in determining how long an unexpected event should be before it is considered important, and what is the permissible miss probability. Once l has been determined, it is a simple matter to calculate the number N of samples which will be gathered from a continuous time history of length T. Specifically,

$$N = \frac{T}{l} \qquad (5.150)$$

This number N will be the required number of sample records, each of length T_r, to yield a desired detection probability for detecting unexpected events of length e.

From each of the N records of length T_r, a sample parameter value $\hat{\Phi}$ would be computed for some quantity of interest. The expected range of values for $\hat{\Phi}$ can then be determined by calculating the probability that $\hat{\Phi}$ occurs between $\mu \pm c\sigma$, where μ and σ are the true mean value and standard deviation of the underlying distribution of $\hat{\Phi}$, and c is positive. Estimates of μ and σ may be obtained from the N sample values of $\hat{\Phi}$. When no assumptions are made about the underlying distribution, the Tchebycheff inequality may be applied. This gives the result

$$\text{Prob} \left[\mu - c\sigma \leq \hat{\Phi} \leq \mu + c\sigma \right] \geq 1 - c^{-2} \qquad (5.151)$$

If a normal (Gaussian) distribution exists, the following relation holds, which yields a higher probability value for any given c. That is,

$$\text{Prob} \left[\mu - c\sigma \leq \hat{\Phi} \leq \mu + c\sigma \right]$$

$$= \int_{\mu - c\sigma}^{\mu + c\sigma} \left(\sigma\sqrt{2\pi} \right)^{-1} \exp \left[\frac{-(\hat{\Phi} - \mu)^2}{2\sigma^2} \right] d\hat{\Phi} \qquad (5.152)$$

A comparison of probability results about the sample parameter values based upon the Tchebycheff inequality and the assumption of normality is shown in the accompanying table.

			c		
	1.0	1.5	2.0	2.5	3.0
Normal	0.6827	0.8664	0.9545	0.9876	0.9973
Tchebycheff	0	0.5556	0.7500	0.8400	0.8889

5.5.2   Periodic Sampling

If data are assumed or verified to be truly random, as opposed to being deterministic in whole or part, then one can choose a fixed time l between samples. When l is in seconds, the period of the sampling is $1/l$ samples per second. Now, Eq. (5.149) states the probability of recording unexpected events for periodic sampling where the validity of this formula is dependent on the data being random.

With periodic rather than random sampling, it is easier to detect underlying linear trends in the data. Once detected and analyzed, these trends can be removed so that further analysis can be devoted to the other data characteristics. The most important of these is the question of stationarity of the data.

If the data are both random and stationary, then the data can be collected at arbitrary random times, and sampled periodically thereafter, without introducing any errors. However, if the data are nonstationary, then results are dependent upon the particular times of observation and should be analyzed by special methods as discussed in Chapter 9. For nonstationary data, a fixed starting time requirement should be imposed and the results should be expressed as a function of this starting time.

5.6 Tests for Basic Characteristics

In order to properly analyze random data from sample time history records, it is necessary to establish three basic characteristics of the data. These basic characteristics are stationarity, randomness, and normality as indicated by Blocks E, F, and G in Figure 5.1. Furthermore, when a collection of records is being analyzed, it is helpful to be able to pool together the results measured from individual records which are equivalent, as indicated by Block C in Figure 5.2. Practical techniques for detecting whether or not sampled data possess these basic characteristics are now outlined and discussed.

5.6.1 Tests for Stationarity

The general concept of stationarity is presented in rigorous terms in Section 3.2. From that material, proof of stationarity would theoretically involve verification that all statistical properties for the random process of interest are invariant with time translations. Such verifications are clearly not feasible in practical terms since there are an infinite number of possible statistics, and a complete description of the random process by an ensemble would be required to compute them. However, by noting certain important assumptions which are generally valid for the vast majority of random data in nature, practical tests for stationarity can be developed.

The first important assumption is as follows. If the data of interest are nonstationary, then the statistical properties computed by time averaging over each of a sequence of short time intervals from a single sample record will vary significantly from one interval to the next. Furthermore, if the data of interest are stationary, then the statistical properties computed for each of the sequence of short time intervals will not vary significantly from one time interval to the next. Here the word "significantly" means that variations are greater than would be expected due to statistical sampling variations. If this assumption is accepted, random data can be tested for stationarity by investigating the behavior of individual sample records rather than an ensemble of sample records. In simpler terms, the above assumption means that proof of self-stationarity for individual sample records, as defined in Section 1.2.4, can be accepted as proof of stationarity for the random process from which the records were obtained. Although one can contrive a hypothetical nonergodic stationary random process where this assumption would not be valid, it will generally be acceptable for data representing actual random phenomena.

The second important assumption is that verification of weak stationarity (time invariance of the mean value and autocorrelation function) will be acceptable for most desired analyses and applications. If this assumption is accepted, then verification of stationarity can be restricted to investigations of only the mean value and autocorrelation functions for the data. This assumption is usually acceptable for two reasons. First, important stationary data analysis procedures such as power spectra and autocorrelation analysis do not require more than weak stationarity to be valid. Second, random data representing actual physical phenomena will generally be strongly stationary if they are weakly stationary. Note that for the case of data with a Gaussian probability density function, weakly stationary data are automatically strongly stationary since all higher-order statistical properties of Gaussian data are determined by the mean value and autocorrelation function.

A third important assumption is that the sample record of the data to be investigated is very long compared to the random fluctuations of the data time history. This condition is necessary so that short-time averages will truly reflect average properties of the data and not just the random fluctuations of the time history in question. In other words, the sample record must be long enough to permit long-term trends to be differentiated from the time history fluctuations. For example, assume one is interested in determining if there are time trends (nonstationarity) in stock market prices. It is clear that long-term trends could not be detected from a sample of prices over a period of only one week. Note that the validity of this assumption is a function of the specific circumstances for each problem. If the assumption is not considered valid, the stationary tests discussed here will not be applicable, and the data must be studied in terms of ensemble averages.

A fourth important assumption, which is not necessary but which will simplify practical testing procedures, is that if the mean square value (or variance) of the data of interest is stationary, then the autocorrelation function (or autocovariance function) for the data is also stationary. This assumption is certainly not as dependable as the first three assumptions. Nevertheless, it is usually valid for the simple reason that it is highly unlikely for nonstationary data to have a time-varying autocorrelation function for any time displacement τ without the value at $\tau = 0$ varying. Since the mean square value is equal to the autocorrelation function at $\tau = 0$ (the variance equals the autocovariance at $\tau = 0$), attention can usually be restricted to the mean square value (or variance) rather than to the entire autocorrelation (or autocovariance) function.

With these assumptions in mind, the stationarity of random data can be tested by investigating a single record $x(t)$ as follows.

1. Divide the sample record into N equal time intervals where the data in each interval may be considered independent. For the case of relatively wide-band data, these time intervals may be contiguous. If the data is narrow-band or of low frequency relative to the individual interval length, it may be necessary to allow a space between each interval to assure that the data in each interval are effectively independent of adjacent intervals.

2. Compute a mean value and mean square value for each interval and align these sample values in time sequence, as follows.

$$\bar{x}_1, \bar{x}_2, \bar{x}_3, \ldots, \bar{x}_N$$
$$\overline{x_1^2}, \overline{x_2^2}, \overline{x_3^2}, \ldots, \overline{x_N^2}$$

3. Test the sequence of mean and mean square values for the presence of underlying trends or variations other than those due to expected sampling variations.

The final test of the sample values for nonstationary trends may be accomplished in many ways. If the sampling distribution for the values is known, various parametric statistical tests discussed in Chapter 4 could be applied. However, as noted in Section 5.4, the sampling distribution for mean values and variances requires a detailed knowledge of the frequency composition of the data. Such knowledge is generally not available at the time one wishes to establish whether or not data are stationary. Hence a nonparametric approach which does not require a knowledge of sampling distributions for the data is more desirable. Two such nonparametric tests which are applicable to this problem are outlined in Section 4.8. These are the run test and the trend test. Either may be applied directly as follows.

Let it hypothesized that the sequence of mean values $(\bar{x}_1, \bar{x}_2, \bar{x}_3, \ldots,$ $\bar{x}_N)$ and the sequence of mean square values $(\overline{x_1^2}, \overline{x_2^2}, \overline{x_3^2}, \ldots, \overline{x_N^2})$ are each independent sample values of a random variable with a true mean value μ_x and mean square value Ψ_x^2, respectively. If this hypothesis is true, the variations in the sequence of sampled values will be random and display no trends. Hence the number of runs in the sequence relative to any given value (for simplicity, take the median value) will be as expected for a sequence of independent random observations of the random variable, as presented in Table 4.11. Moreover, the number of reverse arrangements in the sequence will be as expected for a sequence of independent random observations of the same variable, as presented in Table 4.12. If the number of runs or reverse arrangements is significantly different from the expected number given in Tables 4.11 and 4.12, the hypothesis of stationarity would be rejected. Otherwise, the hypothesis would be accepted. The details of applying either test with numerical illustrations are presented in Examples

4.9 and 4.10. Note that the sample mean values and sample mean square values must be tested separately.

Several important features of these nonparametric tests for stationarity should be noted.

1. A knowledge of the frequency bandwidth of the data under investigation is not required.

2. A knowledge of the exact averaging time used to measure the mean and mean square values is not required.

3. It is not necessary for the data under investigation to be completely random. Valid conclusions are obtained, even when sinusoidal components are present in the data, as long as the fundamental period is short compared to the averaging time used for each mean value and mean square value measurement.

Now consider the case where one is not prepared to accept time invariance of the mean square value as sufficient evidence of time invariance of the autocorrelation function. A test for nonstationary trends in the autocorrelation function may be performed as follows.

1. Filter the sample record into c number of contiguous narrow bandwidth frequency intervals, as one would usually do to compute a power spectrum by analog techniques. From the sampling theorems in Section 5.4.1, the data in each narrow frequency interval of bandwidth B_e will be statistically independent of the data in adjacent frequency intervals as long as the intervals do not overlap and $B_e > 1/T_r$, where T_r is the sample record length.

2. Divide each narrow bandwidth sample record into N equal time intervals as before.

3. Compute a mean square value for each time interval of each frequency interval, and align these sample values in time sequence, as follows,

$$\overline{x_{11}^2},\, \overline{x_{12}^2},\, \overline{x_{13}^2},\, \ldots,\, \overline{x_{1N}^2}$$

$$\overline{x_{21}^2},\, \overline{x_{22}^2},\, \overline{x_{23}^2},\, \ldots,\, \overline{x_{2N}^2}$$

$$\ldots \ldots \ldots \ldots \ldots$$

$$\overline{x_{c1}^2},\, \overline{x_{c2}^2},\, \overline{x_{c3}^2},\, \ldots,\, \overline{x_{cN}^2}$$

Note that there will be cN sample mean square values. Furthermore, except for those values in the first frequency interval including $f = 0$, the sample values will actually be variances. The values in the first frequency interval will include the effect of a nonzero mean value.

4. Test the time sequence of mean square values in each frequency interval for the presence of underlying trends or variations, as before. A total of c tests will be required, plus one additional test if it is desired to test the mean value separately.

The final tests may be accomplished by one of the nonparametric procedures previously discussed. In this case, however, c separate tests must be performed where a rejection of the stationary hypothesis for any one test constitutes a rejection of stationarity for the data. This fact requires careful interpretation of the Type I Error associated with the overall testing procedure. Specifically, if the probability of a Type I Error is α' for the test of each frequency interval, the probability of a Type I Error for the overall test is

$$\alpha = 1 - (1 - \alpha')^c \qquad (5.153)$$

Hence if a Type I Error probability of α is desired for the overall test, then each of the c frequency intervals must be tested at the α' level of significance where

$$\alpha' = 1 - (1 - \alpha)^{1/c} \qquad (5.154)$$

This last procedure will detect time trends in the power spectrum for the data. Since the power spectral density function and autocorrelation function are Fourier transform pairs, time invariance of one directly implies time invariance of the other.

5.6.2 Tests for Randomness

If random data have passed a test for stationarity, then a test for randomness effectively reduces to a test for the presence of sinusoids due to periodic or almost-periodic components in the data. If such sinusoidal components are intense, their presence is usually obvious. However, less intense sinusoidal components in random data may not be so obvious. The most effective procedures for detecting periodic components are those associated with the various analysis procedures which would be employed for random data analysis anyway. Hence, in practical terms, a test for randomness usually evolves from analysis procedures which would be performed assuming the data are random. Specifically, the presence of sinusoidal components in otherwise random data may often be detected by visual inspection of a power spectral density function, an amplitude probability density function, and/or an autocorrelation function measured from stationary data, as discussed in Chapter 1.

To illustrate how a power spectrum can reveal the presence of a sinusoidal component in otherwise random data, refer to Figure 5.11. In this example, the output of a random noise generator was mixed with a sinusoidal signal. The sinusoidal signal was given an rms amplitude equal to one-twentieth of that of the random signal. Plot A, which was made using a relatively wide filter bandwidth, gives little or no indication of the presence of the sinusoid. Plot B, which was made using one-fifth of the previous filter bandwidth, indicates a possible sinusoid quite clearly. Plot C,

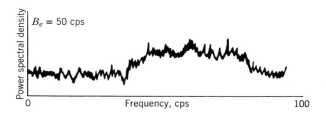

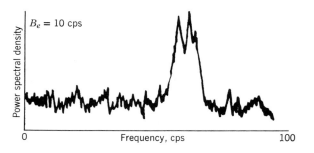

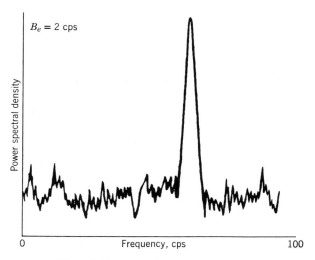

Figure 5.11   Actual power spectra plots.

which was made using a filter bandwidth reduced by another factor of 5, gives a strong indication.

Figure 5.11 illustrates how a highly resolved spectrum will reveal periodic components as sharp peaks, even when the periodicities are of relatively small intensity. A sharp peak in the power spectrum for sample data, however, may also represent narrow-band random data. These two cases can sometimes be distinguished from one another by repeating the power spectral density measurement with the narrowest available analyzer filter bandwidth. If the measured spectral peak represents a sine wave, the indicated bandwidth of the peak will always be equal to the bandwidth of the analyzer filter, no matter how narrow the filter. This method of detection will clearly not work unless the bandwidth for the narrowest analyzer filter is smaller than the bandwidth for possible narrow-band random data. It is also necessary that the available sample record be sufficiently long to make $B_e T_r \gg 1$. Otherwise, uncertainties in the spectral measurements of the random portions of the data will produce spurious peaks which may obscure the peak caused by the sine wave.

The presence of sinusoidal components in otherwise random data may also be revealed by an amplitude probability density function for the data. The probability density plots for sinusoidal and random data are markedly different, as illustrated in Figure 1.13. A random signal will usually have a probability density function which at least resembles the familiar bell-shaped Gaussian characteristic, whereas a sine wave has a dish-shaped probability density function. A mixture of the two takes on prominent characteristics of both. The problem with this procedure is that the sinusoidal component must be fairly intense relative to the random portion of the data before its presence is obvious from the probability density plot. Generally speaking, the presence of the sine wave is difficult to identify if the rms value of the sine wave is less than twice the rms value of the random portion of the data. Furthermore, the presence of more than one sine wave can produce probability density results which are difficult to distinguish from random data. Of course, both these problems can be minimized by filtering the data to isolate single suspicious peaks for probability density analysis.

The most powerful method of detecting sinusoidal components in otherwise random data is presented by an autocorrelogram. For any purely random data, the autocorrelation function will always approach a value equal to the square of the mean value as the time displacement becomes large. On the other hand, the autocorrelation function for a sine wave or collection of sine waves will continue to oscillate no matter how large the time displacement becomes. This fact is illustrated in Figure 1.15.

5.6.3   Tests for Normality

Perhaps the most obvious way to test samples of stationary random data for normality is to measure a probability density function for the data and compare it to the theoretical normal distribution. If the sample record is sufficiently long to permit a measurement with small error compared to the deviations from normality, the lack of normality will be obvious. If the sampling distribution for the probability density estimate is known, a parametric test for normality can be performed even when the statistical error is large. Such parametric tests are outlined and illustrated in Ref. 5, Sec. 17. However, as for stationarity testing discussed in Section 5.6.1, a knowledge of the sampling distribution for probability density measurements requires frequency information for the data which may be difficult to obtain in practical cases. Hence a nonparametric test is desirable.

One of the most convenient nonparametric tests for normality is the chi-square goodness-of-fit test outlined in Section 4.6. This test must be applied to discrete sample values representing the random data of interest. Where the data are being analyzed by digital techniques, no problem exists since the data are already in the form of discrete sample values. For analog data analysis, however, the data must be converted into a digital form to apply the test. The details of applying the chi-square goodness-of-fit test with a numerical illustration are presented in Example 4.7.

5.6.4   Tests for Equivalence

Consider the case where one is given two or more sample records of random data and must determine if the samples were obtained from the same random variable. This problem is basically the same as that of determining whether or not data are stationary, as discussed in Section 5.6.1. In fact, the same basic assumptions outlined in Section 5.6.1 must be used here if a practical test for equivalence is to be formulated. That is, the problem must be reduced to one of detecting differences in mean values and mean square (or variance) values.

The most convenient and direct procedures for testing the equivalence of a collection of sample values are the analysis of variance procedures discussed in Section 4.7. These procedures assume that the sample values being analyzed are normally distributed. However, no knowledge of the mean value or variance of the sampling distribution is required. For the case of sample mean values, the normality assumption is reasonably valid no matter what probability density function the basic random variable has, because of the practical implications of the Central Limit Theorem. The normality assumption for sample mean square values is not strictly valid since, as a general rule, squared random variables are not normally distributed. For example, mean square measurements of normally distributed data have a chi-square sampling distribution, as discussed in Section 4.3.2. In spite of this fact, experience indicates that analysis of variance procedures will yield reasonable results even for mean square (or variance) values if the number of degrees of freedom for the measurement is greater than, say, $n = 2BT = 10$.

Assume that a collection of r sample records is collected for analysis. The sample records may be tested for equivalence by analysis of variance procedures as follows.

1. Divide each of the r sample records into c equal intervals where the data in each interval may be considered independent. The same restrictions noted for the stationary test in Step 1 of Section 5.6.1 apply here.
2. Compute the mean value and mean square value (or variance) for each interval of each record, and align these sample values in a two-way array with time in one direction and record number in the other. For example, the array for sample mean values would be as follows.

$\bar{x}_{11}$	$\bar{x}_{12}$	$\bar{x}_{13}$	—	$\bar{x}_{1c}$
$\bar{x}_{21}$	$\bar{x}_{22}$	$\bar{x}_{23}$	—	$\bar{x}_{2c}$
—	—	—	—	—
$\bar{x}_{r1}$	$\bar{x}_{r2}$	$\bar{x}_{r3}$	—	$\bar{x}_{rc}$

3. Test the arrays of sample mean and mean square (or variance) values for equivalence or variations other than those due to expected sampling variations.

The final test is accomplished by performing the analysis of variance computations outlined in Section 4.7. Note that the procedure recommended here involves only one observation per combination. Multiple observations per combination could be used if desired by simply dividing each sample interval into subintervals. Also, if the data being used have already been tested for stationarity, then only a one-way analysis of variance test (between rows) is required. Note that a test for stationarity and equivalence can be performed simultaneously on such data by using a two-way analysis of variance test.

5.6.5 Equivalence of Power Spectra

The previous section discusses the use of analysis of variance procedures to test selected properties of a collection of records for equivalence. One of the most common problems of interest in this area is the equivalence of power spectra (or autocorrelation functions) for two sample records. A useful technique for this special application will now be described.

An estimate $\hat{G}(f)$ of a power spectral density function $G(f)$ will have a sampling distribution which is approximately normal if the number of degrees of freedom, n, is large, say $n \geq 30$. It is shown in Section 5.3.5 that the sample mean value and variance are given by

$$E[\hat{G}(f)] \approx G(f) \tag{5.155}$$

$$\text{Var}\,[\hat{G}(f)] \approx \frac{2}{n}\,G^2(f) \tag{5.156}$$

Hence a $1 - \alpha$ confidence interval for $G(f)$ based on a measurement $\hat{G}(f)$ may be approximated by

$$[\hat{G}(f)\big(1 - z_{\alpha/2}\sqrt{2/n}\big) \leq G(f) \leq \hat{G}(f)\big(1 + z_{\alpha/2}\sqrt{2/n}\big)] \tag{5.157}$$

where $z_{\alpha/2}$ is the $100\alpha/2$ percentage point of the standardized normal distribution. To arrive at Eq. (5.157), it is assumed that $z_{\alpha/2}\sqrt{2/n} \ll 1$, so that

$$\big(1 \pm z_{\alpha/2}\sqrt{2/n}\big)^{-1} \approx 1 \mp z_{\alpha/2}\sqrt{2/n} \tag{5.158}$$

A logarithmic transformation of the estimate $\hat{G}(f)$ to $\log \hat{G}(f)$ has the effect of producing a distribution which is closer to normal than the original distribution. The sample mean value and variance for $\log \hat{G}(f)$ become

$$E[\log \hat{G}(f)] \approx \log G(f) \tag{5.159}$$
$$\text{Var}[\log \hat{G}(f)] \approx 2/n \tag{5.160}$$

Thus the variance here is independent of frequency. Now, a $1 - \alpha$ confidence interval for $\log G(f)$ may be approximated by

$$[\log \hat{G}(f) - z_{\alpha/2}\sqrt{2/n} \leq \log G(f) \leq \log \hat{G}(f) + z_{\alpha/2}\sqrt{2/n}\,] \tag{5.161}$$

This result can be derived directly from Eq. (5.157) to provide a heuristic explanation for Eqs. (5.159) and (5.160). This derivation uses the assumption that $z_{\alpha/2}\sqrt{2/n} \ll 1$, so that

$$\log\big(1 \pm z_{\alpha/2}\sqrt{2/n}\big) \approx \pm z_{\alpha/2}\sqrt{2/n} \tag{5.162}$$

Consider now two different power spectral density function estimates $\hat{G}_1(f)$ and $\hat{G}_2(f)$ obtained under different conditions, for example, from two different sample records or from two different parts of the same sample record. The problem is to decide whether or not these two power spectra are statistically equivalent over some frequency interval (f_a, f_b) of bandwidth $B = f_b - f_a$.

Assume each of the two power spectral density function estimates is based upon a resolution bandwidth B_e where N_f number of bandwidths are needed to cover the frequency range of interest. That is,

$$N_f = \frac{B}{B_e} \tag{5.163}$$

Further assume the degrees of freedom for each estimate are n_1 and n_2, respectively, meaning that the averaging time (record length) for each estimate may be different even though the resolution bandwidth is the same. From Eqs. (5.159) and (5.160), the sampling distributions for the logarithm of the estimates in the ith bandwidth are approximated by

$$\log \hat{G}_1(f_i) = y \left[\log G_1(f_i), \frac{2}{n_1} \right]$$
$$\log \hat{G}_2(f_i) = y \left[\log G_2(f_i), \frac{2}{n_2} \right] \tag{5.164}$$

where $y[\mu, \sigma^2]$ is a normally distributed random variable with a mean of μ and a variance of σ^2.

Now, if the two sample records in question have the same power spectral density function $G(f) = G_1(f) = G_2(f)$, it follows from Eqs. (5.164) that

$$\log \frac{\hat{G}_1(f_i)}{\hat{G}_2(f_i)} = y \left[0, \frac{2}{n_1} + \frac{2}{n_2} \right] \tag{5.165}$$

Hence the statistic

$$D = \left[N_f \left(\frac{2}{n_1} + \frac{2}{n_2} \right) \right]^{-\frac{1}{2}} \sum_{i=1}^{N_f} \log \frac{\hat{G}_1(f_i)}{\hat{G}_2(f_i)} \tag{5.166}$$

has a standardized normal distribution z. That is,

$$D = y[0, 1] = z \tag{5.167}$$

The result in Eq. (5.167) provides a basis to test the hypothesis that $G_1(f) = G_2(f)$. The region of acceptance for the hypothesis test is

$$[-z_{\alpha/2} \le D \le z_{\alpha/2}] \tag{5.168}$$

where α is the level of significance for the test.

To illustrate this last expression for a level of significance of $\alpha = 0.01$, the acceptance region for a hypothesis that $G_1(f) = G_2(f)$ is given from Table 4.7 by

$$[-2.58 \le D \le 2.58]$$

Hence if D falls inside the range $(-2.58, 2.58)$, the hypothesis that $G_1(f) = G_2(f)$ would be accepted. If D falls outside this range, however, the hypothesis would be rejected with a knowledge that there is a 1 per cent risk that this decision is wrong.

5.7 Multiple-Input Linear System Measurements

Theoretical models for analyzing multiple-input linear systems are discussed in Section 3.5 where two-sided spectral quantities $S(f)$ are used.

These results are valid when the $S(f)$ are replaced by corresponding one-sided measurable spectral quantities $G(f)$. In order to emphasize features of actual measured data and its errors, all formulas will now be stated in terms of $G(f)$.

5.7.1 Multiple Coherence Functions

Consider a collection of q clearly defined inputs $x_i(t)$; $i = 1, 2, \ldots, q$, and one output $y(t)$, as pictured in Figure 5.12. Let $G_i(f) = G_{ii}(f)$ be the

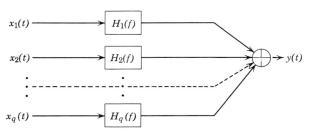

Figure 5.12 Multiple-input linear system.

power spectral density function for $x_i(t)$, and $G_{ij}(f)$ be the cross-spectral density function between $x_i(t)$ and $x_j(t)$. Define the $N \times N$ spectral matrix by

$$\mathbf{G}_{xx}(f) = \begin{bmatrix} G_{11}(f) & G_{12}(f) & \cdots & G_{1q}(f) \\ G_{21}(f) & G_{22}(f) & & G_{2q}(f) \\ \cdot & & & \\ \cdot & & & \\ \cdot & & & \\ G_{q1}(f) & G_{q2}(f) & & G_{qq}(f) \end{bmatrix} \qquad (5.169)$$

The *ordinary coherence function* between $x_i(f)$ and $x_j(t)$ is defined by

$$\gamma_{ij}^2(f) = \frac{|G_{ij}(f)|^2}{G_i(f)\,G_j(f)} \qquad (5.170)$$

The *multiple coherence function* between $x_i(t)$ and all other inputs $x_1(t)$, $x_2(t), \ldots$, excluding $x_i(t)$, is defined by

$$\gamma_{i.x}^2(f) = 1 - [G_i(f)\,G^i(f)]^{-1} \qquad (5.171)$$

where $G^i(f)$ denotes the ith diagonal element of the inverse matrix $[\mathbf{G}_{xx}(f)]^{-1}$ associated with Eq. (5.169). The ordinary and multiple coherence functions are both real-valued quantities which are bounded by zero and unity. That is,

$$0 \le \gamma_{ij}^2(f) \le 1$$
$$0 \le \gamma_{i.x}^2(f) \le 1 \tag{5.172}$$

An augmented $(q + 1, q + 1)$ spectral matrix can also be defined, as in Eq. (3.238), and a multiple coherence function defined between the output $y(t)$ and all of the inputs $x_i(t)$, as per Eq. (5.171). This multiple coherence function, denoted by $\gamma_{y.x}^2(f)$, will also be bounded by zero and unity.

Physical interpretations of the ordinary coherence function are stated in Section 3.4.2, showing how this function measures the linear relationship between the time histories of two different input points. Similarly, the multiple coherence function is a measure of the linear relationship between the time history at one point, and the time histories at the collection of other points. That is, the multiple coherence function indicates whether or not the data at all of the other points linearly produce the results at a given point. Detailed theoretical developments and discussions of multiple coherence functions, as well as other types of partial (conditional) and marginal coherence functions, are presented in Ref. 17. In particular, a *partial coherence function*, as defined in Sections 3.5.6 and 3.5.7, is a multiple coherence function computed from a residual (conditioned) spectral matrix. The importance of multiple coherence functions is demonstrated in later material in this section dealing with variability errors for estimating multiple-input frequency response functions when the inputs are coherent.

Confidence limits for multiple coherence functions in terms of sample multiple coherence functions have been derived empirically in Reference 13 which are applied by following the procedure discussed in Section 5.4.7. For multiple coherence functions, the transformed normal distribution has a mean value $\mu_q(f)$ and variance σ_q^2 given by

$$\mu_q(f) = \frac{q}{(n - 2q)} + \tanh^{-1} \gamma_{i.x}(f)$$

$$\sigma_q^2 = \frac{1}{(n - 2q)} \qquad n = 2B_e T \tag{5.173}$$

where q = number of inputs, and $n = 2B_e T$ is the number of degrees of freedom for the spectral density measurements, as defined in Eq. (5.114). Note that the number of inputs plus the single output is $(q + 1)$. For the special case where $q = 1$, the single input–single output case, Eq. (5.173) reduces to Eq. (5.140).

5.7.2 Multiple Incoherent Input Case

Consider an ideal multiple-input linear system where the output $y(t)$ is due to q incoherent inputs $x_i(t)$; $i = 1, 2, \ldots, q$, as illustrated in Figure 5.12.

From Eq. (3.171), for incoherent inputs, the frequency response function between any measured input point and the output point can be estimated at any frequency f by

$$\hat{H}_i(f) = \frac{\hat{G}_{iy}(f)}{\hat{G}_i(f)} \qquad i = 1, 2, \ldots, q \tag{5.174}$$

This equation is identical in form to the single input–single output case of Eq. (5.130). Hence, from the viewpoint of estimating frequency response functions, the multiple incoherent input case is the same as the single-input case.

The specific assumptions required to obtain an unbiased estimate of the true frequency response function from Eq. (5.174) are as follows:

(a) The system between the various input points and the output point is a constant parameter linear system.

(b) The power spectral and cross-spectral density measurements, $\hat{G}_i(f)$ and $\hat{G}_{iy}(f)$, are unbiased.

(c) The measurement at each input is noise-free (extraneous noise at the output is no problem).

(d) The inputs contributing to the measured output are incoherent.

5.7.3 Multiple Coherent Input Case

Consider now the case where the q inputs in Figure 5.12 may be coherent with one another. From Eq. (3.183), the frequency response function $\hat{H}_i(f)$ between each input point and the output point can be estimated from the matrix relation

$$
\begin{bmatrix}
\hat{H}_1(f) \\
\hat{H}_2(f) \\
\cdot \\
\cdot \\
\cdot \\
\hat{H}_q(f)
\end{bmatrix}
=
\begin{bmatrix}
\hat{G}_{11}(f) & \hat{G}_{12}(f) & \cdots & \hat{G}_{1q}(f) \\
\hat{G}_{21}(f) & \hat{G}_{22}(f) & & \hat{G}_{2q}(f) \\
\cdot \\
\cdot \\
\cdot \\
\hat{G}_{q1}(f) & \hat{G}_{q2}(f) & & \hat{G}_{qq}(f)
\end{bmatrix}^{-1}
\begin{bmatrix}
\hat{G}_{1y}(f) \\
\hat{G}_{2y}(f) \\
\cdot \\
\cdot \\
\cdot \\
\hat{G}_{qy}(f)
\end{bmatrix}
\tag{5.175}
$$

For the special case where the inputs are incoherent, the square matrix reduces to a diagonal matrix, whose inverse is such that Eq. (5.175) becomes a set of independent equations, as given by Eq. (5.174). Hence Eq. (5.175) represents the general form of the relationship needed to compute frequency response functions from measured input-output data.

The specific assumptions required to obtain unbiased estimates of the true frequency response functions from Eq. (5.175) are:

(a) The system between the various input points and the output point is a constant parameter linear system.

(b) The power spectral and cross-spectral density measurements, $\hat{G}_{ij}(f)$ and $\hat{G}_{iy}(f)$, are unbiased.

(c) The measurement at each input is noise-free (extraneous noise at the output is no problem).

(d) All inputs which contribute to the output are measured.

5.7.4 Bias Errors

The estimation of frequency response functions will generally involve a bias (systematic) error as well as a variability (random) error. The bias error results from failure to comply with theoretical assumptions required by the estimation procedure. The variability error results from computing desired quantities using finite samples of data and from the presence of extraneous noise.

The first assumption in computing frequency response functions is that the system between any two measurement points is a constant parameter linear system, as defined and discussed in Chapter 2. Even when the constant parameter part is acceptable, the linearity part may be unacceptable over a wide operating range. An important point is that when these procedures are applied to nonlinear systems, the result is a *"best" linear approximation* for the frequency response function under the specified input conditions. This fact constitutes an important advantage to estimating frequency response functions from actual data rather than from laboratory or simulated data which do not reproduce the actual input conditions.

The second assumption is that the spectral density measurements are unbiased, meaning that the estimates are obtained by a "properly resolved" narrow-band analysis. A spectrum analysis may be considered properly resolved if the analyzer filter bandwidth (or the spectral window for a digital computation) is sufficiently narrow to define each individual peak in the spectral density function of interest. Appropriate analog and digital procedures are discussed in Chapters 6 and 7.

The third assumption deals with the effects of extraneous measurement noise at the input or output, as considered previously in Section 5.4.7. For the multiple incoherent input case, using Eq. (5.174), the gain factor estimate $|\hat{H}_i(f)|$ will be biased such that

$$\frac{E[|\hat{H}_i(f)|]}{|H_i(f)|} = \left[1 + \frac{G_{n_i}(f)}{G_{u_i}(f)}\right]^{-1} \qquad i = 1, 2, \ldots, q \qquad (5.176)$$

where $|H_i(f)|$ = true gain factor between input i and output

$G_{u_i}(f)$ = desired signal spectrum at input i

$G_{n_i}(f)$ = extraneous noise spectrum at input i

Note that the gain factor estimate will be unbiased if $G_{n_i}(f) = 0$, and that extraneous noise at the output is of no concern. The phase factor estimate here will be unbiased independent of extraneous noise either at the input or at the output.

For the multiple coherent case, the problem is more complicated and difficult to analyze because all inputs must be considered which contribute to the output. However, it can be stated that the bias due to unmeasured inputs and/or measurement noise will diminish as the multiple coherence function $\gamma_{y \cdot x}^2(f)$ between the output $y(t)$ and the measured inputs $x_i(t)$ approaches unity. If all inputs contributing to $y(t)$ are accounted for, all input measurements are noise-free, and all transmission paths are constant parameter linear systems, then $\gamma_{y \cdot x}^2(f) = 1$. Hence the value of this multiple coherence function can be used as a measure of the joint validity of the assumptions involved in applying Eq. (5.175).

5.7.5 Variability Errors

The variability of frequency response function estimates is dependent upon the ordinary and multiple coherence between the spectral measurements, as defined in Eqs. (5.170) and (5.171), and the number of degrees of freedom, n, for each spectral measurement, as defined in Eq. (5.114). The variability associated with estimates of the gain factor and phase factor will now be summarized for the multiple incoherent input case and the multiple coherent input case.

Multiple Incoherent Input Case. Assume that the frequency response functions in a multiple incoherent input case are obtained using Eq. (5.174), and that the bias in these estimates is negligible. If the various inputs (known and unknown) are incoherent, the effect of inputs other than the one of interest is the same as the presence of extraneous measurement noise in the output. Such extraneous noise at the output, plus finite sample lengths, introduces a variability error into the estimate of each frequency response function.

From Ref. 17, assuming negligible bias error, the $1 - \alpha$ confidence intervals for the true gain factor $|H_i(f)|$ and true phase factor $\phi_i(f)$ are given at each frequency f, and for each $i = 1, 2, \ldots, q$, by

$$\begin{cases} |\hat{H}_i(f)| - \hat{r}_i(f) \leq |H_i(f)| \leq |\hat{H}_i(f)| + \hat{r}_i(f) \\ \hat{\phi}_i(f) - \Delta\hat{\phi}_i(f) \leq \phi_i(f) \leq \hat{\phi}_i(f) + \Delta\hat{\phi}_i(f) \end{cases} \tag{5.177}$$

where the radial error $\hat{r}_i(f)$ and phase error $\Delta\hat{\phi}_i(f)$ are calculated from

$$\hat{r}_i^2(f) = \frac{2}{n-2}(F_{n_1, n_2; \alpha})[1 - \hat{\gamma}_{yi}^2(f)]\frac{\hat{G}_y(f)}{\hat{G}_i(f)} \tag{5.178}$$

$$\Delta\hat{\phi}_i(f) = \sin^{-1}\left[\frac{r_i(f)}{|\hat{H}_i(f)|}\right] \tag{5.179}$$

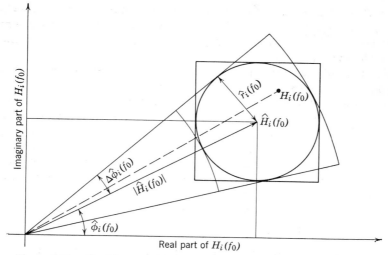

Figure 5.13 Confidence region for frequency response function estimate.

Note that Eq. (5.178) gives the square of the radial error. The various quantities in these equations are

$n = 2B_eT =$ number of degrees of freedom of each spectral estimate

$F_{n_1, n_2; \alpha} =$ 100α percentage point of an F distribution with $n_1 = 2$ and $n_2 = n - 2$ degrees of freedom

$\hat{G}_i(f) =$ power spectrum estimate for the input $x_i(t)$

$\hat{G}_y(f) =$ power spectrum estimate for the output $y(t)$

$\hat{\gamma}_{yi}^2(f) =$ sample estimate of the ordinary coherence function between $y(t)$ and $x_i(t)$

These equations show that the accuracy in estimating frequency response functions improves as $\hat{r}_i(f)$ approaches zero. This improved accuracy occurs for incoherent input cases when:

1. The number of degrees of freedom n increases
2. The ordinary coherence estimate $\hat{\gamma}_{yi}^2(f)$ approaches unity
3. The input spectral density estimate $\hat{G}_i(f)$ increases
4. The output spectral density estimate $\hat{G}_y(f)$ decreases.

A polar diagram for the confidence region represented by Eq. (5.177) is shown in Figure 5.13 at frequency f_0. Different regions apply to each estimated frequency response function $\hat{H}_i(f_0)$ for which different $\hat{r}_i(f_0)$ and $\Delta\hat{\phi}_i(f_0)$ are calculated.

Example 5.7.   Assume a gain factor of 1.25 is estimated at a given frequency f_0 between an input $x(t)$ and an output $y(t)$. Suppose that the respective power spectral density functions are measured as $\hat{G}_x(f_0) = 0.13$ and $\hat{G}_y(f_0) = 0.28$, with $\hat{\gamma}_{yx}^2 = 0.70$. Assume the number of degrees of freedom $n = 100$. Determine a 99 per cent confidence interval for the true gain factor at this frequency, assuming the bias error is negligible.

For this example, $n_1 = 2$ and $n_2 = 98$ degrees of freedom. From Table 4.10(c), for a $1 - \alpha = 0.99$ confidence interval,

$$F_{2,98;\,0.01} = 4.82$$

It follows from Eq. (5.178) that

$$\hat{r}_i^2(f_0) = \left(\frac{2}{98}\right)(4.82)(0.3)\left(\frac{0.28}{0.13}\right) = 0.063$$

and

$$\hat{r}_i(f_0) = 0.25$$

Thus the 99 per cent confidence interval for the gain factor is

$$1.00 \le |H(f_0)| \le 1.50$$

In the absence of noise in the input spectral measurement $\hat{G}_x(f_0)$, this will represent the 99 per cent confidence interval about the unbiased gain factor.

Multiple Coherent Input Case. Assume the frequency response functions in a multiple coherent input case are obtained using Eq. (5.175), and that the bias in these estimates is negligible. Extraneous measurement noise is permitted at the output. Suppose further that possibly some of the inputs contributing to the output have not been measured. The effect of this extraneous noise and unmeasured inputs, plus finite sample lengths, is to introduce a variability error (over and above a possible bias error) into the frequency response function estimates.

From Ref. 17, assuming negligible bias error, the $1 - \alpha$ confidence intervals for the true gain factor $|H_i(f)|$ and true phase factor $\phi_i(f)$ are given at each frequency f by Eqs. (5.177)–(5.179), except that Eq. (5.178) is replaced by

$$\hat{r}_i^2(f) = \frac{2q}{n - 2q}\,(F_{n_1,n_2;\,\alpha})\,\frac{[1 - \hat{\gamma}_{y\cdot x}^2(f)]\hat{G}_y(f)}{[1 - \hat{\gamma}_{i\cdot x}^2(f)]\hat{G}_i(f)} \qquad (5.180)$$

where
q = number of inputs (excluding output)
$n = 2B_e T$ = number of degrees of freedom of each spectral estimate
$F_{n_1,n_2;\alpha}$ = 100α percentage point of an F distribution with $n_1 = 2q$ and $n_2 = n - 2q$ degrees of freedom
$\hat{G}_i(f)$ = power spectrum estimate for the input $x_i(t)$
$\hat{G}_y(f)$ = power spectrum estimate for the output $y(t)$
$\hat{\gamma}_{y\cdot x}^2(f)$ = sample estimate of the multiple coherence function between the output $y(t)$, and all the measured inputs

$\hat{\gamma}_{i.x}^2(f)$ = sample estimate of the multiple coherence function between the input $x_i(t)$, and the other measured inputs excluding $x_i(t)$, as defined by Eq. (5.171)

The accuracy in estimating frequency response functions for coherent input cases improves when:

1. The number of degrees of freedom n increases for a given value of q
2. The multiple coherence estimate $\hat{\gamma}_{y.x}^2(f)$ approaches unity
3. The multiple coherence estimate $\hat{\gamma}_{i.x}^2(f)$ approaches zero
4. The input power spectral density estimate $\hat{G}_i(f)$ increases
5. The output power spectral density estimate $\hat{G}_y(f)$ decreases.

Example 5.8.   Consider an eight input–single output system. Assume a phase factor of 1.94 radians is estimated at a given frequency f_0 between an input $x_i(t)$ and the output $y(t)$, and the corresponding gain factor estimate is 3.20. Suppose the number of degrees of freedom $n = 100$ and the sample estimates $\hat{G}_i(f_0) = 0.11$, $\hat{G}_y(f_0) = 0.82$, $\hat{\gamma}_{y.x}^2(f_0) = 0.90$ and $\hat{\gamma}_{i.x}^2(f_0) = 0.85$. Determine a 95 per cent confidence interval for the true phase factor at this frequency, assuming the bias error is negligible.

For the example, $q = 8$, $n_1 = 16$, $n_2 = 84$ and $\alpha = 0.05$. From Table 4.10(a),

$$F_{16.84;0.05} = 1.77$$

It follows from Eq. (5.180) that

$$\hat{r}_i^2(f_0) = \left(\frac{16}{84}\right)(1.77)\left(\frac{0.10}{0.15}\right)\left(\frac{0.82}{0.11}\right) = 1.67$$

and

$$\hat{r}_i(f_0) = 1.29$$

Then, from Eq. (5.179),

$$\Delta\hat{\phi}_i(f) = \sin^{-1}\left(\frac{1.29}{3.20}\right) = 0.42 \text{ radian}$$

Thus the 95 per cent confidence interval for the true phase factor in radians is

$$1.52 \leq \phi(f_0) \leq 2.36$$

6

ANALOG MEASUREMENT
TECHNIQUES

In many cases, the pertinent data for a physical phenomenon of interest are obtained in the form of a continuous time-varying electrical voltage signal from an appropriate transducer. The amplitude of the transducer output signal is such that it is proportional to the instantaneous value of some parameter of the physical phenomenon of interest. For example, the transducer signal might represent the time history of a structural stress, ocean wave height, vibration displacement, EEG voltage, or communication signal voltage. However, the actual physical parameter represented by the analog signal from the transducer is of no direct concern to the physical procedures of data reduction and analysis. When the pertinent data are available in the form of an analog voltage time history signal, measurements may be performed directly on the signal using electrical and electronic instruments.

As noted earlier, a rudimentary measure of intensity for a stationary random signal is given by the mean square value. A more detailed description of the stationary signal is given in the amplitude domain by a probability density function, in the time domain by an autocorrelation function, and in the frequency domain by a power spectral density function. If two or more stationary random signal records are available, additional information may be obtained from a joint probability density function, a cross-correlation function, and a cross-spectral density function. The basic analog instruments and techniques for measuring these properties from sample records of stationary random data will now be discussed. The basic digital techniques for similar as well as more extensive data reduction and analysis are presented in Chapter 7. Techniques for analyzing nonstationary random data are discussed in Chapter 9.

It should be noted that some of the practical details of the analysis procedures included in this chapter are not rigorous or absolute. In many cases, these details constitute only recommendations based upon the practical experience of the authors and others. Each such recommendation is accompanied by appropriate discussions and qualitative justifications. Nevertheless, the specific applications for the analyzed data or the specific characteristics of the actual instruments used for the analysis may often warrant deviations from the suggested procedures.

6.1 Mean and Mean Square Value Measurements

6.1.1 Basic Instrument Requirements

Mean Values. Given a sample voltage time history record $x(t)$ from a stationary random signal, the mean value μ_x for the signal may be estimated from Eq. (5.10) as follows.

$$\hat{\mu}_x = \frac{1}{T}\int_0^T x(t)\,dt \qquad (6.1)$$

In words, the mean value is estimated by simply averaging the instantaneous value of the signal over the sampling time T.

This operation is accomplished by a direct current voltmeter, which will be called a DC voltmeter for convenience. In general, a DC voltmeter consists of a simple averaging circuit followed by a readout device. The required average may be accomplished in one of two ways. The first approach is to feed the signal into a true integrating circuit (operational amplifier with feedback condenser) which computes, when divided by the sampling time, a one-number average value for the signal after a specific time interval T. This procedure, which will be called true averaging, is a direct functional representation of the mathematical averaging operation defined in Eq. (6.1). The second approach is to feed the signal into a low-pass filter (usually of the RC type) which continuously smooths the signal fluctuations to produce, after three of four RC time constants have elapsed, a continuous estimate for the average value of the signal. This procedure, which will be called RC averaging, is a practical implementation of the mathematical averaging operation defined in Eq. (6.1).

Mean Square Values. The mean square value Ψ_x^2 for the signal may be estimated from Eq. (5.24) as follows.

$$\hat{\Psi}_x^2 = \frac{1}{T}\int_0^T x^2(t)\,dt \qquad (6.2)$$

In words, the mean square value is estimated by the following operations: (1) squaring of the instantaneous value of the signal; (2) averaging the squared instantaneous value over the sampling time. An estimate of the root mean square (rms) value may be obtained by taking the square root of the measured mean square value.

The preceding operations are accomplished by a true mean square (or root mean square) voltmeter, which will be called a TMS voltmeter for convenience. One type of TMS voltmeter in current use instantaneously squares the voltage of the applied signal using a detector with a square law characteristic. The squared voltage signal is time-averaged using either true averaging or RC averaging. When an rms value is desired, the required square root may be accomplished by a proper readout scale calibration. Other types of TMS voltmeters use detectors which compute rms values directly.

6.1.2 Practical Voltmeter Considerations

The mean value of a voltage signal is a measure of the static portion of the signal whereas the variance is a measure of the dynamic portion of the signal. The mean square value is a measure of both static and dynamic portions, as given by the previously derived relationship

$$\Psi_x^2 = \sigma_x^2 + \mu_x^2 \tag{6.3}$$

In many cases, it is necessary to measure the mean square value of a signal by measuring the static (mean value) and dynamic (variance) portions separately. This is true because voltmeters with desirable frequency response characteristics for high-frequency measurements often do not possess DC response capabilities. The measurements produced by such instruments are really variance or standard deviation measurements, although they are usually referred to as mean square or rms measurements.

It should be mentioned that many commercial voltmeters have scales which are calibrated to read the rms voltage of a *sinusoidal* signal, but which do not actually measure the rms voltage of the applied signal. These instruments usually consist of a simple rectifier followed by an equivalent low-pass smoothing filter such that a quantity proportional to either the mean absolute value (average rectified value) or peak value of the applied signal is measured. Note that the mean absolute value $\overline{|x|}$ is defined as follows.

$$\overline{|x|} = \frac{1}{T} \int_0^T |x(t)| \, dt \tag{6.4}$$

For either a peak or mean absolute value measurement, a readout in terms of the rms value of a sine wave may be obtained by a proper readout scale calibration. This is easy to accomplish since the peak, mean absolute, and rms values for a sine wave have fixed relationships to one another.

Assuming the mean value μ_x is zero, these relationships are as follows.

Instantaneous value, $x(t) = X \sin 2\pi f t$

Peak value $X = X$

Mean absolute value, $\overline{|x|} = \dfrac{2}{\pi} X$ (6.5)

Root mean square value, $\Psi_x = \dfrac{1}{\sqrt{2}} X$

Commercial instruments often take advantage of these relationships because peak or mean absolute voltage detection circuits are much cheaper to build than true rms voltage detection circuits. Such instruments are usually called AC voltmeters to indicate that they are usable for only AC (sinusoidal) signals. These AC voltmeters will produce inaccurate readings if they are used to measure complex periodic signals or random signals.

6.1.3 Measurement Accuracy

Any voltage measurement will involve basic errors due to the instrument design capabilities and calibration techniques. Such instrument errors are a function of the initial quality of the instrument and its maintenance. However, the measurement of random signal data involves an additional statistical error defined by the mean square error discussed in Section 5.3. This mean square statistical error will generally include a bias term and a variance term (not to be confused with σ_x^2, the variance of the signal). For both mean and mean square value estimates, which are measured using Eqs. (6.1) and (6.2), it is shown in Sections 5.3.1 and 5.3.2 that these measurements will be unbiased (the bias term equals zero). The variance term in both cases is a function of the spectral characteristics of the signal and the sampling time.

For the special case of bandwidth limited Gaussian white noise with a bandwidth of B cps, the statistical error of a mean value measurement is given in terms of the normalized standard error ϵ by Eq. (5.23) as

$$\epsilon = \frac{\text{s.d. } [\hat{\mu}_x]}{\mu_x} \approx \frac{1}{\sqrt{2BT}} \left(\frac{\sigma_x}{\mu_x} \right) \tag{6.6}$$

For mean square value measurements where $\mu_x = 0$, the normalized standard error is given by Eq. (5.35) as

$$\epsilon = \frac{\text{s.d. } [\hat{\Psi}_x^2]}{\Psi_x^2} \approx \frac{1}{\sqrt{BT}} \tag{6.7}$$

If a TMS voltmeter reads out in rms values instead of mean square values, it can be shown that the appropriate expression for the normalized standard error, assuming $\mu_x = 0$, is

$$\epsilon = \frac{\text{s.d. } [\hat{\Psi}'_x]}{\Psi'_x} \approx \frac{1}{2\sqrt{BT}} \tag{6.8}$$

which is one-half the error for mean square value measurements. In these error formulas, T is the equivalent true averaging time for the measurement. The determination of a proper value for T is discussed in the next section.

Consider now the accuracy of mean value measurements. For those cases where ϵ is relatively small, say $\epsilon \leq 0.2$, the sampling distribution for the mean value measurement in question may be approximated by a normal distribution with a mean value of μ_x and a standard deviation of $\epsilon\mu_x$. The following practical interpretation may then be used. Assume a signal with a true mean value of μ_x is repeatedly sampled at different times, and a mean value estimate $\hat{\mu}_x$ is measured from each sample. For about two-thirds of the measurements obtained, the difference between the measured value and the true value would be less than $\pm\epsilon\mu_x$. For about 95 per cent of the measurements obtained, the difference would be less than $\pm 2\epsilon\mu_x$. That is, $|1 - (\hat{\mu}_x/\mu_x)| < 2\epsilon$ for about 95 per cent of all repeated measurements. In terms of a confidence statement, it can be said with about 95 per cent confidence that the true value lies within the interval between $\hat{\mu}_x/(1 + 2\epsilon)$ and $\hat{\mu}_x/(1 - 2\epsilon)$. A similar interpretation applies to mean square value and rms value measurements.

More accurate confidence statements for mean and mean square value measurements can be established by noting that $\hat{\mu}_x = \bar{x}$ actually has a sampling distribution related to the Student t distribution. Also, assuming $\mu_x = 0$, $\hat{\Psi}'^2 = s^2$ actually has a sampling distribution related to the χ^2 distribution. For the special case of bandwidth limited Gaussian white noise, the number of degrees of freedom for the applicable sampling distribution is $n = 2BT$. Chapter 4 contains details and illustrations explaining how to establish proper confidence intervals using the t and χ^2 distributions.

***Example* 6.1.** Assume a mean square value of $\hat{\Psi}'^2_x = 1$ volt^2 is measured from a sample record of a random signal with a mean value of zero and uniform power spectrum within a bandwidth of $B = 100$ cps. Further assume the averaging time for the measurement is $T = 1$ second. Thus, the normalized standard error for the measurement is $\epsilon = 0.10$. In approximate terms, this means that it can be said with about 95 per cent confidence that the true mean square value is between 0.8 and 1.2 volts^2.

In more precise terms, from Section 4.3.2, the measured value $\hat{\Psi}'^2_x$ has a sampling distribution given by

$$\hat{\Psi}'^2_x \sim \frac{\Psi'^2_x \chi^2_n}{n}$$

where $n = 2BT = 200$ degrees of freedom. Hence, from Table 4.8 the 95 per cent confidence interval for the measurement is 0.814 to 1.21 volts². This illustrates that the normal approximation for the 95 per cent confidence interval given by $\Psi_x^2/(1 \pm 2\epsilon)$ is quite accurate when n is large.

6.1.4 Averaging Time

The averaging time T in Eqs. (6.6)–(6.8) is an idealized quantity. That is, T is the time for a true average as indicated by the integration in Eqs. (6.1)–(6.2). In actual practice, this averaging procedure is often accomplished by using a low-pass RC smoothing filter, as mentioned in Section 6.1.1. Furthermore, the available data are usually limited to some sample record of finite length. These factors must be considered in determining an appropriate value for T in Eqs. (6.6)–(6.8).

First, consider a voltmeter which computes an average by performing an integration over a specific time interval T_a (true averaging). The integration time T_a is equivalent to the idealized averaging time T in Eqs. (6.6)–(6.8). However, the value for T can never be longer than the length of the sample time history record obtained for analysis. If the available sample record length is T_r seconds long, the statistical error of the resulting measurement can never be less than the value given by Eqs. (6.6)–(6.8) where $T = T_r$. In other words, nothing is to be gained by averaging over a given amount of information more than once. Hence, for the case of true averaging, the time T in Eqs. (6.6)–(6.8) should actually be

$$T = T_a \qquad \text{for } T_a \leq T_r$$
$$T = T_r \qquad \text{for } T_r < T_a \tag{6.9}$$

where T_a is the true averaging (integration) time and T_r is the sample record length. Clearly, from Eq. (6.9), the most efficient averaging procedure which will minimize the statistical error is to use a true averaging time which is equal to the length of the available sample record.

Now consider a voltmeter which computes an average by smoothing with a low-pass RC filter having a time constant K (RC averaging). An RC averaging filter produces a continuous measurement which at any instant of time represents a time-weighted average of all inputs that have gone before. For purposes of illustration, assume a mean square value is measured using RC averaging. Typical time histories for RC averaged mean square value measurements are illustrated for both periodic and random signals in Figure 6.1.

As seen in Figure 6.1, RC averaging for a steady-state periodic signal will produce an accurate measurement after a time interval equal to about four or five time constants has elapsed, assuming the time constant is longer than the period of the data. For stationary random signals, the measurement will continue to fluctuate after the original rise. These fluctuations are indicative of the statistical error of the measurement at any instant of time. The question is as follows. For any given averaging time constant and record length, what is the appropriate value for T in Eqs. (6.6)–(6.8) to define the error of the continuous RC averaged measurement at any instant of time? This question will now be answered for the case of mean square value measurements.

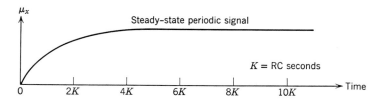

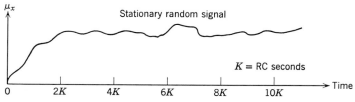

Figure 6.1 Time histories for RC averaged mean square value measurements.

First, consider the case where a mean value for a random signal $y(t)$ is measured by integration over a time interval T as follows.

$$x(T) = \frac{1}{T} \int_0^T y^2(t) \, dt \tag{6.10}$$

The mean and variance for this mean square value measurement are given by

$$\mu_x = E[x(T)] = R_y(0)$$

$$\sigma_x^2 = E[x^2(T)] - \mu_x^2 = \frac{4}{T^2} \int_0^T (T - \tau) R_y^2(\tau) \, d\tau \tag{6.11}$$

Now assume the autocorrelation function $R_y(\tau)$ is given by

$$R_y(\tau) = R_y(0) \, e^{-2B|\tau|} = \mu_x \, e^{-2B|\tau|} \tag{6.12}$$

Here, B is actually equal to an equivalent statistical bandwidth B_s to be defined later, but the subscript s will be dropped for clarity. The normalized mean square error for a measurement $x(T)$ is then

$$\epsilon_x{}^2 = \frac{\sigma_x{}^2}{\mu_x{}^2} = \frac{4}{T^2} \int_0^T (T - \tau)\, e^{-4B|\tau|} \, d\tau$$

$$= \frac{1}{BT} [1 - e^{-4BT}] + \frac{1}{4B^2T^2} [(4BT + 1)\, e^{-4BT} - 1]$$

(6.13)

For the special case of interest where the BT product is relatively large compared to unity, Eq. (6.13) reduces to

$$\epsilon^2 \approx \frac{1}{BT} \qquad \text{for } BT \gg 1$$

(6.14)

Now, consider the case where a mean square value for a random signal $y(t)$ is measured by smoothing the instantaneous squared values with a low-pass RC filter. Let the RC time constant for the smoothing filter be K and the available sample record length be T_r. The mean square value at time T_r is

$$z(K, T_r) = \int_0^{T_r} y^2(t)\, h(T_r - t) \, dt$$

(6.15)

where, for a low-pass RC filter,

$$h(T_r - t) = \frac{1}{K}\, e^{-(T_r-t)/K} \qquad \text{for } (T_r - t) \geq 0$$

The mean and variance for the mean square value $z(K, T_r)$ are given by

$$\mu_z = E[z(K, T_r)] = R_y(0)[1 - e^{-T_r/K}]$$

(6.16a)

$$\sigma_z{}^2 = E[z^2(K, T_r)] - \mu_z{}^2 = \frac{2}{K} \int_0^{T_r} R_y{}^2(\tau)[e^{-\tau/K} - e^{-2T_r/K}\, e^{\tau/K}] \, d\tau$$

(6.16b)

Now, assume as before that the autocorrelation function $R_y(\tau)$ is as given by Eq. (6.12). The variance for the mean square value becomes

$$\sigma_z{}^2 = \frac{2R_y{}^2(0)}{K} \int_0^{T_r} e^{-4B\tau}[e^{-\tau/K} - e^{-2T_r/K}\, e^{\tau/K}] \, d\tau$$

$$= \frac{2R_y{}^2(0)}{K} \left[\frac{1 - e^{-4BT_r}\, e^{-T_r/K}}{4B + (1/K)} + \frac{e^{-4BT_r}\, e^{-T_r/K} - e^{-2T_r/K}}{4B - (1/K)} \right]$$

(6.17)

For the special case where the BK product is relatively large compared to unity, Eq. (6.17) reduces to

$$\sigma_z{}^2 = \frac{R_y{}^2(0)}{2BK} [1 - e^{-2T_r/K}] \qquad \text{for } 4BK \gg 1$$

Hence the normalized variance for a measurement of $z(K, T_r)$ is

$$\epsilon_z^2 = \frac{\sigma_z^2}{\mu_z^2} = \frac{1}{2BK} \left\{ \frac{1 - e^{-2T_r/K}}{[1 - e^{-T_r/K}]^2} \right\} \qquad \text{for } 4BK \gg 1 \qquad (6.18)$$

Equation (6.18) defines the normalized variance for a continuous RC averaged mean square measurement for any given RC averaging time constant and record length. By comparing Eqs. (6.18) and (6.14), an equivalent true averaging time for an RC averaged measurement is obtained as follows

$$T = \frac{2K[1 - e^{-T_r/K}]^2}{[1 - e^{-2T_r/K}]} \qquad (6.19)$$

It can be shown that the above development, when applied to mean value measurements rather than mean square value measurements, will produce the same result presented in Eq. (6.19).

From Eq. (6.19), it is seen that the value for T approaches $2K$ as T_r becomes very long compared to K. Furthermore, by expanding the exponentials, it can be shown that the value for T approaches T_r as K becomes very long compared to T_r. That is

$$\begin{array}{ll} T \approx 2K & \text{for } K \ll T_r \\ T \approx T_r & \text{for } T_r \ll K \end{array} \qquad (6.20)$$

Note that if a mean or mean square value is measured using RC averaging, the resulting measurement generally will be biased as indicated by Eq. (6.16a), which assumes the measurement is computed by viewing the data over one sample record length. This bias error will be substantial for the case where $T_r \leq K$. However, the error can be avoided by forming the sample record into a loop and recirculating the record to obtain a continuous presentation of the data signal. This will allow time for the RC averaging filter to respond fully. After four or five time constants have elapsed, the bias error in the measurement will be negligible. Note that the normalized error expression in Eq. (6.18) still applies to the unbiased estimate obtained by recirculation. This is true because the recirculation effectively changes only a scale factor which does not change the normalized variance of an estimate.

From Eqs. (6.7) and (6.19), the minimum attainable normalized standard error for an RC averaged mean square value measurement is $\epsilon = 1/\sqrt{BT_r}$, which is exactly the same as for a true averaged measurement. Of course, this minimum error can be achieved by RC averaging only in the limit as $K \to \infty$. However, the error approaches the minimum value rapidly as K becomes larger than $T_r/2$. For example, if $K = T_r$, the normalized standard error would be $\epsilon = 1.04\sqrt{BT_r}$, or only 4 per cent greater than the minimum value. Hence very little is to be gained by using an RC averaging time constant which is longer than one sample record length. Note that all of these conclusions apply to mean value measurements as well.

6.2 Probability Density Measurements

6.2.1 Basic Instrument Requirements

Given a sample voltage time history record $x(t)$ from a stationary random signal, the probability density function $p(x)$ for the signal may be estimated from Eq. (5.39) as follows.

$$\hat{p}(x) = \frac{T_x}{TW} \tag{6.21}$$

Here, T_x is the time spent by the signal $x(t)$ within a narrow voltage interval having a width of W volts and a center voltage of x volts. In words, the probability density function is estimated by the following operations.

1. Amplitude filtering of the signal by a narrow amplitude window having a window width of W volts.
2. Measurement of the total time spent by the signal within the window.
3. Averaging of the time spent within the window over the sampling time to obtain the average portion of time spent by the signal within the window.
4. Division of the average portion of the time spent within the window by the window width W.

As the center voltage of the window is moved, a plot of the probability density function versus voltage level is obtained.

The preceding operations are accomplished by an analog amplitude probability density analyzer, which will be called an APD analyzer for convenience. In general, an APD analyzer measures the time spent by a signal within some narrow voltage interval by use of an amplitude window (a pair of Schmidt triggers or similar circuit) which actuates an AND gate on the output of a clock pulse generator. Each time the input signal level from the sample record enters the window, the AND gate opens and passes clock pulses. When the signal level leaves the window, the AND gate closes. This train of pulses from the AND gate is then averaged over the total sampling time to obtain the average portion of time spent by the signal within the window. The required division by the window width W may be obtained by a proper scale calibration. As for voltmeters, the required time averaging may be accomplished by true averaging, or by RC averaging, as discussed in Section 6.1.1. The scan required to cover the voltage range of interest is usually accomplished by shifting the signal in voltage past a fixed amplitude window through mixing the signal with a DC bias voltage.

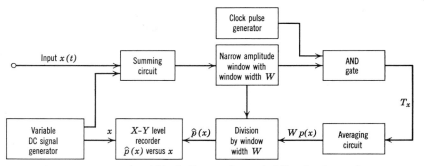

Figure 6.2   Functional block diagram for probability density analyzer.

A functional block diagram for an APD analyzer is shown in Figure 6.2. It should be mentioned that an APD analyzer might be constructed with a collection of contiguous amplitude windows which together cover the voltage range of interest. For this case, no scan would be needed to measure a probability density plot. However, the single-window APD analyzer is far more common in practice.

6.2.2   Statistical Accuracy

The mean square statistical error for probability density function measurements involves both a bias term and a variance term as given by Eq. (5.56). However, if the measurement is properly resolved (to be defined in the next section), the bias term will usually be negligible. The remaining variance term is a function of the spectral characteristics of the signal, the sampling time T, the window width W, and the probability density being measured.

For the special case of bandwidth limited Gaussian white noise with a bandwidth of B cps, the statistical error of a properly resolved probability density measurement is given in terms of the normalized standard error ϵ by Eq. (5.62) as

$$\epsilon = \frac{\text{s.d. } [\hat{p}(x)]}{p(x)} \approx \frac{A_1}{\sqrt{BTW \, \hat{p}(x)}} \tag{6.22}$$

Here, W is the amplitude window width relative to the signal rms value, T is the equivalent true averaging time in seconds, and A_1 is some constant. Theoretical results as well as digital computer studies in Ref. 26 indicate that a value of $A_1 = 0.7$ should be conservative. Experimental results in Ref. 5 indicate that $A_1 = 0.15$ is appropriate for analog instruments with RC averaging when T is replaced by K in Eq. (6.22).

The exact sampling distribution for probability density measurements is unknown. However, for $\epsilon \leq 0.2$, a normal distribution with a mean value of $p(x)$ and a standard deviation of $\epsilon\, p(x)$ is an acceptable approximation. The practical interpretation for ϵ is as discussed in Section 6.1.3.

Example 6.2. Assume a probability density function is to be measured for a random signal with a mean value of zero and a uniform power spectrum within a bandwidth of $B = 1000$ cps. Further assume it is desired to make measurements at signal levels out to three times the rms value with a normalized standard error of 20 per cent ($\epsilon = 0.20$). If the APD analyzer to be used has a window width of one-tenth the signal rms value, what is the required length for the sample data record? Assume $A_1 = 0.7$ in Eq. (6.22).

The maximum requirements for data are generally posed by the measurements at the largest signal level of interest. From Table 4.6, if it is assumed that the random signal in question is approximately Gaussian, the probability density for the signal at three times the rms value would be about $p[x = 3\Psi_x] = 0.0044$. Here, $\Psi_x = \sigma_x$ since $\mu_x = 0$. Using this value in Eq. (6.22) and solving for the averaging time T, the following result is obtained:

$$ T = \frac{A_1{}^2}{p[x = 3\sigma_x]WB\epsilon^2} = \frac{0.5}{(0.0044)(0.1)(1000)(0.04)} \approx 28 \text{ seconds} $$

Hence a sample record length of at least 28 seconds would be required to obtain results with less than a 20 per cent statistical error for levels out to three times the rms value. Note that the measurements with this accuracy out to four times the rms value would require over 20 minutes of data. Of course, this sample record length will permit far more accurate measurements than indicated by $\epsilon = 0.20$ for levels less than the extreme limits. This is true because, for most actual random phenomena, the value of $\hat{p}(x)$ in the denominator of Eq. (6.22) will become larger as x becomes smaller.

6.2.3 Measurement Resolution

It is seen in Eq. (6.22) that the statistical error of probability density measurements is inversely proportional to the width of the amplitude window. One might then conclude that reduced error can easily be obtained by simply increasing the window width. However, increasing the window width reduces the resolution of the analysis, that is, it reduces the ability of the analysis to properly define abrupt changes in the probability density plot. In more quantitative terms, it increases the contribution of the bias term in the general mean square error formula given by Eq. (5.62).

The maximum window width that will permit acceptable measurement resolution is clearly a function of the exact probability density function for the specific random signal being analyzed. However, for the probability density functions which are approximately Gaussian, it can be shown from

Eq. (5.62) that a window width less than one-fifth of the standard deviation for the data will produce resolution with a bias error of less than 1 per cent of reading for measurements out to three standard deviations. Hence, a reasonable resolution criterion is

$$W \leq \tfrac{1}{5}\sigma_x \qquad (6.23)$$

where W is the amplitude window width in volts, and σ_x is the standard deviation of the signal being analyzed in volts.

6.2.4 Averaging Time

Actual APD analyzers may perform the required time average in Eq. (6.21) either by an integration for a specific time interval T_a (true averaging) or by smoothing with a low-pass RC filter (RC averaging). If the APD analyzer employs an integrator to perform the time average, then the requirements of Eq. (6.9) apply. A precise relationship for the case of RC averaging is not known. However, experience indicates that an averaging time constant of $K = T_r$ provides a measurement with near minimum error, after four or five time constants have elapsed, just as for voltmeter measurements. This means, of course, that the sample record must be formed into a loop and recirculated for continuous presentation so that the RC averaging filter will have an opportunity to respond fully to the information on the sample record.

There are two general approaches that one might take to the selection of an averaging time for a probability density analysis. The first approach is to select an averaging time that will maintain a constant statistical error. Referring to Eq. (6.22), this would generally require an averaging time which varies with the value of the probability density being measured. This approach could theoretically reduce the time required to perform an analysis, as will be discussed in the next section. However, the practical problems associated with continually changing the averaging time during an analysis tend to limit its desirability.

The second approach is to always use an averaging time which is as long as the available sample record so that minimum statistical errors are obtained for all probability density values. Although this approach technically results in a longer total analysis time, it is very easy to implement in practice since the averaging time for a given analysis is constant. In line with this second approach, if true averaging is employed, the integration time should be set approximately equal to the sample record length. If RC averaging is employed, it is recommended that the time constant for the RC averaging filter be set equal to the sample record length. That is,

$$T_a = T_r \qquad \text{for true averaging} \qquad (6.24a)$$

$$K = T_r \qquad \text{for RC averaging} \qquad (6.24b)$$

where T_a is the true averaging (integration) time in seconds, T_r is the sample record length in seconds, and K is the RC averaging time constant in seconds.

The suggested averaging times in Eq. (6.24) assume the available sample record is of limited length T_r. There are sometimes situations where the available sample record is effectively unlimited. For example, the sample record of interest might be the output of a noise generator which can be permitted to operate as long as desired. For this case, the selection of an averaging time should be accomplished like the selection of a required record length, as illustrated in Example 6.2.

6.2.5   Scan Rate and Analysis Time

For a multiple window APD analyzer, the probability density at all signal levels of interest would be concurrently measured. This means that the analysis time would effectively be equal to the averaging time T. For a single window APD analyzer, however, the probability density at all signal levels of interest must be measured by scanning through the desired range of values with the single amplitude window while the data are continually displayed for analysis be recirculation of the sample record. The required scan may be accomplished either by discrete steps of the window or by a continuous sweep of the window. A stepped scan is often used with true averaging, whereas a continuous scan is normally used with RC averaging. In either case, if the scan rate is too fast, unnecessary errors will be introduced into the analysis.

For the case of true averaging, the scan rate should be sufficiently slow to permit all information at each signal level to be reflected in each average value computation. That is, the scan rate should be less than one window width per averaging time. Hence the basic scan rate limitation for true averaged probability density measurements is

$$R_s \leq \frac{W}{T_a} \tag{6.25a}$$

where T_a is the true averaging (integration) time in seconds, W is the amplitude window width in volts, and R_s is the scan rate in volts per second.

For the case of RC averaging, the scan rate must be sufficiently slow to allow the RC averaging filter to respond to abrupt changes in the probability density function, as illustrated in Figure 6.1. Otherwise, the RC averaging filter will tend to smooth or fair through abrupt probability density changes producing a bias error. For the worst case of a step change in the probability density function, this bias error will be less than 2 per cent of reading after four RC time constants have elapsed. It follows that each incremental amplitude level must be viewed through the window for at least four RC time constants if this worst-case error of less than 2 per cent is to be achieved. Hence, a recommended conservative scan rate limitation for RC averaged probability density measurements is

$$R_s \leq \frac{W}{4K} \tag{6.25b}$$

where K is the RC averaging time constant in seconds and W is the amplitude window width in volts. Of course, a more rapid scan rate can be used if one is prepared to accept a greater bias error, or if variations in the probability density function are less abrupt. For example, experimental studies on a digital computer indicate that the maximum bias error induced by scanning a Gaussian probability density function from minus three standard deviations to plus three standard deviations is about 3 per cent of reading for a scan rate of $R_s = W/2K$. The maximum error rises to about 10 per cent of reading for a scan rate of $R_s = W/K$.

Assuming it is desired to minimize the statistical error, the averaging time relationships presented in Eq. (6.24) can be substituted into Eq. (6.25) to obtain the maximum scan rate as a function of the sample record length with the following results. For the case of true averaging, $R_s \leq W/T_r$ since $T_a = T_r$ for minimum statistical error. For the case of RC averaging, $R_s \leq W/4T_r$ since $K = T_r$ is recommended.

Now consider the total required analysis time. If the total voltage range for an APD analysis is V volts, then it follows from Eq. (6.25) that the minimum analysis time would be

$$T_s \geq \begin{cases} \dfrac{T_a V}{W} & \text{for true averaging} \tag{6.26a} \\[3mm] \dfrac{4KV}{W} & \text{for RC averaging} \tag{6.26b} \end{cases}$$

***Example* 6.3.**   Assume the probability density function for a random signal with a mean value of zero and an rms value of 1 volt is to be estimated from a sample record of length $T_r = 30$ seconds over a range of values from -3 volts to $+3$ volts ($V = 6$ volts) using an APD analyzer with a window width of $W = 0.1$ volt. If true averaging is used, $T_a = 30$ seconds and the maximum scan rate is $R_s = 0.0033$ volt per second. Hence the minimum analysis time would be $T_s = 1800$ seconds, or 30 minutes. If RC averaging is used, $K = 30$ seconds and the maximum recommended scan rate is $R_s = 0.0008$ volt per second. Hence the minimum analysis time would be $T_s = 7200$ seconds or 2 hours.

6.3   Autocorrelation Measurements

6.3.1   Basic Instrument Requirements

Given a sample voltage time history record $x(t)$ from a stationary random signal, the autocorrelation function $R_x(\tau)$ for the signal may be estimated from Eq. (5.65) as follows.

$$\hat{R}_x(\tau) = \frac{1}{T} \int_0^T x(t)\, x(t + \tau)\, dt \qquad (6.27)$$

In words, the autocorrelation function is estimated by the following operations.

1. Delaying the signal by a time displacement equal to τ seconds, called the lag time.
2. Multiplying the signal value at any instant by the value that had occurred τ seconds before.
3. Averaging the instantaneous product value over the sampling time.

As the lag time is moved, a plot of the autocorrelation function versus lag time (autocorrelogram) is obtained.

The preceding operations are accomplished by an analog autocorrelation function analyzer, which will be called an ACF analyzer for convenience. In general, an ACF analyzer displaces the signal in time by use of a magnetic signal recorder with a variable lag time between the record and playback. This can be accomplished, for example, with a magnetic drum recorder where the location of the playback head is variable relative to the location of the record head. The input and output of the lag time generator are then multiplied and time-averaged. The required time average may be accomplished either by true averaging or by RC averaging, as discussed in Section 6.1.1. The lag time is variable over a range from zero to the longest sampling times that are anticipated. Since the autocorrelation function is an even function, it is not necessary to make measurements with negative lag times. A functional block diagram for an ACF analyzer is shown in Figure 6.3. As for the case of APD analyzers discussed in Section 6.2.1, an ACF analyzer might be constructed with a collection of equally spaced lag time generators which together cover the time displacement range of interest. For this case, no lag time scan would be needed to measure the autocorrelogram. Note that the estimate $\hat{R}_x(\tau)$ actually obtained in Figure 6.3 is the average of $x(t - \tau)x(t)$ which equals the average of $x(t)\, x(t + \tau)$ for stationary signals.

6.3.2 Statistical Accuracy

The mean square statistical error for autocorrelation function measurements involves only a variance term as given by Eq. (5.75). That is, the bias term is equal to zero, assuming the available sample record length $T_r \geq T + \tau$. The variance term is a function of the spectral characteristics of the signal, the sampling time T, and the autocorrelation value being measured.

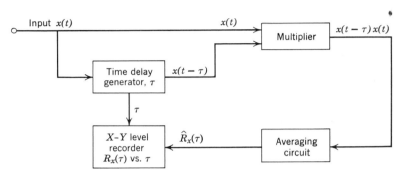

Figure 6.3   Functional block diagram for autocorrelation analyzer.

For the special case of bandwidth limited Gaussian white noise with a bandwidth of B cps, the statistical error of an autocorrelation function measurement is given in terms of the normalized standard error ϵ by Eq. (5.78) as

$$\epsilon = \frac{\text{s.d. } [\hat{R}_x(\tau)]}{R_x(\tau)} \approx \frac{1}{\sqrt{2BT}}\left(1 + \frac{R_x^2(0)}{R_x^2(\tau)}\right)^{1/2} \tag{6.28}$$

where T is the equivalent true averaging time in seconds.

The exact sampling distribution for autocorrelation function measurements is well defined only for zero lag time where $\hat{R}_x(0) = \hat{\Psi}_x^2$. However, for $\epsilon \leq 0.2$, the normal approximation discussed in Section 6.1.3 can be used to establish approximate confidence intervals.

***Example* 6.4.**   Assume an autocorrelation function is to be measured for a random signal with a Gaussian probability density function and a uniform power spectrum within a bandwidth of $B = 1000$ cps. Further assume it is desired to make measurements of correlation values down to 10 per cent of the maximum value with a normalized standard error of 10 per cent or $\epsilon = 0.10$. What is the required length for the sample data record?

The maximum requirements for data are posed by the measurements at the smallest autocorrelation values of interest. For this problem, the smallest value of interest is $R_x(\tau) = 0.10R_x(0)$. Using this value in Eq. (6.28), and solving for the averaging time T, the following result is obtained.

$$T = \frac{1 + R_x^2(0)/R_x^2(\tau)}{2B\epsilon^2} = \frac{101}{2(1000)(0.01)} = 5.05 \text{ seconds}$$

Hence a sample record length of at least 5 seconds would be required to obtain results with less than a 10 per cent error for correlation values down to 10 per cent of the maximum value. This sample record length will, of course, permit more accurate measurements than indicated by $\epsilon = 0.10$ for correlation values greater than $0.10R_x(0)$ since the correlation function $R_x(\tau)$ appears in the denominator of Eq. (6.28).

6.3.3   Measurement Resolution

As seen from Eq. (6.27), the autocorrelation function $R_x(\tau)$ must be estimated at various different lag times τ to obtain a correlogram. This may be accomplished in one of two ways. The first way is to measure a correlation value with the lag time fixed at a specific time displacement of interest. The lag time would then be changed to a new time displacement and the correlation value would again be measured. This stepped scan procedure is usually employed by ACF analyzers which incorporate an integration type averaging circuit so that the resulting correlogram will appear as a series of discrete correlation values measured at specific lag times. The second way is to measure correlation values while the lag time is continuously varied through the time displacement range of interest. This continuous scan procedure is normally employed by ACF analyzers which incorporate an RC averaging circuit, so that a continuous correlogram is obtained.

For the first method involving a stepped scan, the interval between the lag times determines how well the correlation function is resolved. As the interval is made smaller, the resolution of the measured correlogram will be improved. However, the number of correlation measurements required to cover a given time displacement range will be increased. Hence the selection of a lag time interval will always involve a compromise between measurement resolution and analysis time. The maximum permissible interval which can be employed for any given analysis is, of course, a function of the exact correlogram for the specific random signal being analyzed. For general applications, however, it can be said that at least two correlation values per cycle are needed to define data at any given frequency. This follows directly from the fact that correlation functions and power spectral density functions are Fourier transform pairs. Thus, a minimum resolution criterion for autocorrelation measurements is given by

$$h \leq \frac{1}{2f_m} \tag{6.29}$$

where h is the interval between lag times in seconds and f_m is the maximum frequency of significant data in cps.

For the second method involving a continuous scan lag time, a slightly different interpretation of measurement resolution is required. This procedure produces a continuous correlogram (assuming RC averaging is used) where correlation values appear to be defined for every lag time over the time displacement range of the analysis. However, the value at any given lag time is actually a time-weighted average of the correlation characteristics at all lag times that had been previously scanned. These effects tend to smooth out rapid changes in the correlogram and thus introduce a bias error which reduces the resolution of the measurement. As the lag time scan rate is made slower, the resolution of the measured correlogram will be improved. However, as for the case of measurements at discrete lag times, the analysis time will be increased producing the same requirement for a compromise between measurement resolution and analysis time. The maximum permissible scan rate which can be employed while maintaining acceptable resolution is discussed in Section 6.3.5.

6.3.4 Averaging Time

The general discussions and relationships for averaging time presented for probability density measurements in Section 6.2.4 also apply for autocorrelation measurements. More specifically, the most practical approach to autocorrelation analysis is to select an averaging time which is as long as the available sample record so that minimum statistical errors are obtained for all correlation values. Hence, the integration time for true averaging or the time constant for RC averaging should be as given in Eq. (6.24). If the available sample record length is unlimited, the selection of an averaging time should be accomplished like the selection of a required sample record length, as illustrated in Example 6.4.

6.3.5 Scan Rate and Analysis Time

For a multiple lag time ACF analyzer, the autocorrelation functions at all time displacements of interest would be concurrently measured. This means that the analysis time would effectively be equal to the averaging time T. However, for a single lag time ACF analyzer, the autocorrelation function at various time displacements of interest must be measured by scanning with a single lag time generator while the sample record is continuously recirculated. If this scan is too fast, unnecessary errors will be introduced into the analysis.

For a stepped scan where true averaging is used, if all the information at each time delay is to be reflected in the measurement, the scan rate must clearly be limited to one lag time per averaging time. Hence the basic scan rate limitation for a stepped scan with true averaging is

$$R_s \leq \frac{h}{T_a} \tag{6.30a}$$

where T_a is the true averaging (integration) time in seconds, h is the interval between lag times in seconds, and R_s is the scan rate in seconds per second.

For a continuous scan where RC averaging is used, if abrupt changes in the correlation function are to be accurately detailed for an equivalent resolution interval of h, it is suggested that the scan rate be limited to one resolution interval per four time constants for the reasons given in Section 6.2.5. Hence the recommended scan rate limitation for a continuous scan with RC averaging is

$$R_s \leq \frac{h}{4K} \tag{6.30b}$$

where K is the RC averaging time in seconds and h is the desired resolution interval in seconds.

Assuming it is desired to minimize the statistical error, the averaging time relationships presented in Eq. (6.24) can be substituted into Eq. (6.30) to obtain the maximum scan rate as a function of the sample record length with the following results. For the case of true averaging, $R_s \leq h/T_r$ since $T_a = T_r$ for minimum error. For the case of RC averaging, $R_s \leq h/4T_r$ since $K = T_r$ is recommended.

Now consider the total required analysis time. If the total lag time range for an ACF analysis is D seconds, then it follows from Eq. (6.30) that the minimum analysis time would be

$$T_s \geq \begin{cases} T_a D/h & \text{for true averaging} \tag{6.31a} \\ 4KD/h & \text{for RC averaging} \tag{6.31b} \end{cases}$$

Example 6.5. Assume the autocorrelation function for a random signal is to be estimated from a sample record of length $T_r = 5$ seconds over a time displacement range of 0 to 0.5 second ($D = 0.5$ second), where time displacements down to $h = 0.0025$ second are to be resolved. If true averaging is used, $T_a = 5$ seconds and the maximum scan rate is $R_s = 0.0005$ second/second. Hence, the minimum analysis time would be $T_s = 1000$ seconds or about 17 minutes. If RC averaging is used, $K = 5$ seconds and the recommended maximum scan rate is $R_s = 0.000125$ second/second. Hence the minimum analysis time would be $T_s = 4000$ seconds or about 1.1 hours.

6.4 Power Spectral Density Measurements

6.4.1 Basic Instrument Requirements

Given a sample voltage time history record $x(t)$ from a stationary random signal, the power spectral density function $G_x(f)$ for the signal may be estimated from Eq. (5.82) as follows.

$$\hat{G}_x(f) = \frac{1}{B_e T} \int_0^T x^2(t, f, B_e)\, dt \qquad (6.32)$$

Here, $x(t, f, B_e)$ is that portion of $x(t)$ passed by a narrow band-pass filter with a bandwidth of B_e cps and a center frequency of f cps. In words, the power spectral density function is estimated by the following operations.

1. Frequency filtering of the signal by a narrow band-pass filter having a bandwidth of B_e cps.
2. Squaring of the instantaneous value of the filtered signal.
3. Averaging the squared instantaneous value over the sampling time.
4. Division of the mean square output by the bandwidth B_e.

As the center frequency of the narrow band-pass filter is moved, a plot of the power spectral density function versus frequency (power spectrum) is obtained.

The preceding operations are accomplished by an analog power spectral density analyzer, which will be called a PSD analyzer for convenience. Most PSD analyzers perform the filtering operation by heterodyning the input data signal past a highly selective narrow band-pass filter with a fixed center frequency. The mean square value computation is effectively equivalent to a TMS voltmeter measurement as discussed in Section 6.1.1. The required division by the bandwidth B_e may be obtained by a proper scale calibration. A functional block diagram for a PSD analyzer is shown in Figure 6.4. As for the case of APD and ACF analyzers discussed in Sections 6.2.1 and 6.3.1, a PSD analyzer can be constructed with a collection of contiguous narrow band-pass filters which together cover the frequency range of interest. For this case, no frequency scan would be needed to measure a power spectrum. Such multiple filter PSD analyzers are widely used in practice.

It should be mentioned that a PSD analyzer is nothing more than a common harmonic wave analyzer with a TMS voltmeter circuit. The conventional harmonic wave analyzer usually employs a simple AC voltmeter circuit which computes a mean absolute value for the filtered signal. If one is prepared to make definite assumptions concerning the probability density function for the signal to be analyzed, the use of a conventional wave analyzer as a PSD analyzer is possible.

More specifically, assume the random signal to be analyzed has a Gaussian probability density function. Further assume a power spectrum is to be measured using an instrument which computes a mean absolute value as given by Eq. (6.4). For a Gaussian density function with zero

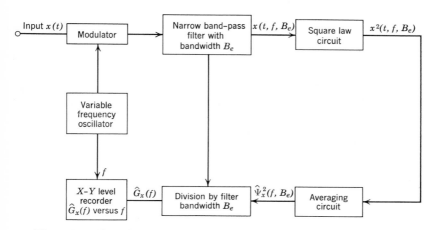

Figure 6.4   Functional block diagram for power spectral density analyzer.

mean, the mean absolute value is

$$\overline{|x|} = \frac{2\sqrt{2}}{\pi} \hat{\Psi}'_x \tag{6.33}$$

It follows that the power spectral density function may be estimated from Eq. (6.32) as follows.

$$\hat{G}_x(f) = \frac{\pi^2}{8B_e} \left(\overline{|x(f, B_e)|} \right)^2 \tag{6.34}$$

For a constant bandwidth analysis, the coefficient $\pi^2/(8B_e)$ is simply a calibration constant. The required square of the mean absolute value $\overline{|x|}$ may be obtained by an appropriate readout scale calibration. In fact, if the analyzer output is passed through a logarithmic converter, the squaring may be accomplished by a proper adjustment of the readout sensitivity.

One problem with this procedure is that the Gaussian assumption must be reasonably valid. As the data deviates from the ideal Gaussian form, the ratio of the rms to the mean absolute value changes and the conversion factor in Eq. (6.33) becomes inaccurate. This problem has been considered by many investigators in the past. The general consensus is that a mean square value measurement capability for a PSD analyzer is not a compelling necessity, but is still very desirable because it does eliminate a possible error from the analysis procedure and simplifies the calibration.

6.4.2 Statistical Accuracy

The mean square statistical error for power spectral density function measurements involves both a bias term and a variance term, as given by Eq. (5.97). However, if the measurement is properly resolved (to be defined in the next section), the bias term will usually be negligible. The remaining variance term is a function of the analyzer filter bandwidth B_e and the sampling time T. Specifically, the statistical error of a properly resolved power spectral density measurement is given in terms of the normalized standard error ϵ by Eq. (5.104) as

$$\epsilon = \frac{\text{s.d. } [\hat{G}_x(f)]}{G_x(f)} \approx \frac{1}{\sqrt{B_e T}} \tag{6.35}$$

Here, B_e is the bandwidth of the analyzer narrow bandwidth filter in cps and T is the equivalent true averaging time in seconds.

Since power spectral density measurements are effectively mean square value measurements, the appropriate sampling distribution is as discussed and illustrated in Example 6.1. For this case, however, the bandwidth of interest is the filter bandwidth B_e rather than the entire signal bandwidth B. Hence the number of degrees of freedom for the applicable χ^2 sampling distribution is $n = 2B_e T$. This fact makes accuracy statements for power spectral density measurements far more practical than for other types of measurements since the bandwidth B_e is always well defined. Additional discussion of this bandwidth term is presented in Section 6.4.6.

Example **6.6.** Assume a power spectrum is to be measured for a random signal with a normalized standard error of 20 per cent ($\epsilon = 0.20$). If the PSD analyzer to be used has a filter bandwidth of $B_e = 5$ cps, what is the required length for the sample data record?

The maximum requirements for data are a function only of the PSD analyzer filter bandwidth. Using Eq. (6.35) and solving for the averaging time T, the following result is obtained:

$$T = \frac{1}{B_e \epsilon^2} = \frac{1}{(5)(0.04)} = 5 \text{ seconds}$$

Hence a sample record of at least 5 seconds would be required to obtain results with less than 20 per cent statistical error at any given center frequency.

6.4.3 Measurement Resolution

It is seen from Eq. (6.35) that the statistical error of power spectral density estimates is inversely proportional to the bandwidth of the analyzer filter. It appears that the measurement error can easily be reduced by simply increasing the filter bandwidth. However, increasing the filter bandwidth reduces the resolution of the analysis by increasing the contribution of the bias term in the general mean square error formula given by Eq. (5.104). Hence, the selection of a PSD analyzer filter bandwidth involves the same considerations that apply for the selection of an APD analyzer amplitude window width, as discussed in Section 6.2.3. For the case of power spectral density analysis, however, the problem is even more critical since a power spectrum of common random data is more likely to display abrupt changes and sharp peaks than a probability density plot.

A practical resolution criterion for power spectral density measurements of narrow bandwidth random data representing the resonant response of simple systems has been studied theoretically and experimentally in Ref. 15. That reference, along with experience, indicates that a reasonable criterion for acceptable resolution in practice is an analyzer filter bandwidth that is one-fourth the bandwidth of the narrowest peak in the power spectrum being measured. That is,

$$B_e < \tfrac{1}{4} B_{sr} \qquad (6.36)$$

where B_e is the analyzer filter bandwidth in cps and B_{sr} is the half-power point bandwidth of a power spectral density peak in cps. This criterion should limit bias errors to less than about 3 per cent when measuring power spectra for most physically meaningful random data, assuming $B_e T \gg 1$. Further discussions of the resolution problem and alternate filter bandwidth selection criteria are presented in Section 6.4.7.

6.4.4 Averaging Time

The general discussions and relationships for averaging time presented for voltmeter measurements in Section 6.1.4 also apply for power spectral density measurements. Specifically, if true averaging is used, the integration time should be set equal to the sample record length. If RC averaging is used, it is recommended that the time constant for the RC averaging filter be set equal to the sample record length for the reasons outlined in Section 6.1.4. That is,

$$T_a = T_r \qquad \text{for true averaging} \qquad (6.37a)$$

$$K = T_r \qquad \text{for RC averaging} \qquad (6.37b)$$

where T_a is the true averaging (integration) time in seconds, T_r is the sample record length in seconds, and K is the RC averaging time constant in seconds.

The recommended averaging times in Eq. (6.37) will produce measurements with the same statistical error at all frequencies, as long as the PSD analyzer filter bandwidth is not changed. There are situations in actual practice, however, where it is desirable to change the filter bandwidth during an analysis. As discussed in Chapter 2, the frequency response functions for physical systems often display sharp peaks with frequency bandwidths that are proportional to the center frequency of the peak. Because the response power spectrum for a physical system is proportional to the square of the frequency response function magnitude (gain factor), these constant percentage bandwidth peaks tend to appear in random signals representing the response of such systems. Referring to Eq. (6.36), it follows that the bandwidth B_e for a power spectral density analysis can often be increased in direct proportion to the frequency of the analysis while still maintaining proper measurement resolution. The result will be increased measurement accuracy at higher frequencies. Another approach is to maintain a constant measurement accuracy by reducing the averaging time as the analysis frequency increases. This second approach can significantly reduce the total required analysis time as will be seen in the next section.

6.4.5   Scan Rate and Analysis Time

The scan rate considerations for a power spectral density analysis are exactly the same as discussed for a probability density analysis in Section 6.2.5, except the frequency bandwidth B_e replaces the amplitude window width W. Hence, the basic scan rate limitation for power spectral density measurements is

$$R_s \leq \begin{cases} B_e/T_a & \text{for true averaging} \qquad (6.38a) \\ B_e/4K & \text{for RC averaging} \qquad (6.38b) \end{cases}$$

where T_a is the true averaging (integration) time in seconds, K is the RC averaging time constant in seconds, B_e is the analyzer filter bandwidth in cps, and R_s is the scan rate in cps per second.

Note that there is an additional scan rate restriction imposed by the required rise time of the narrow band-pass analyzer filter. The rise time for an ideal band-pass filter of bandwidth B_e is about $T_e = 1/B_e$ seconds. This means that the scan rate must be restricted to less than $B_e/T_e = B_e^2$ cps/second if the analyzer filter is to respond fully to abrupt changes in the power spectrum being analyzed. Comparing this relationship to the scan rate restriction given by Eq. (6.38), it is seen that Eq. (6.38) is always more restrictive if the B_eT product is greater than unity. Since the B_eT product in practice must be greater than unity if reasonable accuracy is to be achieved in the measurements, the restrictions given by Eq. (6.38) will apply and the B_e^2 scan rate restriction can be ignored.

Assuming it is desired to minimize the statistical error, the averaging time relationships presented in Eq. (6.37) can be substituted into Eq. (6.38) to obtain the maximum scan rate as a function of the sample record length with the following results. For the case of true averaging, $R_s \leq B_e/T_r$ since $T_a = T_r$ for minimum error. For the case of RC averaging, $R_s \leq B_e/4T_r$ since $K = T_r$ to be within 4 per cent of minimum statistical error.

Now consider the total required analysis time. If the total frequency range for a PSD analysis is F cps, then it follows from Eq. (6.38) that the minimum analysis time would be as follows.

$$T_s \geq \begin{cases} T_aF/B_e & \text{for true averaging} & (6.39a) \\ 4KF/B_e & \text{for RC averaging} & (6.39b) \end{cases}$$

Example 6.7. Assume the power spectrum for a random signal is to be estimated from a sample record of length $T_r = 5$ seconds over a frequency range from 10 to 1000 cps ($F = 990$ cps) using a PSD analyzer with a filter bandwidth of $B_e = 5$ cps. If true averaging is used, $T_a = 5$ seconds and the maximum scan rate is $R_s = 1.0$ cps per second. Hence the minimum analysis time would be $T_s = 990$ seconds or 16.5 minutes. If RC averaging is used, $K = 5$ seconds and the maximum recommended scan rate is $R_s = 0.25$ cps per second. This gives a minimum analysis time of $T_s = 3960$ seconds or 66 minutes.

Consider the case where the analyzer filter bandwidth is changed during the analysis in a manner which maintains proper resolution. Let the bandwidth be changed to $B_e = 10$ cps when the center frequency reaches 100 cps, to $B_e = 20$ cps when the center frequency reaches 200 cps, and to $B_e = 50$ cps when the center frequency reaches 500 cps. The frequency range of the spectrum analysis has now been broken up into four subranges, each scanned with a different bandwidth. Assuming the averaging time is not changed, and that true averaging is used, the maximum scan rate for each subrange is as follows.

$B_1 = 5$ cps	$F_1 = 90$ cps	$R_{s1} = 1.0$ cps/sec
$B_2 = 10$ cps	$F_2 = 100$ cps	$R_{s2} = 2.0$ cps/sec
$B_3 = 20$ cps	$F_3 = 300$ cps	$R_{s3} = 4.0$ cps/sec
$B_4 = 50$ cps	$F_4 = 500$ cps	$R_{s4} = 10.0$ cps/sec

The total analysis time would be

$$T_s = \frac{F_1}{R_{s1}} + \frac{F_2}{R_{s2}} + \frac{F_3}{R_{s3}} + \frac{F_4}{R_{s4}} = 90 + 50 + 75 + 50 = 265 \text{ seconds}$$

The total analysis time is now 265 seconds or less than 5 minutes, compared to 16.5 minutes for the analysis with a constant bandwidth of $B_e = 5$ cps.

Finally, consider the case where the analysis averaging time is changed when the bandwidth is changed. Assume that a normalized standard error of $\epsilon = 1/\sqrt{B_e T_a} = 0.20$ is acceptable for the entire analysis. Then, the maximum scan rate for each subrange is as follows.

$$
\begin{array}{lll}
B_1 = \;\; 5 \text{ cps} & T_{a1} = 5 \quad \text{sec} & R_{s1} = \quad\;\; 1.0 \text{ cps/sec} \\
B_2 = 10 \text{ cps} & T_{a2} = 2.5 \;\; \text{sec} & R_{s2} = \quad\;\; 4.0 \text{ cps/sec} \\
B_3 = 20 \text{ cps} & T_{a3} = 1.25 \text{ sec} & R_{s3} = \quad 16.0 \text{ cps/sec} \\
B_4 = 50 \text{ cps} & T_{a4} = 0.5 \;\; \text{sec} & R_{s4} = 100.0 \text{ cps/sec}
\end{array}
$$

The total analysis time would now be $T_s \approx 139$ seconds or only about 2.3 minutes. These examples clearly illustrate how proper analyzer filter bandwidth selections and averaging times can greatly reduce the time required to perform a power spectral density analysis. Note that additional reduction in analysis time can often be achieved by expanding the frequency range of the data, as discussed in Section 6.4.7.

6.4.6 Frequency Bandwidth Considerations

From Eq. (6.32), it is seen that a knowledge of the PSD analyzer filter bandwidth is required to obtain accurate power spectral density measurements. Furthermore, from Eq. (6.35), the value of the filter bandwidth influences the normalized standard error for the measurement. The bandwidth B_e in these equations is an idealized quantity, that is, B_e is the bandwidth of a narrow band-pass filter which is assumed to have a perfect rectangular band-pass characteristic. The narrow band-pass filters in PSD analyzers do not have such perfect characteristics. Hence, given an actual PSD analyzer filter, the following question arises. What is the proper value for the bandwidth in Eqs. (6.32) and (6.35)? The answer to this question will now be discussed.

The frequency bandwidth of a narrow band-pass filter may be described in many different ways. It is appropriate here to define and clarify three different descriptions for bandwidth which are of interest to the power spectral density measurement problem. These three bandwidths are the *half-power point bandwidth* B_r, the *noise bandwidth* B_n, and the *equivalent statistical bandwidth* B_s. Given any linear filter with a frequency response function of $H(f)$, these three frequency bandwidth terms are defined mathematically as follows.

half power $$B_r = f_2 - f_1 \qquad \text{where } |H(f_1)|^2 = |H(f_2)|^2 = \tfrac{1}{2}|H_m|^2 \qquad (6.40a)$$

noise $$B_n = \frac{\displaystyle\int_0^\infty |H(f)|^2 \, df}{|H_m|^2} \qquad (6.40b)$$

statistical $$B_s = \frac{\left[\displaystyle\int_0^\infty |H(f)|^2 \, df\right]^2}{\displaystyle\int_0^\infty |H(f)|^4 \, df} \qquad (6.40c)$$

$|H(f)|$ is the magnitude of the frequency response function (gain factor) at any frequency f and $|H_m|$ is the maximum value of the gain factor.

The half-power point bandwidth B_r, defined in Eq. (6.40a), is the frequency interval between the upper and lower frequencies where the filter attenuates an applied signal by 3 db below maximum transmissibility. This description of bandwidth is convenient because it is easy to measure, but is otherwise of little physical significance for random signal applications.

The noise bandwidth B_n, defined in Eq. (6.40b), is the bandwidth of a hypothetical rectangular filter which would pass a signal with the same mean square value as the actual filter when the input is white noise. In other words, B_n is that measure of bandwidth which will satisfy the relationship $\Psi_x^2 = BG_x$ for filters which do not have ideal rectangular bandpass characteristics. Hence B_n is clearly a convenient measure of bandwidth to use for normalizing narrow-band mean square value measurements, as required for analog power spectral density measurements in accordance with Eq. (6.32).

The equivalent statistical bandwidth B_s, defined in Eq. (6.40c), is the bandwidth of a hypothetical rectangular filter which would pass a signal with the same mean square value statistical error as the actual filter when the input is white noise. In other words, B_s is the description of filter bandwidth which is technically appropriate for the normalized standard error given in Eq. (6.35).

For the case of an ideal rectangular filter, the three descriptions of bandwidth are all equal. For any other filter characteristic, however, the bandwidth terms will generally be different. For example, consider the case of a narrow band-pass filter consisting of a single-tuned resonant circuit where the bandwidth is small compared to the filter center frequency. The gain factor for a single-tuned filter is given by

$$|H(f)| = \left[\frac{a^2}{a^2 + (f - f_r)^2} + \frac{a^2}{a^2 + (f + f_r)^2}\right]^{1/2} \qquad a \ll f_r \qquad (6.41)$$

Note that the maximum value for $|H(f)|$ occurs when $f \approx f_r$ and is approximately equal to unity, as shown below.

$$|H_m| \approx |H(f_r)| = \left[1 + \frac{a^2}{a^2 + 4f_r^2}\right]^{\frac{1}{2}} \approx 1 \quad \text{if} \quad a \ll f_r \quad (6.42)$$

A typical plot of the gain factor versus frequency for a single-tuned band-pass filter is shown in Figure 6.5. This plot is for the special case where the

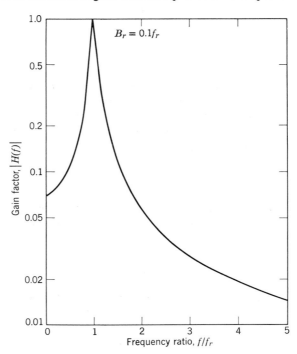

Figure 6.5 Gain factor for single-tuned band-pass filter.

half-power point bandwidth is one-tenth of the center frequency, that is, $B_r = 2a = 0.1f_r$.

From Eq. (6.40a), the half-power point bandwidth for this filter is clearly

$$B_r = (f_r + a) - (f_r - a) = 2a \quad (6.43a)$$

From Eq. (6.40b), the noise bandwidth is

$$B_n = \int_0^\infty \left[\frac{a^2}{a^2 + (f - f_r)^2} + \frac{a^2}{a^2 + (f + f_r)^2}\right] df = \pi a \quad (6.43b)$$

Finally, from Eq. (6.40c), the equivalent statistical bandwidth is

$$B_s = \frac{\left\{\int_0^\infty \left[\dfrac{a^2}{a^2 + (f - f_r)^2} + \dfrac{a^2}{a^2 + (f + f_r)^2}\right] df\right\}^2}{\int_0^\infty \left[\dfrac{a^2}{a^2 + (f - f_r)^2} + \dfrac{a^2}{a^2 + (f + f_r)^2}\right]^2 df} = \frac{(\pi a)^2}{\pi a/2} = 2\pi a \tag{6.43c}$$

Hence, compared to the half-power point bandwidth, the noise bandwidth and equivalent statistical bandwidth for a single-tuned filter are

$$B_n = \frac{\pi}{2} B_r \tag{6.44a}$$

$$B_s = \pi B_r \tag{6.44b}$$

The meaning of the preceding results is as follows. Assume a power spectral density function is to be measured using a PSD analyzer with a single-tuned band-pass filter having a half-power point bandwidth of B_r cps. Then the proper estimate for power spectral density from Eq. (6.32) will be obtained by using B_n for B_e. This gives

$$\hat{G}_x(f) = \frac{2}{\pi B_r T}\int_0^T x^2(t, f, B_r)\, dt \tag{6.45}$$

On the other hand, the precise expression for the normalized standard error for the measurement from Eq. (6.35) will be obtained by using B_s for B_e. This gives

$$\epsilon = \frac{1}{\sqrt{\pi B_r T}} \tag{6.46}$$

The preceding discussion indicates that the value of bandwidth used in Eq. (6.32) should be different from that used in Eq. (6.35). Although this is technically true, the use of any one of the bandwidth values in Eq. (6.40) will generally be acceptable for all relationships in actual practice. This is true because the filters used in modern PSD analyzers have highly selective band-pass characteristics which closely approximate the ideal rectangular form. There is little difference between the half-power point, noise, and equivalent statistical bandwidths for most actual filters. For this reason, the filter bandwidth in all equations related to power spectra measurements and errors will be assumed ideal and denoted by B_e, where it is understood that this is only an approximation for the proper value of bandwidth.

6.4.7   Other Practical Considerations

The efficient and accurate analysis of random data by analog procedures involves a good deal of art as well as science. There are numerous practical techniques which, when applied with understanding and experience, can greatly reduce data analysis time and increase analysis accuracy. A few such practical techniques associated with analog power spectral density analysis are now discussed.

Expanding Data Frequency Range. In many cases, the upper frequency capability of an analog PSD analyzer may be substantially higher than the highest frequency of interest in the data to be analyzed. If this is true, the frequency range of the data can be expanded for analysis by speeding up the recirculation of the sample data record. This will permit wider bandwidths and shorter averaging times to be used for the analysis. The net result is that, for any given resolution and statistical accuracy, the total analysis time will be decreased by the same factor that the data recirculation rate is increased.

For example, assume the recirculation speed is increased by a factor of two. All spectral peaks in the data will be doubled in bandwidth while the effective record length is cut in half. This means that the analyzer filter bandwidth required for a given resolution can be doubled and the averaging time required for a given random error can be cut in half. It follows that the scan rate given by Eq. (6.38) will increase by a factor of four. Of course, the frequency range F that must be scanned is also increased by a factor of two. Hence, from Eq. (6.39), the total analysis time is cut in half. The frequency range expansion technique is clearly a valuable practical tool for analog power spectral density analysis, and should be used whenever possible.

Pre-analysis Editing. Referring to the discussion of measurement resolution in Section 6.4.3, it is the sharp peaks in the power spectrum being analyzed that cause bias errors and necessitate the use of narrow bandwidth filters for the analysis. If the power spectrum is reasonably smooth, at least over selected frequency intervals, the analysis can be performed using a relatively wide filter bandwidth without introducing serious bias errors. The problem here is to determine if sharp spectral peaks are present in the data, and, if so, where they occur.

A common approach to this problem is to establish a coarse frequency composition for the data before a detailed analysis is performed. This can be accomplished by rapidly scanning the frequency range of the data with a relatively wide analyzer filter bandwidth. Another technique is to use a multiple filter spectrum analyzer. In either case, the location of sharp peaks in the power spectrum of the data can be identified for more careful analysis using a narrow bandwidth filter, while the remainder of the spectrum is estimated using a much wider filter bandwidth. Such pre-analysis editing procedures can greatly reduce over-all data analysis time.

Minimizing Mean Square Error. It is sometimes suggested in the literature on power spectral density analysis that the selection of the analyzer filter bandwidth should be based upon a criterion which minimizes the total mean square error for the analysis, as given by Eq. (5.104). In other words, it is suggested that a bandwidth be selected which will balance the bias and random errors so that the sum of their squares will be a minimum. This suggestion is certainly logical from a theoretical viewpoint, particularly for the case where the available sample record length is shorter than desired. The pre-editing technique discussed previously is more or less a crude implementation of this suggestion. Before such a criterion can be rigorously applied, however, it is necessary to define a power spectrum for the data to be analyzed in sufficient detail to permit Eq. (5.104) to be accurately minimized. In other words, one must know the shape of the power spectrum to be estimated. Of course, the suggested resolution criterion in Eq. (6.36) also presupposes some knowledge of the power spectrum to be analyzed, but the information required to apply Eq. (6.36) is rudimentary and easy to establish in practice.

The important point here is as follows. The bias term in Eq. (5.104) increases with the fourth power of bandwidth while the random term decreases with only the first power of bandwidth. Hence, it is important that any mistake in the selection of the analyzer filter bandwidth be in the direction of too narrow a selection rather than too wide. It is this fact that leads to the suggested filter bandwidth criterion in Eq. (6.36), which effectively assures a relatively small bias error (less than 3 per cent in most cases) independent of the random error. Another point is as follows. Once the power spectrum has been estimated, the uncertainty fluctuations (scatter) in the estimate due to random error can be reduced by smoothing out these fluctuations in the resulting power spectrum. This assumes that uncertainty fluctuations can be distinguished from underlying spectral trends. However, the a priori knowledge of the power spectrum required for this type of frequency smoothing is no more extensive than the a priori knowledge required to minimize the total mean square error expression in Eq. (5.104), and the result will usually be a more accurate estimate.

Prewhitening. Another method for increasing the accuracy of power spectral density analysis is the use of prewhitening. Prewhitening means filtering the data prior to analysis to remove spectral peaks and obtain as smooth a power spectrum as possible. Relatively wide filter bandwidths can then be used for the analysis without introducing significant bias errors. The problem in applying prewhitening is the same as the problem in minimizing the total mean square error of an estimate, as discussed previously: effective prewhitening requires a knowledge of the power spectrum to be estimated. Another difficulty when analog data analysis procedures are used is that highly flexible filters are needed for the pre-whitening operation. Analog filters with the necessary flexibility are expensive and difficult to build. Prewhitening techniques are usually more suitable for digital data analysis techniques where filters of any desired form can be rapidly synthesized. Nevertheless, prewhitening can sometimes be employed to improve the accuracy of analog data analysis, if great care is exercised and sufficient analog filtering equipment is available.

6.5 Joint Probability Density Measurements

6.5.1 Basic Instrument Requirements

Given two sample voltage time history records $x(t)$ and $y(t)$ from two stationary random signals, the joint probability density function $p(x, y)$ for the two signals may be estimated from Eq. (5.60) as follows.

$$\hat{p}(x, y) = \frac{T_{x,y}}{T W_x W_y} \tag{6.47}$$

$T_{x,y}$ is the time spent by the signals $x(t)$ and $y(t)$ simultaneously within the narrow voltage intervals having widths of W_x and W_y volts and center voltages of x and y volts, respectively. In words, the joint amplitude probability density function is estimated by the following operations.

1. Individual amplitude filtering of the two signals $x(t)$ and $y(t)$ by two narrow amplitude windows having widths of W_x and W_y volts, respectively.
2. Measurement of the total joint time spent by the two signals while they are simultaneously within the windows.
3. Averaging of the joint time spent within the windows over the sampling time, to obtain the average portion of time spent by the two signals while they are simultaneously within the windows.
4. Division of the average portion of time spent within the windows by the product of the window widths W_x W_y.

As the center voltage of each window is moved, a three-dimensional plot of the joint probability density function versus voltage levels x and y is obtained.

The preceding operations are accomplished by an analog joint probability density analyzer, which will be called a JPD analyzer for convenience. A JPD analyzer effectively consists of two simple APD analyzers as discussed in Section 6.2.1, except the amplitude windows in the two individual analyzers are followed by a single AND gate on the output of a clock pulse generator. When the input signal level from one sample record falls within the first amplitude window while the input signal level from a second sample record simultaneously falls within the second ampli-tude window, the AND gate opens and passes clock pulses indicating the joint time spent simultaneously within the windows. The train of pulses from the AND gate is then averaged by either true averaging or RC aver-aging, as for the case of the simple APD analyzer. A functional block diagram for a JPD analyzer is shown in Figure 6.6.

6.5.2 Statistical Accuracy

The mean square statistical error for joint probability density measure-ments is not well defined. Some heuristic guidelines about the general form of the error are presented in Section 5.3.3.

6.5.3 Measurement Resolution   6.5.4   Averaging Time

The considerations associated with these two factors are exactly the same as for probability density measurements discussed in Sections 6.2.3 and 6.2.4.

6.5.5 Scan Rate and Analysis Time

The general limitations imposed upon the scan rate for joint prob-ability density analysis are exactly the same as for simple probability den-sity analysis discussed in Section 6.2.5. However, there are now two signals whose range of values must be scanned for a joint probability density analysis. In effect this means that the x window must be scanned through the entire range of interest for $x(t)$, while the y window is fixed at each of the numerous positions required to cover the entire range of interest for $y(t)$. If the total range of values of interest for $x(t)$ and $y(t)$ is V_x and V_y volts, respectively, the minimum analysis time is

$$T_s \geq \begin{cases} \dfrac{T_a V_x V_y}{W_x W_y} & \text{for true averaging} & (6.48a) \\[3mm] \dfrac{4K V_x V_y}{W_x W_y} & \text{for RC averaging} & (6.48b) \end{cases}$$

where T_a is the integration time in seconds, K is the RC averaging time constant in seconds, and W_x and W_y are the amplitude window widths in volts.

Example 6.8.   Assume the joint probability density function for two random signals with mean values of zero and rms values of 1 volt is to be estimated from two sample records, each of length $T = 30$ seconds, over an amplitude range from -3 volts to $+3$ volts ($V_x = V_y = 6$ volts) using a JPD analyzer having window widths of $W_x = W_y = 0.1$ volt. If true averaging is used, $T_a = 30$ seconds and it follows from Eq. (6.25) that the

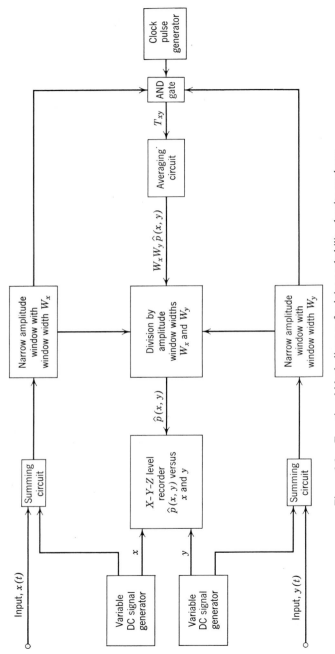

Figure 6.6 Functional block diagram for joint probability density analyzer.

maximum scan rate for W_x is $R_s = 0.0033$ volt per second for each position of W_y. Hence the minimum analysis time is 1800 seconds or 30 minutes for each position of W_y. There are a minimum of $V_y \div W_y = 60$ required positions for W_y which gives a minimum total analysis time of $T_s > 1800$ minutes or 30 hours. This example clearly illustrates the practical difficulties associated with joint probability density analysis. Specifically, unusually long analysis times are generally required to obtain properly resolved results.

6.6   Cross-Correlation Measurements

6.6.1   Basic Instrument Requirements

Given two sample voltage time history records $x(t)$ and $y(t)$ from two stationary random signals, the cross-correlation function $R_{xy}(\tau)$ for the two signals may be estimated from Eq. (5.65) as follows.

$$\hat{R}_{xy}(\tau) = \frac{1}{T}\int_0^T x(t)\,y(t+\tau)\,dt \qquad (6.49)$$

In words, the cross-correlation function is estimated by the following operations.

1. Delaying the signal $x(t)$ relative to the signal $y(t)$ by a time displacement equal to τ seconds, called the lag time.
2. Multiplying the value of $y(t)$ at any instant by the value of $x(t)$ that had occurred τ seconds before.
3. Averaging the instantaneous value product over the sampling time.

As the lag time is moved, a plot of the cross-correlation function versus lag time (cross-correlogram) is obtained.

The preceding operations are accomplished by an analog cross-correlation function analyzer, which will be called a CCF analyzer for convenience. In general, a CCF analyzer is exactly the same as the ACF analyzer discussed in Section 6.3.1, except the direct input to the multiplier and the input to the lag time generator are independent. A functional block diagram for a CCF analyzer is shown in Figure 6.7. Note that the estimate $\hat{R}_{xy}(\tau)$ actually obtained in Figure 6.7 is the average of $x(t-\tau)\,y(t)$ which equals the average of $x(t)\,y(t+\tau)$ for stationary signals.

6.6.2   Statistical Accuracy

The mean square statistical error for cross-correlation function measurements involves only a variance term as given by Eq. (5.75). The bias term is equal to zero, assuming $T_r \geq T + \tau$. The variance term is a function of the spectral characteristics of the two signals, the sampling time T, and the cross-correlation value being measured.

For the special case of two bandwidth limited Gaussian white noise

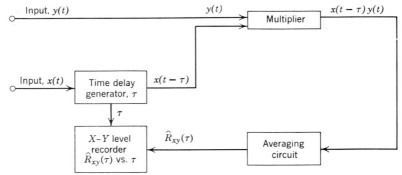

Figure 6.7 Functional block diagram for cross-correlation analyzer.

signals with identical bandwidths B, the statistical error of the cross-correlation function measurement is given in terms of the normalized standard error ϵ by Eq. (5.78) as

$$\epsilon = \frac{\text{s.d. } [\hat{R}_{xy}(\tau)]}{R_{xy}(\tau)} \approx \frac{1}{\sqrt{2BT}}\left(1 + \frac{R_x(0)\,R_y(0)}{R_{xy}^2(\tau)}\right)^{1/2} \qquad (6.50)$$

where T is the equivalent true averaging time in seconds. Observe the similarity between Eq. (6.50) and the error expression for autocorrelation function measurements given by Eq. (6.28). The discussions and illustrations of Eq. (6.28) apply here.

6.6.3 Measurement Resolution   6.6.4 Averaging Time
6.6.5 Scan Rate and Analysis Time

The considerations associated with these three factors are exactly the same as for autocorrelation function measurements discussed in Sections 6.3.3 through 6.3.5.

6.7 Cross-Spectral Density Measurements

6.7.1 Basic Instrument Requirements

Given two sample voltage time history records $x(t)$ and $y(t)$ from two stationary random signals, the cross-spectral density function $G_{xy}(f)$ for the two signals may be estimated from Eq. (1.50) as follows.

$$\hat{G}_{xy}(f) = \hat{C}_{xy}(f) - j\,\hat{Q}_{xy}(f) \qquad (6.51)$$

$$\hat{C}_{xy}(f) = \frac{1}{T}\int_0^T x(t, f, B_e)\,y(t, f, B_e)\,dt \qquad (6.51a)$$

$$\hat{Q}_{xy}(f) = \frac{1}{T}\int_0^T x(t, f, B_e)\,y^\circ(t, f, B_e)\,dt \qquad (6.51b)$$

The symbol $y°(t, f, B_e)$ denotes a 90-degree phase shift from $y(t, f, B_e)$. In words, the cross-spectral density function is estimated by the following operations.

1. Individual frequency filtering of the two signals $x(t)$ and $y(t)$ by narrow band-pass filters having identical bandwidths of B_e cps and the same center frequency.
2. Multiplying the instantaneous values of the two filtered signals with no phase shift.
3. Multiplying the instantaneous values of the two filtered signals with one shifted 90 degrees out of phase with the other.
4. Averaging each of the two instantaneous product values over the sampling time.
5. Division of each of the two mean products by the bandwidth B_e.

As the center frequency of the two band-pass filters is moved, a plot of the real and imaginary parts of the cross-spectral density function versus frequency (cross-spectrum) is obtained.

The preceding operations are accomplished by an analog cross-spectral density analyzer, which will be called a CSD analyzer for convenience. In general, a CSD analyzer consists of two PSD analyzers as discussed in Section 6.4.1, except that multipliers replace the squaring circuits and a 90-degree phase shift circuit is added. The narrow band-pass filters in the two component analyzers must be well matched to prevent unwanted phase shifts. A functional block diagram for a CSD analyzer is shown in Figure 6.8.

6.7.2 Statistical Accuracy

The mean square statistical error for cross-spectral density function measurements may be considered in terms of the error associated individually with the measurement of the co-spectral density and the quad-spectral density. The error for each term is a function of coherency, but it can be bounded as shown in Section 5.3.5. Specifically, if bias terms are ignored, the statistical error of a co-spectral density measurement is bounded in terms of the normalized standard error by

$$\epsilon = \frac{\text{s.d. } [\hat{C}_{xy}(f)]}{\sqrt{G_x(f) \, G_y(f)}} \leq \frac{1}{\sqrt{B_e T}} \tag{6.52}$$

where B_e is the bandwidth of the analyzer narrow bandwidth filters in cps and T is the equivalent true averaging time in seconds. A similar expression applies to quad-spectral density measurements. It should be emphasized that Eq. (6.52) is only a bound on the error. A much smaller error than

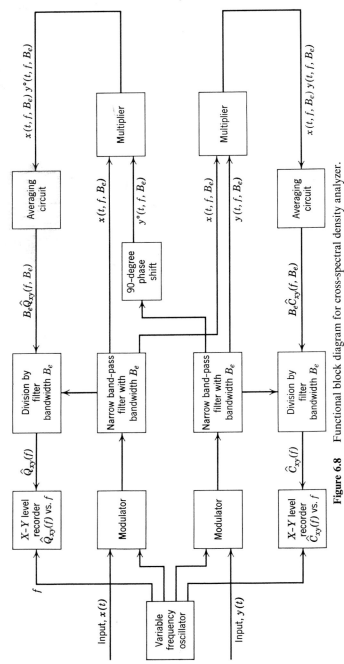

Figure 6.8 Functional block diagram for cross-spectral density analyzer.

that given by Eq. (6.52) will occur for cross-spectral density measurements between two highly coherent signals.

6.7.3   Measurement Resolution   6.7.4   Averaging Time
6.7.5   Scan Rate and Analysis Time

The considerations associated with these three factors are exactly the same as for power spectral density measurements discussed in Sections 6.4.3–6.4.5.

7

DIGITAL COMPUTER TECHNIQUES

Chapter 6 was devoted to analog techniques which should be followed for certain processing of random data. This chapter discusses similar as well as more extensive processing questions for digital computer techniques, and points out essential requirements that must be satisfied if statistically equivalent results are to be obtained by analog and digital methods. Discrete representations of continuous data involve problems of digitizing, replacing integrals by sums, and relating record lengths and frequency bandwidths to corresponding digital parameters. Statistical errors associated with digital computer calculations must be determined in terms of these digital parameters. A full understanding of these digital computer techniques is required for the design of large-scale experimental programs where random data considerations are of concern. This is particularly true for the multiple input problems which are discussed in the last section. The material includes digital computer flow charts appropriate for analysis of single random records, joint random records, and multiple input records.

7.1   Digitizing of Continuous Data

The process of *digitizing* consists of converting continuous data into discrete numbers. There are two main parts involved in a digitization procedure. The first part is *sampling*, which is defining the points at which the data are observed. It is important to have a sufficient number of samples to describe properly the significant information in the high frequencies. On the other hand, sampling at points which are too close together will yield correlated and highly redundant data, and increase greatly both the labor and cost of calculations. To cut down the number of samples, one should decrease the sampling rate to the lowest rate which will avoid aliasing errors.

278

$x(t)$

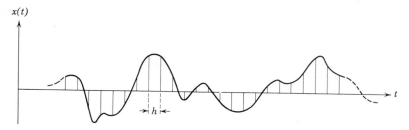

Figure 7.1   Sampling of continuous record.

An illustration of equispaced sampling that converts continuous data into discrete data is shown in Figure 7.1. Clearly, if the sampled values are separated too far apart, these sampling values could represent either low or high frequencies in the original data. This property is called *aliasing*, and constitutes a source of error which does not occur in analog processing of data.

To be specific on this matter of aliasing, if the time interval Δt between samples is h seconds, then the sampling rate is $1/h$ samples per second. Now, the useful data will be from 0 to $1/2h$ cycles per second since frequencies in the data which are higher than $1/2h$ cps will be folded into the lower frequency range from 0 to $1/2h$ cps and confused with data in this lower range. The cutoff frequency

$$f_c = \frac{1}{2h} \tag{7.1}$$

is known as the *Nyquist frequency*. Folding of the frequency axis is illustrated in Figure 7.2.

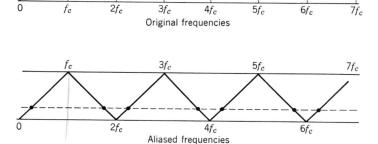

Figure 7.2   Folding about the Nyquist cutoff frequency f_c.

For any frequency f in the range $0 \leq f \leq f_c$, the higher frequencies which are aliased with f are defined by

$$(2f_c \pm f), (4f_c \pm f), \ldots, (2nf_c \pm f), \ldots \tag{7.2}$$

To prove this fact, observe that for $t = 1/2f_c$,

$$\cos 2\pi ft = \cos 2\pi(2nf_c \pm f)\frac{1}{2f_c} = \cos\frac{\pi f}{f_c}$$

Thus all data at frequencies $2nf_c \pm f$ have the same cosine function as data at frequency f when data are sampled at points $1/2f_c$ apart. For example,

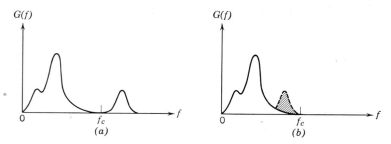

Figure 7.3   Aliased power spectra due to folding. (*a*) True spectra. (*b*) Aliased spectra.

if $f_c = 100$ cps, then data at 30 cps would be aliased with data at frequencies 170 cps, 230 cps, 370 cps, 430 cps, and so forth. Similarly, the power at these higher confounding frequencies is aliased with the power in the lower frequencies. This occurs because for $t = 1/2f_c$, the power quantities $\sin^2 2\pi ft$ and $\cos^2 2\pi ft$ do not distinguish between a frequency f and frequencies $2nf_c \pm f$. Hence when the cutoff frequency f_c is as shown in Figure 7.3, a true power spectral density function as pictured in Figure 7.3(*a*) would be folded into the aliased power spectral density function as illustrated in Figure 7.3(*b*).

Two practical methods exist for handling this aliasing problem. The first method is to choose h sufficiently small so that it is physically unreasonable for data to exist above the associated cutoff frequency f_c. For example, assume that information below 1000 cps is desired from some given data. This means that $h = 0.50$ msec would technically be sufficient. However, further assume that there is reason to believe that the data may contain contributions up to perhaps 2000 cps. Then, the Nyquist frequency should be established at $f_c = 2000$ cps which requires that $h = 0.25$ msec in order to avoid aliasing. In general, it is a good rule to select f_c to be one-and-a-half or two times greater than the maximum frequency of interest. The second method is to filter the data prior to sampling so that information above a maximum desired cutoff frequency is no longer contained in the filtered data. Then, choosing f_c equal to the maximum frequency of interest will give accurate results for frequencies below f_c. The second method is preferred over the first method to save on computing time and costs.

The second part of concern in a digitizing procedure is the matter of *quantization*, which is the actual conversion of the observed values to

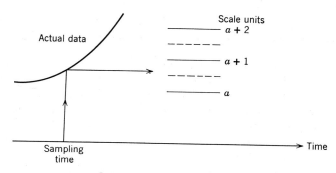

Figure 7.4   Quantization error.

numerical form. No matter how fine the scale, a choice between two consecutive values is required. This matter is illustrated on Figure 7.4. In this figure one would choose $a + 1$ as the closest numerical value to the desired time value.

If one assumes that the quantization errors follow a uniform probability distribution over one scale unit, then these errors will have a mean value of zero and a standard deviation of approximately 0.29 scale unit. This is easily shown as follows:

Let $p(x)$ be the quantization error probability density function defined by

$$p(x) = 1 \qquad -0.50 \le x \le 0.50$$

$$= 0 \qquad \text{otherwise}$$

Then, the mean value μ_x is clearly zero since $p(x)$ is symmetric about $x = 0$, and the variance

$$\sigma_x{}^2 = \int_{-\infty}^{\infty} (x - \mu_x)^2 \, p(x) \, dx = \int_{-0.5}^{0.5} x^2 \, dx = \tfrac{1}{12}$$

The standard deviation is

$$\sigma_x = \sqrt{\tfrac{1}{12}} \approx 0.29 \text{ scale unit} \tag{7.3}$$

This is the rms value of the quantization error, which may be considered as an rms noise on desired signals.

To apply this result, suppose the full range of a signal is quantized at 256 scale units. What is the rms noise-to-signal ratio? The answer is $0.29/256 \approx 0.001$. This illustrates that, for most practical problems, quantization errors should be negligible when rms values of signals are quantized at 256 or more scale units. For some applications, still fewer quantization levels will be satisfactory.

7.2   Basic Statistical Calculations for a Single Record

A number of basic statistical calculations will now be described which might be carried out in digital form for single time history records. This listing is not exhaustive and should not be automatically applied to all records. Parts of this procedure which may not be needed for certain applications should be omitted, and other parts should be extended as required for special applications. This listing does describe, however, the main operations which should be available for general digital computer processing of random data. Sample size requirements for these calculations were derived previously in Section 5.4, assuming the records are from ergodic processes.

7.2.1   Arithmetic Quantities

Digitizing of Data and Selection of Sample Size.   Let $\{u_n\}$; $n = 1, 2, \ldots, N$ be the data values of a single time history record $u(t)$ found at the points $t_n = t_0 + nh$; $n = 1, 2, \ldots, N$. The point t_0 is arbitrary and does not enter into the later formulas. These points are a distance h apart and determine the cutoff frequency $f_c = 1/2h$. The sample size N should be selected, if possible, on the basis of desired accuracies for later estimates. Rules for this selection are discussed in Section 7.3.1. In equation form, the original data values are

$$u_n = u(t_0 + nh) \qquad n = 1, 2, \ldots, N \tag{7.4}$$

Calculation of the Mean Value.   The sample mean value is given by

$$\bar{u} = \frac{1}{N} \sum_{n=1}^{N} u_n \tag{7.5}$$

where N is the number of data samples and u_n are the data values. The quantity $\bar{u}$ calculated here is an unbiased estimate of the true mean value μ_n. For independent data samples, the normalized standard error is $1/\sqrt{N}$.

Transformation of Data to Zero Mean Value.   In order that subsequent formulas and calculations may be simplified, it is desirable at this time to transform the data to have a zero mean value. Define a new time history record $x(t) = u(t) - \bar{u}$. Then, $x(t)$ has data values $\{x_n\}$ given by

$$x_n = x(t_0 + nh) = u_n - \bar{u} \qquad n = 1, 2, \ldots, N \qquad (7.6)$$

Note that $\bar{x} = 0$. The reason for representing the original data values by $\{u_n\}$ instead of $\{x_n\}$ is to have the $\{x_n\}$ notation indicate a zero sample mean value. Subsequent formulas will now be stated in terms of the transformed data values $\{x_n\}$.

Calculation of the Mean Square Value.   The sample mean square value is given by

$$\overline{x^2} = \frac{1}{N} \sum_{n=1}^{N} (x_n)^2 \qquad (7.7)$$

where N is the number of data samples and x_n is the transformed data values with $\bar{x} = 0$. The quantity $\overline{x^2}$ calculated here is a biased estimate of the true mean square value Ψ_x^2. For independent samples, the normalized standard error is $\sqrt{2/N}$.

Calculation of the Standard Deviation.   The sample standard deviation is given by

$$s = \left[\sum_{n=1}^{N} \frac{(x_n)^2}{N-1} \right]^{1/2} \qquad (7.8)$$

where N is the number of data samples and x_n are transformed data values with $\bar{x} = 0$. The quantities s and s^2 calculated here are unbiased estimates of the true standard deviation and variance, σ_x and σ_x^2, respectively. Note that

$$\overline{x^2} = \left(\frac{N-1}{N} \right) s^2 \qquad (7.9)$$

Standardization to Unit Standard Deviation.   A further transformation on the data may be convenient at this time if the computer calculations are to be performed with fixed, as opposed to floating, arithmetic. Multiplying the transformed values x_n, by $1/s$ yields

$$z_n = \frac{x_n}{s} \qquad n = 1, 2, \ldots, N \qquad (7.10)$$

This results in final data with a sample mean of zero and a sample standard deviation of unity.

7.2.2   Probability Functions

Probability Density and Distribution Functions.   Probability density and distribution functions are theoretically related by

$$p(x) = \frac{d\,P(x)}{dx} \qquad P(x) = \int_{-\infty}^{x} p(\xi)\,d\xi \qquad (7.11)$$

An estimate $\hat{p}(x)$ is obtained digitally by dividing the range for x into an appropriate number of class intervals and by tabulating the number of observations and the percentage of data in each interval. This gives a probability density histogram, as illustrated in Table 7.1. An estimate $\hat{P}(x)$ is obtained digitally by cumulating the number of observations and the percentage of data from the class intervals.

Table 7.1   Probability Density Histogram Representing $\hat{p}(x)$. (Numbers in each box represent observed number of occurrences and percentage of data)

	1	2	4	6	5	3	3	1	
	0.04	0.08	0.16	0.24	0.20	0.12	0.12	0.04	$\rightarrow x$
Class interval	1	2	3	4	5	6	7	8	

In order to later apply optimally a χ^2 goodness-of-fit test of the data to the Gaussian and Rayleigh distributions, the number of class intervals K should be chosen as indicated in Section 4.6. For values of N greater than 2000, at the 5 per cent level of significance, one should use the formula

$$K = 1.87(N - 1)^{2/5} \qquad (7.12)$$

The sample mean and the sample variance for a given sequence of N transformed data values x_n are unique. However, the sample probability density function is not unique because it is determined by the choice of end points a and b of the interval $[a, b]$ for the range of x, and by the choice of the number K of class intervals in which $[a, b]$ is divided. When a, b, and K are changed, the sample probability density function will change also. This follows from the way the sample probability density function is computed, which is to tabulate the number of occurrences of x which fall inside each of the K class intervals of $[a, b]$, as well as the number of x which fall outside of $[a, b]$.

A formal statement of this procedure will now be given. After selecting the interval $[a, b]$ and the number K, let

$$c = \frac{b - a}{K} \qquad (7.13)$$

$$d_i = a + ic \qquad i = 0, 1, 2, \ldots, K$$

Note that $d_0 = a$ and $d_K = b$. Next, define a sequence of $K + 2$ numbers $\{N_i\}$; $i = 0, 1, 2, \ldots, K + 1$, by the conditions

$$N_0 = [\text{number of } x \text{ such that } x \leq d_0]$$
$$N_1 = [\text{number of } x \text{ such that } d_0 < x \leq d_1]$$
$$N_2 = [\text{number of } x \text{ such that } d_1 < x \leq d_2]$$

$$\cdot$$
$$\cdot$$
$$\cdot$$

$$N_i = [\text{number of } x \text{ such that } d_{i-1} < x \leq d_i] \tag{7.14}$$

$$\cdot$$
$$\cdot$$
$$\cdot$$

$$N_K = [\text{number of } x \text{ such that } d_{K-1} < x \leq d_K]$$
$$N_{K+1} = [\text{number of } x \text{ such that } x > d_K]$$

This procedure will sort out the N data values of x so that the number sequence $\{N_i\}$ satisfies

$$N = \sum_{i=0}^{K+1} N_i \tag{7.15}$$

One method of doing this sorting on a digital computer is to examine each of the x_n; $n = 1, 2, \ldots, N$, in turn as follows.

1. If $x_n \leq a$, add the integer one to N_0.
2. If $a < x_n \leq b$, compute $I = (x_n - a)/c$. Then, select i as the largest integer less than or equal to I, and add the integer one to N_i.
3. If $x_n > b$, add the integer one to N_{K+1}.

This technique is easily programmed on binary machines having floating point operations.

Four output forms for the sequence $\{N_i\}$ can be used. The first output is the *histogram* which is simply the sequence $\{N_i\}$ without changes. The second output is the sample *percentage of data* in each class interval defined for $i = 0, 1, 2, \ldots, K + 1$, by

$$\hat{P}_i = \text{Prob } [d_{i-1} < x \leq d_i] = \frac{N_i}{N} \tag{7.16}$$

The third output is the sequence of sample probability *density* functions $\{\hat{p}_i\}$ defined at the midpoints of the K class intervals in $[a, b]$ by

$$\hat{p}_i = \frac{\hat{P}_i}{c} = \left(\frac{N_i}{N}\right)\left(\frac{K}{b - a}\right) \qquad i = 1, 2, \ldots, K \tag{7.17}$$

The fourth output is the sequence of sample probability *distribution* functions $\{\hat{P}(i)\}$ defined at the class interval end points where $i = 0, 1, 2, \ldots,$ $K + 1$, by

$$\hat{P}(i) = \text{Prob}\,[-\infty < x \le d_i] = \sum_{j=0}^{i} \hat{P}_j = c \sum_{j=0}^{i} \hat{p}_j \tag{7.18}$$

Note here that $\hat{P}(i)$ is defined differently from $\hat{P}_i$. Note also that $\hat{P}(K + 1) = 1$ so that it is necessary to evaluate $\hat{P}(i)$ only at the $K + 1$ class interval end points beginning with a and ending with b.

Gaussian Probability Density and Distribution Function. An estimate for the Gaussian probability density and distribution function is given by

$$\hat{p}(x) = \left(s\sqrt{2\pi}\right)^{-1} e^{-x^2/2s^2} \qquad \hat{P}(x) = \int_{-\infty}^{x} \hat{p}(\xi)\, d\xi \tag{7.19}$$

where s is the sample standard deviation for $\{x_n\}$, computed by Eq. (7.8). To compare these results with the preceding digital histogram estimates, the sample Gaussian probability density function should be evaluated at the midpoints of the K class intervals in $[a, b]$ and the sample Gaussian distribution function should be evaluated at the $K + 1$ class interval end points beginning with a and ending with b.

Rayleigh Probability Density and Distribution Function. An estimate for a Rayleigh probability density and distribution function is given by

$$\hat{p}_R(x) = \frac{x}{s^2} e^{-x^2/2s^2} \qquad \hat{P}_R(x) = \int_{-\infty}^{x} \hat{p}_R(x)\, dx \tag{7.20}$$

where s is the sample standard deviation for $\{x_n\}$, computed by Eq. (7.8). To compare these results with digital histogram estimates, the sample density function $\hat{p}_R(x)$ should be evaluated at the midpoints of the K class intervals in $[a, b]$, and the sample distribution function $\hat{P}_R(x)$ should be evaluated at the $K + 1$ class interval end points beginning with a and ending with b.

Tests for Gaussian and Rayleigh Distributions. The χ^2 goodness-of-fit test may be applied as a test for either the Gaussian or the Rayleigh distribution. Full details of this test for the Gaussian distribution (a test for normality) are illustrated by Example 4.7.

Tests for Stationarity and Randomness. Statistical requirements for testing data for stationarity and randomness are discussed in Sections 5.6.1 and 5.6.2. It is not recommended that these tests be performed on all data or even on any data unless justified. These tests should be used only for data whose properties are questioned by a trained analyst and important enough to deserve such treatment.

7.2.3 Fourier Series Representation

If a transformed sample record $x(t)$ is periodic with a period of T_p and a fundamental frequency $f_1 = 1/T_p$, then $x(t)$ can be represented by the Fourier series

$$x(t) = \frac{a_0}{2} + \sum_{q=1}^{\infty}(a_q \cos 2\pi q f_1 t + b_q \sin 2\pi q f_1 t)$$

where

$$a_q = \frac{2}{T}\int_0^T x(t) \cos 2\pi q f_1 t \, dt \qquad q = 0, 1, 2, \ldots$$

$$b_q = \frac{2}{T}\int_0^T x(t) \sin 2\pi q f_1 t \, dt \qquad q = 1, 2, 3, \ldots$$

Assume a sample record $x(t)$ is of finite length $T_r = T_p$, the fundamental period of the data. Further assume that the record is sampled at an *even* number of N equally spaced points a distance h apart where h has been selected to produce a sufficiently high-frequency cutoff $f_c = 1/2h$. Consider the initial point of the record to be zero and denote the transformed data values, as before, by

$$x_n = x(nh) \qquad n = 1, 2, \ldots, N \tag{7.21}$$

One may calculate the finite version of a Fourier series which will pass through these N data values. For any point t in the interval $(0, T_p)$ one obtains

$$x(t) = A_0 + \sum_{q=1}^{N/2} A_q \cos\left(\frac{2\pi q t}{T_p}\right) + \sum_{q=1}^{(N/2)-1} B_q \sin\left(\frac{2\pi q t}{T_p}\right) \tag{7.22}$$

At the particular points $t = nh$; $n = 1, 2, \ldots, N$, where $T_p = Nh$,

$$x_n = x(nh) = A_0 + \sum_{q=1}^{N/2} A_q \cos\left(\frac{2\pi q n}{N}\right) + \sum_{q=1}^{(N/2)-1} B_q \sin\left(\frac{2\pi q n}{N}\right) \tag{7.23}$$

The coefficients A_q and B_q are given by

$$A_0 = \frac{1}{N}\sum_{n=1}^{N} x_n = \bar{x} = 0$$

$$A_q = \frac{2}{N}\sum_{n=1}^{N} x_n \cos\frac{2\pi q n}{N} \qquad q = 1, 2, \ldots, \frac{N}{2} - 1$$

$$A_{N/2} = \frac{1}{N}\sum_{n=1}^{N} x_n \cos \pi n \tag{7.24}$$

$$B_q = \frac{1}{N}\sum_{n=1}^{N} x_n \sin\frac{2\pi q n}{N} \qquad q = 1, 2, \ldots, \frac{N}{2} - 1$$

Note that $A_0 = 0$ since $x(t)$ is transformed data where $\bar{x}$ is made equal to zero. In the preceding formulas, N is the number of data samples, x_n are the data values, A_q are the finite analogues of Fourier cosine coefficients, B_q are the finite analogues of Fourier sine coefficients, h is the time interval between data values, and T_p is the period. For large N, the digital computation requirements for determining the coefficients A_q and B_q can become quite extensive. However, the determination of these coefficients might still be of enough interest to justify the necessary computations.

7.3 Autocorrelation and Power Spectra Calculations

Basic formulas will now be given to calculate autocorrelation and power spectral density functions for single records from digitized data. These formulas are the discrete representations of the continuous formulas listed in Chapters 3, 5, and 6. The discussion will begin by stating rules for selecting the sample size N and other parameters so as to achieve digitally accurate results.

7.3.1 Choice of Sample Size and Other Parameters

Sampling Interval. Choose the sampling interval $h = \Delta t$ such that

$$h = \frac{1}{2f_c} \tag{7.25}$$

where $1/f_c$ is smallest "period" in record. This choice of h must be small enough so that aliasing will not be a problem. Although two points per cycle of the cutoff frequency f_c is a theoretical requirement, more points are recommended in practice for improved results.

Two cases are of interest here. For accurate correlation function measurements where the correlation function has frequencies near f_c, one should choose $h = 1/4f_c$. If power spectra measurements are the prime consideration, then choosing $h = 2/5f_c$ should be sufficient. Of course, for reasons of economy, one should select h as close to $1/2f_c$ as can be justified.

Number of Correlation Lag Values. Choose the maximum number of correlation lag values m such that

$$m = \frac{1}{B_e h} \tag{7.26}$$

where B_e is the desired equivalent resolution bandwidth for power spectra calculations. Note that

$$B_e = \frac{1}{mh} \tag{7.27}$$

Thus B_e will be small for a given h when m is large.

Sample Size N and Record Length T_r**.** Choose the sample size N such that

$$N = \frac{m}{\epsilon^2} \qquad (7.28)$$

where ϵ is the normalized standard error desired for spectral calculations. The associated minimum record length T_r is

$$T_r = Nh \qquad (7.29)$$

Degrees of Freedom and Standard Error. The number of degrees of freedom for spectral calculations is

$$n = 2B_e T_r = \frac{2N}{m} \qquad (7.30)$$

The normalized standard error is given by

$$\epsilon = \sqrt{m/N} \qquad (7.31)$$

Thus, ϵ will be small for a given N when m is small.

Example 7.1. Suppose it is desired that $\epsilon = 0.10$ when $f_c = 2000$ cps and $m = 50$. Compute values for h, B_e, N, and T_r.

$$h = \frac{1}{2f_c} = 0.25 \text{ msec}$$

$$B_e = \frac{1}{mh} = 80 \text{ cps}$$

$$N = \frac{m}{\epsilon^2} = 5000$$

$$T_r = Nh = 1.25 \text{ second}$$

Example 7.2. Suppose it is desired that $B_e = 20$ cps when $f_c = 1000$ cps and $\epsilon = 0.10$. Compute values for h, m, N, and T_r.

$$h = \frac{1}{2f_c} = 0.50 \text{ msec}$$

$$m = \frac{1}{B_e h} = 100$$

$$N = \frac{m}{\epsilon^2} = 10,000$$

$$T_r = Nh = 5.0 \text{ second}$$

Example **7.3.**   Suppose it is desired that $B_e = 25$ cps when $f_c = 500$ cps and $T_r = 20$ sec. Compute values for h, m, N, and ϵ.

$$h = \frac{1}{2f_c} = 1.0 \text{ msec}$$

$$m = \frac{1}{B_e h} = 40$$

$$N = \frac{T_r}{h} = 2000$$

$$\epsilon = \sqrt{\frac{m}{N}} \approx 0.14$$

7.3.2   Autocorrelation Functions

For N data values $\{x_n\}$, $n = 1, 2, \ldots, N$, from a transformed record $x(t)$ which is stationary with $\bar{x} = 0$, the estimated autocorrelation function at the displacement rh is defined by the formula

$$\hat{R}_r = \hat{R}_x(rh) = \frac{1}{N - r} \sum_{n=1}^{N-r} x_n x_{n+r} \qquad r = 0, 1, 2, \ldots, m \qquad (7.32)$$

where r is the *lag number*, m is the *maximum* lag number, and $\hat{R}_r$ is the estimate of the true value R_r at lag r, corresponding to the displacement rh.

The maximum lag number m determines the later equivalent frequency bandwidth resolution for the power spectral density function in the frequency interval $(0, f_c)$. This equivalent bandwidth for the computational procedure discussed here is given by any of the following.

$$B_e = \frac{2f_c}{m} = \frac{1}{mh} = \frac{1}{\tau_{\max}} \qquad (7.33)$$

In words, the equivalent bandwidth B_e is twice the range found by dividing the frequency interval $(0, f_c)$ into m equally spaced parts f_c/m apart [B_e divides the theoretical frequency interval $(-f_c, f_c)$ into m equally spaced parts]. Thus, from knowledge of f_c, one can choose m in advance so as to have a desired B_e. For small statistical uncertainty in later estimates of the power spectral density function, one should choose $m \ll N$ since the maximum number of statistical degrees of freedom associated with these estimates is given by $2N/m$. On the other hand, high resolution (small B_e) will result if m is large, Thus a compromise choice for m is necessary in practice.

Since the quantity m represents the maximum number of correlation lag values, the maximum displacement is

$$\tau_{\max} = mh \qquad (7.34)$$

As a rule of thumb, it is desirable to keep the maximum lag m less than one-tenth the sample size N. This will tend to avoid certain instabilities that can occur in autocorrelation function estimates. This is related to the fact that, although the sample autocorrelation function as defined by Eq. (7.32) is a good estimate of any individual point of the correlation function, the estimate considered with respect to all points of the correlation function simultaneously is not a good estimate. These facts lead to the requirement of smoothing the "raw" power spectral density function estimates, which is discussed later.

The sample autocorrelation function may also be defined at lag r by

$$\hat{R}_r = \hat{R}_x(rh) = \frac{1}{N} \sum_{n=1}^{N-r} x_n x_{n+r} \qquad r = 0, 1, 2, \ldots, m \qquad (7.35)$$

where the division by N remains constant instead of changing to $N - r$ as in Eq. (7.32). Use of this equation gives a biased estimate for the autocorrelation function. However, for N large and m small with respect to N, the values obtained by using Eq. (7.35) differ very little from those obtained by use of Eq. (7.32), and has little effect on the later power spectrum estimates, although significant changes can occur in coherence function estimates.

The autocorrelation function may take on negative as well as positive values. A normalized value for the autocorrelation function is obtained by dividing $\hat{R}_r$ by $\hat{R}_0$ where

$$\hat{R}_0 = \hat{R}_x(0) = \frac{1}{N} \sum_{n=1}^{N} (x_n)^2 = \overline{x^2} \qquad (7.36)$$

Note that the quantity $\hat{R}_0$ is a sample estimate of the true mean square value in the data. The quantity $\hat{R}_0$ is related to the sample variance s^2 by the relation

$$\hat{R}_0 = \left(\frac{N-1}{N} \right) s^2 \qquad (7.37)$$

Thus, for large N, there is negligible difference between $\hat{R}_0$ and s^2. When $\hat{R}_r$ is normalized, one obtains the quantity $\hat{R}_r/\hat{R}_0$ which theoretically will be between plus and minus one, that is,

$$-1 \leq \frac{\hat{R}_r}{\hat{R}_0} \leq 1 \qquad (7.38)$$

7.3.3   Power Spectral Density Functions

For sampled data from a transformed record $x(t)$ which is stationary with $\bar{x} = 0$, a "raw" estimate $\tilde{G}_x(f)$ of a true power spectral density function $G_x(f)$ is defined for an arbitrary f in the range $0 \leq f \leq f_c$ by

$$\tilde{G}_x(f) = 2h \left[\hat{R}_0 + 2 \sum_{r=1}^{m-1} \hat{R}_r \cos \left(\frac{\pi r f}{f_c} \right) + \hat{R}_m \cos \left(\frac{\pi m f}{f_c} \right) \right] \qquad (7.39)$$

where h is the time interval between samples, $\hat{R}_r$ is the estimate of the auto-correlation function at lag r, m is the maximum lag number, $f_c = 1/2h$ is the cutoff frequency, and $\tilde{G}_x(f)$ is the "raw" estimate of true value $G_x(f)$ at frequency f. The function $\tilde{G}_x(f)$ defined by Eq. (7.39) is often termed the "periodogram."

The total mean square value of the record in the frequency range $0 \leq f \leq f_c$ is given by

$$\int_0^{f_c} \tilde{G}_x(f)\, df = \hat{R}_0 = \hat{R}_x(0) \tag{7.40}$$

The power spectral density function estimate $\tilde{G}_x(f)$ should not be confused with a mathematical two-sided power spectral density function estimate $\tilde{S}_x(f)$ which is defined for negative as well as positive f by

$$\tilde{S}_x(f) = \tilde{S}_x(-f) = \frac{\tilde{G}_x(f)}{2} \tag{7.41}$$

Here

$$\int_{-f_c}^{f_c} \tilde{S}_x(f)\, df = \hat{R}_x(0) \tag{7.42}$$

It is recommended that the values of the function $\tilde{G}_x(f)$ be calculated only at the $m + 1$ special discrete frequencies where

$$f = \frac{kf_c}{m} \qquad k = 0, 1, 2, \ldots, m \tag{7.43}$$

This will provide $m/2$ independent spectral estimates since spectral estimates at points less than $2f_c/m$ apart will be correlated. At these discrete frequency points,

$$\tilde{G}_k = \tilde{G}_x\left(\frac{kf_c}{m}\right) = 2h\left[\hat{R}_0 + 2\sum_{r=1}^{m-1} \hat{R}_r \cos\left(\frac{\pi r k}{m}\right) + (-1)^k \hat{R}_m\right] \tag{7.44}$$

The index k is called the *harmonic number*, and $\tilde{G}_k$ is the "raw" estimate of the power spectral density function at harmonic k, corresponding to the frequency $f = kf_c/m$.

A convenient check formula which requires all of the $m + 1$ estimates of $\tilde{G}_k$ is

$$\hat{R}_x(0) = \frac{1}{2hm}\left[\frac{1}{2}\tilde{G}_0 + \sum_{k=1}^{m-1}\tilde{G}_k + \frac{1}{2}\tilde{G}_m\right] \tag{7.45}$$

A final "smooth" estimate of the power spectral density may now be found by further frequency smoothing called "Hanning," Ref. 6, p. 14.

Let $\hat{G}_k$ represent this "smooth" estimate at harmonic k, where the $\wedge$ replaces the $\sim$. Then at the $m + 1$ frequencies $f = kf_c/m; k = 0, 1, 2, \ldots,$ m, one obtains

$$\hat{G}_0 = 0.5\tilde{G}_0 + 0.5\tilde{G}_1$$

$$\hat{G}_k = 0.25\tilde{G}_{k-1} + 0.5\tilde{G}_k + 0.25\tilde{G}_{k+1} \qquad k = 1, 2, \ldots, m - 1 \quad (7.46)$$

$$\hat{G}_m = 0.5\tilde{G}_{m-1} + 0.5\tilde{G}_m$$

Equation (7.46) is implemented easily on a binary digital computer compared to other smoothing procedures. These other procedures provide different bias errors and uncertainty errors which may be preferred for certain applications. In general, the Hanning method should be satisfactory.

Smoothing is necessary since the periodogram (raw estimate) given by Eq. (7.39) is an inefficient estimate of the true spectral density. To be specific, the variability of these estimates does not decrease with increased record length or sample size. This leads to the requirement of smoothing the periodogram or equivalently, weighting the correlation function nonuniformly.

An alternative equivalent way to obtain Eq. (7.46) is in terms of a Hanning *lag window* weighting function D_r defined by

$$D_r = D(rh) = \frac{1}{2}\left(1 + \cos\frac{\pi r}{m}\right) \qquad r = 0, 1, 2, \ldots, m$$
$$= 0 \qquad\qquad\qquad r > m \qquad (7.47)$$

Note that $D_0 = 1$ and $D_m = 0$. Equation (7.47) may now be combined with Eq. (7.44) to yield a condensed formula for the smooth estimates at harmonics $k = 0, 1, 2, \ldots, m$. Specifically,

$$\hat{G}_k = \hat{G}_x\left(\frac{kf_c}{m}\right) = 2h\left[\hat{R}_0 + 2\sum_{r=1}^{m-1} D_r \hat{R}_r \cos\left(\frac{\pi r k}{m}\right)\right] \qquad (7.48)$$

where $\hat{R}_r$ is obtained from Eq. (7.32) or Eq. (7.35).

To verify Eq. (7.48), observe that for $k = 0$,

$$\hat{G}_0 = 2h\left[\hat{R}_0 + 2\sum_{r=1}^{m-1} D_r \hat{R}_r\right]$$

$$= 2h\left[\hat{R}_0 + \sum_{r=1}^{m-1} \hat{R}_r\left(1 + \cos\frac{\pi r}{m}\right)\right]$$

$$= 0.5\hat{G}_0 + 0.5\hat{G}_1$$

Also, for $k = m$,

$$\hat{G}_m = 2h\left[\hat{R}_0 + \sum_{r=1}^{m-1} \hat{R}_r\left(1 + \cos\frac{\pi r}{m}\right)\cos\pi r\right]$$

$$= 2h\left\{\hat{R}_0 + \sum_{r=1}^{m-1} \hat{R}_r\left[\cos\frac{\pi r(m-1)}{m} + \cos\pi r\right]\right\}$$

$$= 0.5\hat{G}_{m-1} + 0.5\tilde{G}_m$$

Finally, for all $k = 1, 2, \ldots, m-1$,

$$\hat{G}_k = 2h\left[\hat{R}_0 + \sum_{r=1}^{m-1} \hat{R}_r\left(1 + \cos\frac{\pi r}{m}\right)\cos\frac{\pi r k}{m}\right]$$

$$= 2h\left\{\hat{R}_0 + \sum_{r=1}^{m-1} \hat{R}_r\left[\frac{1}{2}\cos\frac{\pi r}{m}(k-1) + \cos\frac{\pi r}{m} + \frac{1}{2}\cos\frac{\pi r}{m}(k+1)\right]\right\}$$

$$= 0.25\hat{G}_{k-1} + 0.5\hat{G}_k + 0.25\tilde{G}_{k+1}$$

Thus, Eq. (7.48) is identical with Eq. (7.46).

When the computation of frequency response functions and the associated coherence functions is the main goal, certain variations in the above formulas may sometimes be appropriate. In particular, the application of the Parzen lag weighting function to the correlation functions for the purpose of obtaining spectral estimates may occasionally be more useful. This lag window weighting function is given from Ref. 22 by the formula,

$$
\begin{aligned}
D_r' &= 1 - 6\left(\frac{r}{m}\right)^2 + 6\left(\frac{r}{m}\right)^3 & r &= 0, 1, 2, \ldots, \frac{m}{2} \\
&= 2\left(1 - \left[\frac{r}{m}\right]\right)^3 & r &= \frac{m}{2} + 1, \ldots, m \\
&= 0 & r &> m
\end{aligned}
\tag{7.49}
$$

where the prime is used merely to distinguish Eq. (7.49) from Eq. (7.47). Note here that $D_0' = 1$ and $D_m' = 0$. The use of this Parzen window maintains the sample coherence function between its theoretical values of ± 1, as opposed to the Hanning window of Eq. (7.47) which allows a sample coherence function to vary over wider limits depending on the form of the power spectrum. The final "smooth" formula of the power spectral density estimate at harmonic k is the same form as Eq. (7.48). Specifically,

$$\hat{G}_k = \hat{G}_x\left(\frac{kf_c}{m}\right) = 2h\left[\hat{R}_0 + \sum_{r=1}^{m-1} D_r'\hat{R}_r\cos\frac{\pi r k}{m}\right] \tag{7.50}$$

where D_r' is given here by Eq. (7.49) instead of by Eq. (7.47).

A procedure often described and recommended in spectral analysis techniques is *prewhitening* or *coloring*. The process of prewhitening amounts to applying a special filter (digital or analog) to the data which will result in the filtered data having a flat (white) spectrum. The filter must therefore have a frequency response which has valleys where the spectrum of the data has peaks and vice versa. A flat spectrum is desired for the filtered data since this assumption is made in the derivation of uncertainty formulas. To obtain the original desired spectrum, a *recoloring* operation has to take place at the finish of the computations. This involves the application of a filter which is the reverse of the prewhitening filter. Since prewhitening requires advanced knowledge of the spectrum, it is not specifically mentioned here in any of the data processing procedures except in one instance.

The procedure of translating out suspected time delays in two-dimensional data analysis is recommended in Section 7.4.5 and amounts to a simple form of two-dimensional prewhitening of the cross-power spectrum. This is a straightforward procedure if a significant peak in the cross-correlation function is detected. Although other prewhitening procedures are not discussed, such procedures may be useful in special applications if one has some advance knowledge of the spectrum.

Another general method of computing power spectra may be recommended and has been applied under certain restricted conditions. This method, in effect, simulates the analog procedure. That is, the data are filtered (digitally), squared, and averaged. In general, this procedure offers no advantage in data processing over transforming the correlation function if the filtering method uses the same bandwidth and interval spacing as the correlation method. It has the disadvantage of losing the correlation information. However, this is an important application of digital filtering techniques which may be pertinent for special problems, such as spectral analysis with variable filter bandwidths.

7.4 Joint Statistical Calculations for Two Records

In the formulas to follow, it is assumed that two time history records $u(t)$, $v(t)$ are from stationary processes and exist only for $t_0 \leq t \leq t_0 + T_r$, where t_0 is arbitrary and may be zero. Assume the sampling time interval is $\Delta t = h$ which corresponds to a cutoff frequency of $f_c = 1/2h$. Let the respective sample values for $u(t)$ and $v(t)$ be donated by

$$u_n = u(t_0 + nh) \qquad n = 1, 2, 3, \ldots, N$$
$$v_n = v(t_0 + nh) \qquad T_r = Nh$$

$$(7.51)$$

The first quantities to compute are the sample mean values

$$\bar{u} = \frac{1}{N} \sum_{n=1}^{N} u_n \qquad \bar{v} = \frac{1}{N} \sum_{n=1}^{N} v_n \qquad (7.52)$$

Then, compute the transformed data values

$$x_n = u_n - \bar{u} \qquad y_n = v_n - \bar{v}; \qquad n = 1, 2, \ldots, N \qquad (7.53)$$

corresponding to new time records $x(t) = u(t) - \bar{u}$ and $y(t) = v(t) - \bar{v}$, where $\bar{x} = 0$ and $\bar{y} = 0$.

The next three subsections are concerned with joint probability density functions, cross-correlation functions, and cross-spectral density functions computed from transformed data values x_n and y_n.

7.4.1 Joint Probability Functions

Joint Probability Density and Distribution Functions. The joint probability density function $p(x, y)$ is theoretically given by

$$p(x, y) = \frac{\partial}{\partial y}\left(\frac{\partial P(x, y)}{\partial x}\right) \qquad (7.54)$$

where $P(x, y)$ is the joint probability distribution function. An estimate $\hat{p}(x, y)$ obtained digitally by tabulating results in the form of a two-dimensional probability density histogram. That is, each variable, x and y, is divided into an appropriate number of class intervals and the number

Table 7.3   Two-Dimensional Histogram

0	1	1	2	1	1	0	1	0
1	3	4	5	7	6	3	2	1
1	2	7	15	19	13	6	2	1
3	4	8	18	25	16	8	4	2
1	3	6	14	17	16	6	3	1
1	2	5	6	8	5	5	1	0
0	1	1	2	3	2	2	1	0

of observations and the percentage of data in each rectangle are tabulated. See Table 7.3 for an illustration as to how a two-dimensional histogram might appear.

The joint probability distribution function $P(x, y)$ is theoretically given by

$$P(x, y) = \int_{-\infty}^{y} \int_{-\infty}^{x} p(\xi, \eta) \, d\xi \, d\eta \qquad (7.55)$$

where $p(\xi, \eta)$ is the joint probability density function. An estimate $\hat{P}(x, y)$ is obtained digitally from the preceding tabulation by first cumulating the number of observations and percentages in the x direction from the x-class intervals, and then in the y direction from the y-class intervals.

Joint Gaussian Probability Density Function. An estimate of the joint Gaussian probability density function is given by

$$\hat{p}(x, y) = \frac{\exp\left(\dfrac{-1}{2[1 - \hat{\rho}_{xy}{}^2(0)]}\left[\left(\dfrac{x}{s_x}\right)^2 - 2\hat{\rho}_{xy}(0)\left(\dfrac{x}{s_x}\right)\left(\dfrac{y}{s_y}\right) + \left(\dfrac{y}{s_y}\right)^2\right]\right)}{2\pi s_x s_y \sqrt{1 - \hat{\rho}_{xy}{}^2(0)}} \qquad (7.56)$$

where s_x is the sample standard deviation for $x(t)$, s_y is the sample standard deviation for $y(t)$, and $\hat{\rho}_{xy}(0)$ is the sample covariance coefficient for $x(t)$ and $y(t)$, a special case of Eq. (7.62) at $r = 0$. To compare this result with the preceding two-dimensional digital histogram estimate, the sample joint probability density function should be evaluated at the midpoints of the rectangles determined by the x and y class intervals.

The joint Gaussian probability density function is easily described in terms of "equiprobability ellipses." If one considers the points that give a constant value to the sample density function, it is seen that they form an ellipse, namely,

$$c^2 = [2(1 - \hat{\rho}_{xy}{}^2(0))]^{-1}\left[\left(\frac{x}{s_x}\right)^2 - 2\hat{\rho}_{xy}(0)\left(\frac{x}{s_x}\right)\left(\frac{y}{s_y}\right) + \left(\frac{y}{s_y}\right)^2\right] \qquad (7.57)$$

where c^2 is a constant. It can be shown (see Ref. 8, p. 288) that the percentage of observations in the whole plane outside this ellipse is

$$\int_{c}^{\infty} 2ce^{-c^2} \, dc = e^{-c^2} \qquad (7.58)$$

To apply this result, one might calculate Eq. (7.58) for the 50, 25, 5, and 1 per cent values. This gives ellipses which include, respectively, 50, 75, 95, and 99 per cent of the observations. The values for c^2 corresponding to these ellipses are listed in Table 7.4.

Conditional Probability Density Function. The conditional probability density function $p(y \mid x)$ for y given x (that is, for a specific value of x), is denoted by

$$p(y \mid x) = \frac{p(x, y)}{p(x)} \qquad \text{assuming } p(x) \neq 0 \qquad (7.59)$$

where $p(x, y)$ is the joint probability density function of x and y, and $p(x)$ is the probability density function of x.

A digital estimate $\hat{p}(y \mid x)$ may be obtained by choosing a column of the two-dimensional digital histogram estimate for the joint probability density function, and normalizing each entry by dividing by the total number (or

Table 7.4   Values of c^2 for Equiprobability Ellipses

Percentage of Observations Included in Ellipse	Corresponding Value of c^2
50	0.693
75	1.386
95	2.996
99	4.605

total percentage) in that column. For each fixed class interval of x one may obtain in this way a conditional density function for y. To obtain conditional densities for x given y, one uses rows instead of columns.

7.4.2   Cross-Correlation Functions

As in Section 7.3.2, choose a maximum lag number m which will give a desired equivalent frequency resolution $B_e = 1/mh$ as well as a desired number of degrees of freedom $2N/m$. The autocorrelation functions and power spectral density functions are calculated for the transformed variables $x(t)$ and $y(t)$ in terms of the data values, x_n and y_n, separately according to the formulas listed previously. Formulas to calculate their joint cross-correlation functions and cross-spectral functions in terms of the transformed data will now be given.

Unbiased estimates for the sample cross-correlation functions at lag numbers $r = 0, 1, 2, \ldots, m$, are defined by

$$\hat{R}_{xy}(rh) = \frac{1}{N - r} \sum_{n=1}^{N-r} x_n y_{n+r} \qquad (7.60)$$

$$\hat{R}_{yx}(rh) = \frac{1}{N - r} \sum_{n=1}^{N-r} y_n x_{n+r} \qquad (7.61)$$

Note that the two cross-correlation functions $\hat{R}_{xy}(rh)$ and $\hat{R}_{yx}(rh)$ differ by the interchange of the x_n and y_n data values. Instead of dividing by $N - r$

in Eqs. (7.60) and (7.61), if $N \gg m$, it may be more convenient as in Eq. (7.35) to divide by N.

The sample cross-correlation function $\hat{R}_{xy}(rh)$ may be normalized to have values between plus and minus one by dividing them by $\sqrt{\hat{R}_x(0)}\sqrt{\hat{R}_y(0)}$. This defines a sample cross-correlation coefficient

$$\hat{\rho}_{xy}(rh) = \frac{\hat{R}_{xy}(rh)}{\sqrt{\hat{R}_x(0)}\sqrt{\hat{R}_y(0)}} \qquad r = 0, 1, 2, \ldots, m \qquad (7.62)$$

which theoretically should satisfy $-1 \le \hat{\rho}_{xy}(rh) \le 1$. A similar formula exists for $\hat{\rho}_{yx}(rh)$.

For later determination of the cross-spectral density function estimate $\hat{G}_{xy}(f)$ between $x(t)$ and $y(t)$, calculate for $r = 0, 1, 2, \ldots, m$, the two quantities (even and odd parts of the cross-correlation function)

$$\hat{A}_r \equiv \hat{A}_{xy}(rh) = \tfrac{1}{2}[\hat{R}_{xy}(rh) + \hat{R}_{yx}(rh)] \qquad (7.63)$$
$$\hat{B}_r = \hat{B}_{xy}(rh) = \tfrac{1}{2}[\hat{R}_{xy}(rh) - \hat{R}_{yx}(rh)] \qquad (7.64)$$

7.4.3   Cross-Spectral Density Functions

As discussed in previous chapters, the cross-spectral density function is a complex-valued quantity defined by

$$G_{xy}(f) = C_{xy}(f) - j\, Q_{xy}(f) \qquad (7.65)$$

where $C_{xy}(f)$ is called the co-spectral density function and $Q_{xy}(f)$ is called the quadrature spectral density function. An equivalent representation for $G_{xy}(f)$ is

$$G_{xy}(f) = |G_{xy}(f)|\, e^{-j\theta_{xy}(f)} \qquad (7.66)$$

where $|G_{xy}(f)|$ is the absolute value of $G_{xy}(f)$, and $\theta_{xy}(f)$ is the phase angle contained in $G_{xy}(f)$. Two resulting relations are

$$|G_{xy}(f)| = [C_{xy}^{\,2}(f) + Q_{xy}^{\,2}(f)]^{\frac{1}{2}} \qquad (7.67)$$

$$\theta_{xy}(f) = \tan^{-1}\left[\frac{Q_{xy}(f)}{C_{xy}(f)}\right] \qquad (7.68)$$

"Raw" estimates from sampled data for the co-spectral density function and the quadrature spectral density function may be found as follows. The formulas are for one-sided spectra which are nonzero only for $f \ge 0$.

At an arbitrary value of f in the range $0 \le f \le f_c$, "raw" estimates for $\tilde{C}_{xy}(f)$ and $\tilde{Q}_{xy}(f)$ are

$$\tilde{C}_{xy}(f) = 2h\left[\hat{A}_0 + 2\sum_{r=1}^{m-1}\hat{A}_r \cos\left(\frac{\pi r f}{f_c}\right) + \hat{A}_m \cos\left(\frac{\pi m f}{f_c}\right)\right] \qquad (7.69)$$

$$\tilde{Q}_{xy}(f) = 2h\left[2\sum_{r=1}^{m-1}\hat{B}_r \sin\left(\frac{\pi r f}{f_c}\right) + \hat{B}_m \sin\left(\frac{\pi m f}{f_c}\right)\right] \qquad (7.70)$$

where the $\hat{A}_r$ and $\hat{B}_r$ are given by Eqs. (7.63) and (7.64). As before, these functions should be calculated only at the $m + 1$ special discrete frequencies of harmonic number k where

$$f = \frac{kf_c}{m} \qquad k = 0, 1, 2, \ldots, m \tag{7.71}$$

At these discrete frequency points,

$$\tilde{C}_k = \tilde{C}_{xy}\left(\frac{kf_c}{m}\right) = 2h\left[\hat{A}_0 + 2\sum_{r=1}^{m-1}\hat{A}_r \cos\left(\frac{\pi rk}{m}\right) + (-1)^k\hat{A}_m\right] \tag{7.72}$$

$$\tilde{Q}_k = \tilde{Q}_{xy}\left(\frac{kf_c}{m}\right) = 4h\sum_{r=1}^{m-1}\hat{B}_r \sin\left(\frac{\pi rk}{m}\right) \tag{7.73}$$

"Smooth" estimates for C_k and Q_k at harmonic k may now be calculated as in Eq. (7.46) by using the Hanning method. This yields

$$\hat{C}_0 = 0.5\tilde{C}_0 + 0.5\tilde{C}_1$$
$$\hat{Q}_0 = 0.5\tilde{Q}_0 + 0.5\tilde{Q}_1$$
$$\hat{C}_k = 0.25\tilde{C}_{k+1} + 0.5\tilde{C}_k + 0.25\tilde{C}_{k+1}$$
$$\qquad\qquad\qquad\qquad\qquad\qquad\qquad\qquad k = 1, 2, \ldots, m - 1 \tag{7.74}$$
$$\hat{Q}_k = 0.25\tilde{Q}_{k-1} + 0.5\tilde{Q}_k + 0.25\tilde{Q}_{k+1}$$
$$\hat{C}_m = 0.5\tilde{C}_{m-1} + 0.5\tilde{C}_m$$
$$\hat{Q}_m = 0.5\tilde{Q}_{m-1} + 0.5\tilde{Q}_m$$

At the $m + 1$ discrete frequencies $f = k\,f_c/m;\ k = 0, 1, 2, \ldots, m$, one obtains the "smooth" cross-spectral density estimates

$$\hat{G}_{xy}\left(\frac{kf_c}{m}\right) = \hat{C}_k - j\hat{Q}_k = \left|\hat{G}_{xy}\left(\frac{kf_c}{m}\right)\right| e^{-j\theta_{xy}(kfc/m)} \tag{7.75}$$

where

$$\left|\hat{G}_{xy}\left(\frac{kf_c}{m}\right)\right| = (\hat{C}_k^2 + \hat{Q}_k^2)^{1/2} \tag{7.76}$$

$$\hat{\theta}_{xy}\left(\frac{kf_c}{m}\right) = \tan^{-1}\left(\frac{\hat{Q}_k}{\hat{C}_k}\right) \tag{7.77}$$

7.4.4 Correction for Linear Trend

The previous analysis assumes that the transformed records $x(t)$ and $y(t)$ are from stationary processes with zero mean values. If the mean value is not zero, then the power spectral density function will exhibit a large peak (theroetically infinite) at zero frequency which will distort estimates at other frequencies. This is the reason why original records $u(t)$ and $v(t)$ are corrected by subtracting off their sample mean values.

A second correction may be needed to subtract off a slowly varying linear trend (that is, nonzero slope of $u(t)$ or $v(t)$ with respect to time) about which $u(t)$ or $v(t)$ may be oscillating. This may be due to instrumentation drifts or to an actual underlying linear trend in the data over a long record length T_r. Whatever the cause, better estimates of the desired spectral density functions will be obtained by taking proper account of possible linear trends in the data. Otherwise, this also will cause large distortions of the estimates, particularly at low frequencies.

Let the original random record $u(t)$ be represented by

$$u(t) = \bar{u} + \bar{\alpha}_u\left(t - \frac{T_r}{2}\right) + x(t) \qquad 0 \le t \le T_r \qquad (7.78)$$

where $\bar{u}$ denotes the sample mean value of $u(t)$ over $(0, T_r)$, the parameter $\bar{\alpha}_u$ denotes the average slope of $u(t)$ with respect to t, and $x(t)$ is the corrected sample record with zero mean value and zero average slope. The previous analysis assumed $\bar{\alpha}_u = 0$.

By integrating $u(t)$ over 0 to $T_r/3$, and subtracting from the integral over $2T_r/3$ to T_r, one can solve for $\bar{\alpha}_u$ as follows.

$$\bar{\alpha}_u = \frac{1}{(T_r/3)(2T_r/3)}\left[\int_{2T_r/3}^{T_r} u(t)\,dt - \int_0^{T_r/3} u(t)\,dt\right] \qquad (7.79)$$

In terms of the data samples $\{u_n\}$, $n = 1, 2, \ldots, N$, where $T_r = Nh$,

$$\bar{\alpha}_u = \frac{1}{hv(N-v)}\left[\sum_{n=N-v}^{N} u_n - \sum_{n=1}^{v} u_n\right] \qquad v = \left[\frac{N}{3}\right] \qquad (7.80)$$

where v is the largest integer less than or equal to $[N/3]$.

In terms of the original data values $\{u_n\}$, the sample mean value $\bar{u}$, and the average slope $\bar{\alpha}_u$, the autocorrelation function estimate of Eq. (7.32) becomes

$$\hat{R}_x(rh) = \left(\frac{1}{N-r}\sum_{n=1}^{N-r} u_n u_{n+r}\right) - \bar{u}^2 - \tfrac{1}{12}\bar{\alpha}_u{}^2\lambda_r \qquad (7.81)$$

where $\bar{u}$ is calculated by Eq. (7.5), $\bar{\alpha}_u$ by Eq. (7.80), and

$$\lambda_r = N^2h^2\left[1 - 2\left(\frac{r}{N}\right) - 2\left(\frac{r}{N}\right)^2\right] \qquad r = 0, 1, 2, \ldots, m \qquad (7.82)$$

Note that for $m \ll N$, the quantity $\lambda_r \approx N^2h^2$ for all r. The smooth power spectral density function calculated by Eq. (7.48) or (7.50) corresponds to the corrected record $x(t)$, with autocorrelation function of Eq. (7.81).

Similarly, a pair of original records $u(t)$ and $v(t)$ with nonzero mean values $\bar{u}$, $\bar{v}$, and nonzero average slopes $\bar{\alpha}_u$, $\bar{\alpha}_v$, may be represented by

$$u(t) = \bar{u} + \bar{\alpha}_u\left(t - \frac{T_r}{2}\right) + x(t)$$

$$0 \leq t \leq T_r \qquad (7.83)$$

$$v(t) = \bar{v} + \bar{\alpha}_v\left(t - \frac{T_r}{2}\right) + y(t)$$

where $x(t)$ and $y(t)$ are corrected ergodic records with zero mean values and zero average slopes.

In place of Eq. (7.60), the cross-correlation function estimate becomes

$$\hat{R}_{xy}(rh) = \left(\frac{1}{N-r}\sum_{n=1}^{N-r} u_n v_{n+r}\right) - \bar{u}\bar{v} - \frac{r}{2}(\bar{u}\bar{\alpha}_v - \bar{v}\bar{\alpha}_u) - \tfrac{1}{12}\bar{\alpha}_u\bar{\alpha}_v\lambda_r \quad (7.84)$$

where λ_r is given by Eq. (7.82). The smooth cross-spectral density function calculated by Eq. (7.75) corresponds to the corrected records $x(t)$ and $y(t)$, with cross-correlation function of Eq. (7.84).

7.4.5 Requirements for Significant Cross-Correlation Peaks

A special feature which should be considered for the digital computer program is the translation of the lag window weighting center to the peak of the sample cross-correlation function. That is, the maximum of the cross-correlation function does not necessarily occur at zero displacement as is the case for the autocorrelation function. To properly compute frequency response function estimates, one should attempt to center the lag window weighting around the peak (assuming a significant peak exists) of the cross-correlation function in order that the maximum information in the data is properly utilized. This causes a modification of the formulas for the cross-spectral density. For this time shifting to be applied properly, one must assume that sufficient values have been computed on either side of the peak in the cross-correlation function to allow a reasonable number of frequency values of the power spectral density to be computed. An alternative procedure is to translate the original data in time such that time delays are eliminated.

Let τ_0 be the value of τ at which the cross-correlation function attains its maximum value. Then, in place of Eqs. (7.63) and (7.64), one should compute

$$\hat{A}_{xy}'(rh) = \tfrac{1}{2}[\hat{R}_{xy}(rh + \tau_0) + \hat{R}_{yx}(rh - \tau_0)] \qquad (7.85)$$

$$\hat{B}_{xy}'(rh) = \tfrac{1}{2}[\hat{R}_{xy}(rh + \tau_0) - \hat{R}_{yx}(rh - \tau_0)] \qquad (7.86)$$

where the prime is used to distinguish these equations from the previous ones. Substitution of Eqs. (7.85) and (7.86) into Eqs. (7.72) and (7.73) yields primed "raw" estimates $\tilde{C}_k{}'$ and $\tilde{Q}_k{}'$. Smoothing by the Hanning method of Eq. (7.74) yields primed "smooth" estimates $\hat{C}_k{}'$ and $\hat{Q}_k{}'$. Finally, the desired smooth values of the original untranslated co-spectra and quadrature spectra are calculated at the harmonic numbers $k = 0, 1, 2, \ldots, m$ by

$$\hat{C}_k = \hat{C}_k{}' \cos\left(\frac{2\pi k f_c \tau_0}{m}\right) - \hat{Q}_k{}' \sin\left(\frac{2\pi k f_c \tau_0}{m}\right) \tag{7.87}$$

$$\hat{Q}_k = \hat{C}_k{}' \sin\left(\frac{2\pi k f_c \tau_0}{m}\right) + \hat{Q}_k{}' \cos\left(\frac{2\pi k f_c \tau_0}{m}\right) \tag{7.88}$$

When $\tau_0 = 0$, these equations give the previous results.

The digital computer could be programmed to perform a search of the cross-correlation values to find the time value τ_0 at which the highest peak in $\hat{R}_{xy}(\tau)$ is observed. This might be either a peak in the positive or the negative direction, and the greatest peak in absolute value should be found. Alternatively, a more proper procedure might actually be where an ordinary computer run is first made. One then inspects the data and notes where the significant peak in the cross-correlation function has occurred (assuming a peak does occur). This value is then used as an input parameter for a subsequent computer run where this more refined computing method would be employed. Note also in the preceding formulas that the value of m might have to be modified since sufficient values of the cross-correlation function might not be computed to one side or the other of the largest peak. In this case, the m in these formulas would have to be the largest number of points that are available.

7.4.6 Frequency Response Functions

From Chapter 2, the frequency response function $H(f)$ of a linear system is a complex-valued function defined by

$$H(f) = |H(f)|\, e^{-j\phi(f)} \tag{7.89}$$

where $|H(f)|$ is the gain factor of the system and $\phi(f)$ is the phase factor of the system. From Eq. (5.138), if a stationary input $x(t)$ produces an output $y(t)$, the system gain factor can be estimated by

$$|\hat{H}(f)| = \left(\frac{\hat{G}_y(f)}{\hat{G}_x(f)}\right)^{\!\!1/2} \tag{7.90}$$

Hence, at the discrete frequencies $f = kf_c/m$, $k = 0, 1, 2, \ldots, m$, the gain factor may be estimated digitally by

$$|\hat{H}_k| = \left|\hat{H}\left(\frac{kf_c}{m}\right)\right| = \left(\frac{\hat{G}_{k,y}}{\hat{G}_{k,x}}\right)^{\!\!1/2} \tag{7.91}$$

where $\hat{G}_{k,x}$ and $\hat{G}_{k,y}$ represent the digital values of the power spectrum estimates at harmonic k for $x(t)$ and $y(t)$, respectively. Note that Eq. (7.90) gives an unbiased estimate of $|H(f)|$ only for the ideal case where there is no extraneous noise at either the input or output and no other inputs contribute to $y(t)$.

For either single input–single output problems where extraneous noise is present only at the output, or multiple input–single output problems where the inputs are uncorrelated, another more general method for estimating the system frequency response function (including both gain and phase factors) is given by Eq. (5.130), namely,

$$\hat{H}(f) = \frac{\hat{G}_{xy}(f)}{\hat{G}_x(f)} \tag{7.92}$$

It follows that

$$|\hat{H}(f)| = \frac{|\hat{G}_{xy}(f)|}{\hat{G}_x(f)} \quad \text{and} \quad \hat{\phi}(f) = \hat{\theta}_{xy}(f) \tag{7.93}$$

Hence, at the discrete frequencies $f = kf_c/m$; $k = 0, 1, 2, \ldots, m$, the gain factor and phase factor may be estimated digitally by

$$|\hat{H}_k| = \frac{(\hat{C}_k^2 + \hat{Q}_k^2)^{1/2}}{\hat{G}_{k,x}} \tag{7.94}$$

$$\hat{\phi}_k = \tan^{-1}\left(\frac{\hat{Q}_k}{\hat{C}_k}\right) \tag{7.95}$$

where $\hat{G}_{k,x}$ represents the digital value of the power spectrum estimate at harmonic k for $x(t)$, and $\hat{C}_k$ and $\hat{Q}_k$ represent the digital values of the co-spectrum estimate and quad-spectrum estimate at harmonic k between $x(t)$ and $y(t)$.

7.4.7   Coherence Functions

From Section 3.4.2, the coherence function $\gamma_{xy}^2(f)$ between two stationary records $x(t)$ and $y(t)$ is defined by

$$\gamma_{xy}^2(f) = \frac{|G_{xy}(f)|^2}{G_x(f)\, G_y(f)} \tag{7.96}$$

where $G_x(f)$ and $G_y(f)$ are the power spectral density functions of $x(t)$ and $y(t)$, respectively, and $G_{xy}(f)$ is the cross-spectral density function between $x(t)$ and $y(t)$. The coherence function theoretically should satisfy $0 \le \gamma_{xy}^2(f) \le 1$ for all f.

In terms of digital calculations, at the discrete frequencies $f = kf_c/m$; $k = 0, 1, 2, \ldots, m$, the coherence function is estimated by

$$\hat{\gamma}_k^2 = \frac{\hat{C}_k^2 + \hat{Q}_k^2}{\hat{G}_{k,x}\hat{G}_{k,y}} \tag{7.97}$$

where $\hat{G}_{k,x}$ and $\hat{G}_{k,y}$ represent the digital values of the power spectrum estimates at harmonic k for $x(t)$ and $y(t)$, respectively, whereas $\hat{C}_k$ and $\hat{Q}_k$ represent the digital values of the co-spectrum estimate and quad-spectrum estimate at harmonic k between $x(t)$ and $y(t)$.

Formulas for calculating more complicated partial coherence functions are discussed in Section 7.5, which deals with multiple input problems. All terms entering into partial coherence computations are described there so as to make these computations as clear as possible.

7.4.8   Computational Sequence and Digital Computer Flow Charts

The preceding work is summarized in the block diagrams of Figures 7.5 and 7.6 which show the order for computing desired sample functions for two transformed time history records $x(t)$ and $y(t)$. In the frequency response function calculation in Figure 7.6, $x(t)$ is considered as an input and $y(t)$ as an output through a linear system. For simplicity in notation, the hat ($\wedge$) is omitted for all the sample quantities in these figures.

The digital computer flow charts of Figure 7.7 show the operations to be performed by the digital computer program for the statistical analysis of single and joint time history records. The essential sequence of the operations could be approximately as indicated, if all the preceding analysis is desired. Other routines, such as tests for stationarity and randomness,

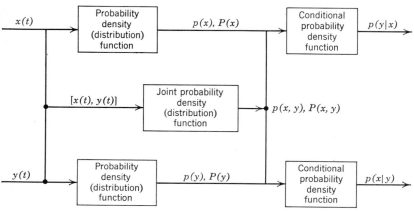

Figure 7.5   Probability functions for two records.

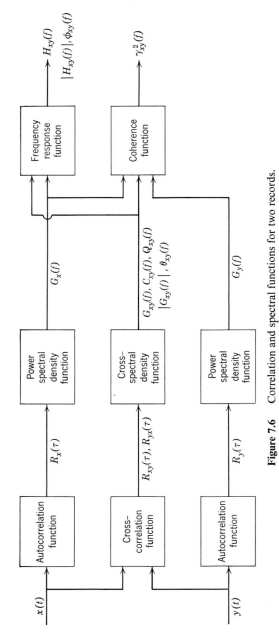

Figure 7.6 Correlation and spectral functions for two records.

can be added to incorporate additional desired tests. Moreover, if only certain parts of the program, such as power spectra alone, are requested, these can be computed directly by omitting intervening steps dealing with other information. In practice, specific machines and programs may also permit parallel operations to be performed which would modify these flow charts to permit more efficient processing.

7.5 Calculations for Multiple-Input Problems

Basic mathematical theory for multiple-input problems is discussed in Section 3.5. Calculations for these problems will be easier to explain if definite problems are considered rather than the general case. For this reason, the equations in this section will be specialized to the case of six inputs rather than an arbitrary number of inputs. The following material describes in some detail the necessary multiple frequency response computations, coherence and partial coherence function computations, and interpretation of results for this special problem. Digital computer flow diagrams are developed which are preliminary to later programming work. For simplicity in notation, the hat ($\wedge$) is omitted here for the estimated quantities both in the text and in the flow diagrams.

Assume that six (possibly correlated) input time history signals and a single-output time history signal are measured for some physical problem. For example, the six input signal points might be the wheels of a truck being driven on a rough road, whereas the output signal point is a specific location on the truck chassis. The basic objective is to properly characterize the signal transmission properties between the six input points (for example, wheels) and the output point (for example, truck location where the response is being measured). A schematic idealization of this six input–single output signal transmission problem is illustrated in Figure 7.8.

7.5.1 Multiple Frequency Response Function Computations

One must realize in this discussion that the important quantities entering into the computations are the cross-spectral density functions which are complex numbers. Two procedures are therefore optional as to the actual programming for the computer of the various formulas. If a complex arithmetic package is available as part of a compiler, or possibly as a separate package for other purposes, then this may be used directly to perform all operations. This is possible since all normal operations which may be performed on real numbers may also be performed on complex numbers. Of course, the amount of computation is considerably greater than for real numbers since, for example, multiplying two complex numbers together requires essentially four times as much work as multiplying

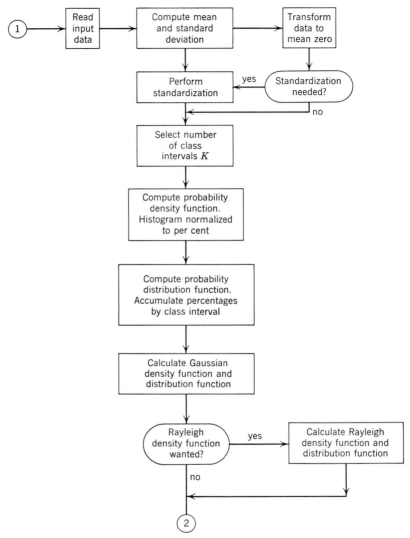

Figure 7.7 Digital computer flow charts for analysis of single and joint records.

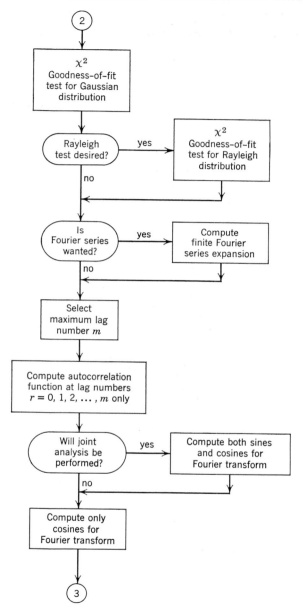

Figure 7.7   (Continued)

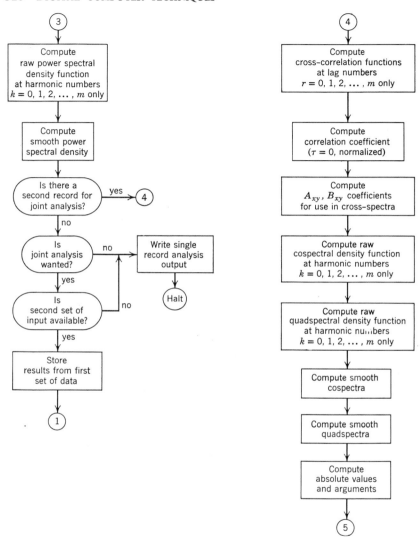

Figure 7.7   (Continued)

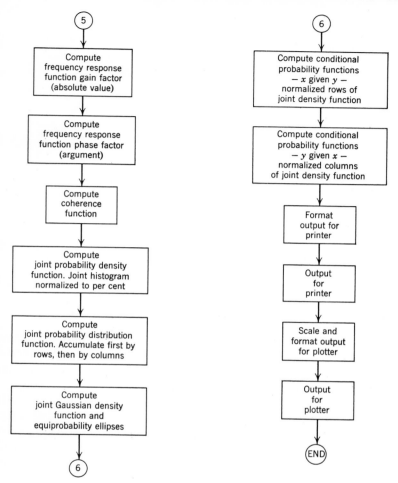

Figure 7.7 (Continued)

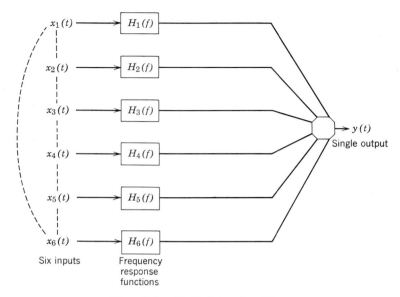

Figure 7.8   Multiple-input problem.

two real numbers together. Likewise, division operations are much more time-consuming. If a complex arithmetic package is not available, then all quantities can be handled in terms of their real and imaginary parts, and formulas can be written to calculate each part separately.

The formulas to be presented will be given in complex-valued matrix from since this is the most convenient notation for the present six input–single output problem. First of all, seven ordinary power spectral density functions must be computed, one for each input and the output. Then twenty-one cross-spectral density functions must be computed. This number includes fifteen cross-spectral density functions between all the inputs, and six between each of the inputs and the output. A 7×7 matrix of forty-nine elements is obtained with the lower-left elements being given as complex conjugates of the upper-right elements. This requires considerable computation, especially if many frequency values are necessary. Therefore, one should be extremely careful in choosing the number of frequency values at which these functions are computed in order that the computations may be minimized.

For the subsequent discussion, define a six-dimensional input vector $x(t)$ which has as components the six-input time histories being measured. That is, let

$$\mathbf{x}(t) = [x_1(t), x_2(t), \ldots, x_6(t)] \tag{7.98}$$

Next define a six-dimensional cross-spectrum vector of the output $y(t)$ with the inputs $x_i(t)$. That is,

$$\mathbf{G}_{xy} = [G_{1y}, G_{2y}, \ldots, G_{6y}] \tag{7.99}$$

where

$$G_{iy} \equiv G_{x_i y}(f) \qquad i = 1, 2, \ldots, 6 \tag{7.100}$$

Note that in the vector notation, the function of f notation is omitted in the interests of simplicity. Also, let $H_i = H_i(f)$ represent the frequency response function between the input x_i and the output y. Then define the N-dimensional frequency response function vector,

$$\mathbf{H} = [H_1, H_2, \ldots, H_6] \tag{7.101}$$

Finally, define the 6×6 matrix of the cross-spectra of all the inputs $x(t)$ by

$$\mathbf{G}_{xx} = \begin{bmatrix} G_{11} & G_{12} & \cdots & G_{16} \\ G_{21} & G_{22} & & G_{26} \\ \cdot & & & \\ \cdot & & & \\ \cdot & & & \\ G_{61} & G_{62} & & G_{66} \end{bmatrix} \tag{7.102}$$

where

$$G_{ij} = G_{x_i x_j}(f) \qquad i, j = 1, 2, \ldots, 6 \tag{7.103}$$

Fortunately, the symmetry of the matrix of Eq. (7.102) reduces the computational requirements in the sense that $G_{ji} = G_{ij}{}^*$, where the asterisk (*) indicates complex conjugate. The main diagonal consisting of the ordinary power spectra must be computed, and the upper-right portion of fifteen cross-spectra must be explicitly computed. The lower-left values are then obtained immediately by setting the imaginary part negative and reflecting across the main diagonal.

Let a prime denote the transpose of a vector. Then a six-dimensional linear system may be defined which specifies the frequency response functions in terms of the cross-spectral density functions. The formula is

$$\mathbf{G}_{xy}{}' = \mathbf{G}_{xx}\mathbf{H}' \tag{7.104}$$

Writing out in full, one has

$$\begin{bmatrix} G_{1y} \\ G_{2y} \\ \cdot \\ \cdot \\ \cdot \\ G_{6y} \end{bmatrix} = \begin{bmatrix} G_{11} & G_{12} & \cdots & G_{16} \\ G_{21} & G_{22} & & G_{26} \\ & & & \\ & & & \\ G_{61} & G_{62} & & G_{66} \end{bmatrix} \begin{bmatrix} H_1 \\ H_2 \\ \cdot \\ \cdot \\ \cdot \\ H_6 \end{bmatrix} \tag{7.105}$$

The matrix (7.105) is equivalent to a set of six simultaneous linear equations which may now be solved for the frequency response function vector **H**. The values obtained for these frequency response functions are valid whether or not the inputs are correlated. The solution of these equations requires the inversion of the 6×6 complex matrix of the cross-spectral density functions of the six inputs. This matrix is Hermitian, that is, it is equal to its transposed conjugate. This fact simplifies certain aspects of the computations as mentioned previously. However, the inversion of a complex matrix requires a special comment. A method for the inversion of a complex matrix which may be applied proceeds as follows.

Let the complex matrix $\mathbf{G}_{xx}$ be written in terms of its real and imaginary parts. That is,

$$\mathbf{G}_{xx} = \mathbf{A} + j\mathbf{B} \tag{7.106}$$

Then, the inverse of the matrix $\mathbf{G}_{xx}$ may be written as

$$\mathbf{G}_{xx}^{-1} = \mathbf{A}_1 - j\mathbf{B}_1 \tag{7.107}$$

where

$$\mathbf{A}_1 = (\mathbf{A} + \mathbf{B}\mathbf{A}^{-1}\mathbf{B})^{-1} \qquad \mathbf{B}_1 = \mathbf{A}_1\mathbf{B}\mathbf{A}^{-1} \tag{7.108}$$

In words, the real part **A** of the matrix $\mathbf{G}_{xx}$ must be inverted. Also, the matrix $\mathbf{A}_1$ given by Eq. (7.108) must be computed, which involves taking another inverse. Therefore, the inverting of the 6×6 complex matrix requires the inversion of two 6×6 real matrices plus several matrix multiplications. No particular method for inverting a real matrix will be specified here since most computing installations have their own subroutines available. A method should be employed, if possible, which takes advantage of the symmetry and antisymmetry of the real and imaginary parts, respectively, of the matrix $\mathbf{G}_{xx}$.

After this inverse matrix is computed, the six frequency response functions are obtained from the formula

$$\mathbf{H}' = \mathbf{G}_{xx}^{-1}\mathbf{G}_{xy}' \tag{7.109}$$

which is equivalent to

$$\begin{bmatrix} H_1 \\ H_2 \\ \cdot \\ \cdot \\ \cdot \\ H_6 \end{bmatrix} = \begin{bmatrix} G_{11} & G_{12} & \cdots & G_{16} \\ G_{21} & G_{22} & & G_{26} \\ & & & \\ & & & \\ & & & \\ G_{61} & G_{62} & & G_{66} \end{bmatrix}^{-1} \begin{bmatrix} G_{1y} \\ G_{2y} \\ \cdot \\ \cdot \\ \cdot \\ G_{6y} \end{bmatrix} \tag{7.110}$$

It is tacitly assumed that the matrix $\mathbf{G}_{xx}$ is nonsingular and that the Inverse exists. If it is singular (of rank less than 6), then at least one row is a linear combination of others, which means at least two inputs are perfectly coherent. This would mean less than six inputs effectively are present. These matters require separate consideration and special handling.

7.5.2 Coherence and Partial Coherence Function Computations

The digital formula for an ordinary coherence function is given by Eq. (7.97). This formula may be applied to any pair of the inputs or, more reasonably, to any input paired with the output to obtain ordinary coherence function values between all inputs and the output. Formulas for the partial coherence function will now be presented. First, define a 7×7 matrix which consists of the original 6×6 matrix of the cross-spectral densities of the input functions, and let this matrix be augmented by a cross-spectral density function vector of the inputs with the output. That is, let

$$\mathbf{G}_{yxx} = \begin{bmatrix} G_{yy} & G_{y1} & G_{y2} & \cdots & G_{y6} \\ G_{1y} & G_{11} & G_{12} & & G_{16} \\ G_{2y} & G_{21} & G_{22} & & G_{26} \\ & & \vdots & & \\ G_{6y} & G_{61} & G_{62} & & G_{66} \end{bmatrix} \tag{7.111}$$

where $G_{yi} = G_{iy}{}^{*}$.

From this matrix, the residual (conditioned) spectral matrix between x_1 and y is obtained by the following matrix formula.

$$\mathbf{G}_{xy \cdot 2 \cdots 6} = \begin{bmatrix} G_{yy} & G_{y1} \\ G_{1y} & G_{11} \end{bmatrix}$$

$$- \begin{bmatrix} G_{y2} & \cdots & G_{y6} \\ G_{12} & \cdots & G_{16} \end{bmatrix} \begin{bmatrix} G_{22} & \cdots & G_{26} \\ & \ddots & \\ G_{62} & \cdots & G_{66} \end{bmatrix}^{-1} \begin{bmatrix} G_{2y} & G_{21} \\ & \ddots & \\ G_{6y} & G_{61} \end{bmatrix} \tag{7.112}$$

$$= \begin{bmatrix} G_{yy.2 \cdots 6} & G_{y1.2 \cdots 6} \\ G_{1y.2 \cdots 6} & G_{11.2 \cdots 6} \end{bmatrix}$$

The partial coherence function between x_1 and y is now given by the equation

$$\gamma_{1y.2 \cdots 6}^{2} = \frac{|G_{1y.2 \cdots 6}|^{2}}{G_{yy.2 \cdots 6} G_{11.2 \cdots 6}} \tag{7.113}$$

where the individual terms in Eq. (7.113), called residual spectra, are obtained from Eq. (7.112). The notation in this equation is intended to indicate that relations are being investigated between variables x_1 and y, while effects of other variables $x_2, \ldots, x_6$ are subtracted out. The partial coherence formula of Eq. (7.113) involves the residual input spectrum, residual output spectrum, and residual cross-spectrum, quantities which are direct extensions of the ordinary input spectrum, output spectrum, and cross-spectrum for two variables alone.

Observe that extensive computations are required in order to arrive at the partial coherence function. This is because a 5×5 matrix has to be inverted to obtain Eq. (7.112) for each value of a partial coherence function that is to be computed. Note also that this generally is a complex-valued matrix. However, the partial coherence function quantities as given by Eq. (7.113) are real values. This is due to the fact that, although the residual cross-spectrum between x_1 and y is a complex number, its absolute value squared is real, and this is the quantity entering into Eq. (7.113). Moreover, the residual input spectrum and the residual output spectrum are real numbers.

An alternative way to calculate $H_1(f)$, rather than by Eq. (7.110), is to use the formula

$$H_1(f) = \frac{G_{1y.2 \cdots 6}(f)}{G_{11.2 \cdots 6}(f)} \tag{7.114}$$

where the terms in Eq. (7.114) are obtained from Eq. (7.112). This is a direct extension of the well-known result for the single input–single output linear system where the numerator is simply $G_{1y}(f)$ and the denominator is simply $G_{11}(f)$.

It should be possible to apply a recursive technique to obtain several subsequent inverse matrices after one has been found. For example, under proper conditions, a matrix inverse may be expanded in a Taylor series as if it were a scalar variable. Assume $\mathbf{A}$ is a matrix with known inverse $\mathbf{A}^{-1}$, and that the inverse of a matrix $\mathbf{B} = \mathbf{A} + \Delta\mathbf{A}$ is desired. Then $\mathbf{B}^{-1}$ may be approximated by

$$\mathbf{B}^{-1} = (\mathbf{A} + \Delta\mathbf{A})^{-1} \approx \mathbf{A}^{-1}(\mathbf{I} - \mathbf{A}^{-1}\Delta\mathbf{A} + (\mathbf{A}^{-1}\Delta\mathbf{A})^2) \tag{7.115}$$

where $\mathbf{I}$ is the identity matrix.

Equation (7.115) requires that the norm (in some appropriate sense) of $\Delta\mathbf{A}$ is sufficiently less than the norm of $\mathbf{A}$, such that a term $(\mathbf{A}^{-1}\Delta\mathbf{A})^3$ is negligible. If $\Delta\mathbf{A}$ is sufficiently small, possibly even the $(\mathbf{A}^{-1}\Delta\mathbf{A})^2$ term can be discarded from the approximation Eq. (7.115). The inverse matrix, $\mathbf{B}^{-1}$, may therefore be obtained via matrix multiplications and additions which will usually be faster than finding the inverse directly.

One must apply these procedures with caution since round-off and truncation errors will generally build up after a few applications of the method. Hence, at appropriate intervals, the application of the recursive procedure of Eq. (7.115) must be interrupted and an inverse must be computed directly.

All the calculations indicated above only serve to compute the partial coherence functions between the input x_1 and the output y. There are five other partial coherence functions to be computed, those between the input x_2 and y, the input x_3 and y, up to between the input x_6 and y. In order to obtain these, one takes the matrix indicated by Eq. (7.111) and first trades positions between the second and third rows and the second and third columns. Then Eqs. (7.112) and (7.113) are recomputed. This will give the coherence function between the second input x_2 and the output y. Repeat this process for all six variables.

This concludes the description of applicable formulas necessary to compute the frequency response functions for a multiple input situation and the associated partial coherence functions. The ordinary coherence functions are not adequate for this multiple input situation since the correlation occurring between the various input variables may obscure the true relations between any given input and the output. If the ordinary coherence function were computed, one might obtain high coherencies when in fact they did not exist, and vice versa. The computation of the partial coherencies, however, subtracts out the effects due to correlation between the variables and the true relations between any given input and the output is exposed. These matters are discussed more fully in Sections 3.5 and 5.7. The statistical accuracy of these frequency response function measurements requires further computation and analysis as discussed in Sections 5.7.4 and 5.7.5 involving multiple coherence functions.

7.5.3 Digital Computer Flow Chart

Assume that a large-scale digital computer is employed for the computations. Further assume this computer has seven magnetic tape units available for use as data input units. Hence each input time history and the output time history are available on separate tape units. There must also be available at least one tape for final computer output in addition to at least one tape (or large capacity magnetic drum or disc file) on which to store intermediate computational results. The computational procedure might then take place in the sequence indicated by the following digital computer flow chart of Figure 7.9. All terms shown should be calculated at discrete frequencies as indicated in earlier sections of this chapter.

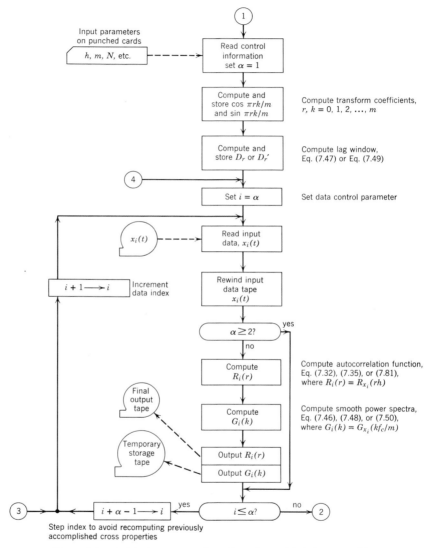

Figure 7.9   Digital computer flow chart for multiple input problem.

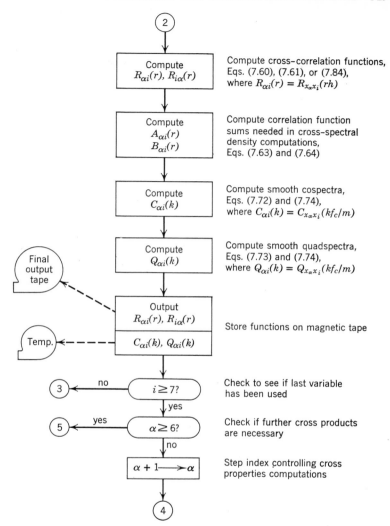

Figure 7.9 (Continued)

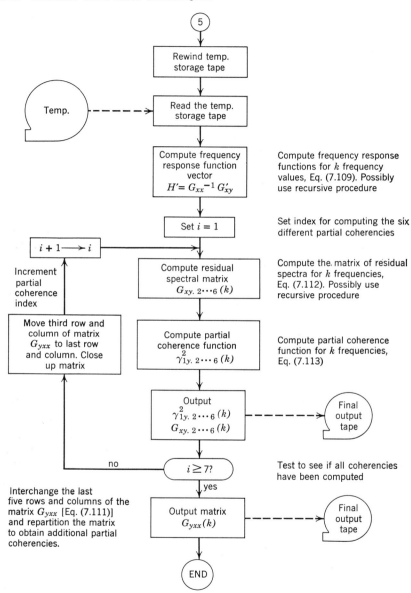

Figure 7.9 (Continued)

8

ILLUSTRATION OF
EXPERIMENTAL PROCEDURES

The basic statistical background needed to design an experiment and evaluate the resulting data is covered in Chapter 4. Many of the practical procedures discussed in that chapter ultimately involve the testing of a hypothesis. To help clarify the usefulness of hypothesis testing as a general tool of experimental design and data evaluation, a detailed discussion based upon actual experimental data is now presented.

Referring to Eq. (5.93), the variance for an unbiased power spectral density estimate, $\hat{G}(f)$, is theoretically given by

$$\text{Var}[\hat{G}(f)] = \frac{G^2(f)}{B_e T} \tag{8.1}$$

where B_e is the frequency resolution bandwidth in cps, T is the sampling time in seconds, and $G(f)$ is the true spectral density being estimated. From Section 6.1.4, if the averaging procedure required to measure $\hat{G}(f)$ is performed by smoothing with a low-pass RC filter where the available sample record is of unlimited length T_r, then $T = 2K$, where K is the RC averaging time constant in seconds. Hence, for this case, Eq. (8.1) becomes

$$\text{Var}[\hat{G}(f)] = \frac{G^2(f)}{2B_e K} \qquad K \ll T_r \tag{8.2}$$

In terms of a normalized variance, the relationship is

$$\epsilon^2 = \frac{\text{Var}[\hat{G}(f)]}{G^2(f)} = \frac{1}{2B_e K} \qquad K \ll T_r \tag{8.3}$$

Since most analog PSD analyzers perform averaging by smoothing with a low-pass RC filter, Eq. (8.3) represents an important practical relationship. An experimental program designed to verify the preceding

321

relationship will now be detailed. The data used for the discussion consist of actual analog power spectral density measurements taken from Ref. 5.

8.1 Design of the Experiment

The general purpose of the experiment is to verify the theoretical expression for the normalized variance of RC averaged power spectral density estimates, as given by Eq. (8.3). The basic procedure is to gather a series of N statistically independent power spectral density estimates, $\hat{G}_i$, $i = 1, 2, 3, \ldots, N$, for a specific set of measurement parameters, B_e, K, and f_c. A variance for the series of estimates is then computed and an experimental value for ϵ^2 is determined. The procedure is repeated for different values of B_e, K, and f_c. The resulting set of empirical values for ϵ^2 are then used to test the validity of Eq. (8.3).

For each set of N statistically independent estimates, $\hat{G}_i$, a sample mean and variance are computed as follows.

$$\bar{G} = \frac{1}{N} \sum_{i=1}^{N} \hat{G}_i \tag{8.4a}$$

$$s^2 = \frac{1}{N-1} \sum_{i=1}^{N} (\hat{G}_i - \bar{G})^2 = \frac{1}{N-1} \left[\sum_{i=1}^{N} \hat{G}_i^2 - \bar{G} \sum_{i=1}^{N} \hat{G}_i \right] \tag{8.4b}$$

Assuming that the power spectrum of the signal being measured is relatively uniform over the resolution bandwidth B_e, the expected value for the above sample mean is the true power spectral density G. The expected value for the sample variance is the true variance of the estimate $\text{Var}[\hat{G}]$, which will be denoted by σ^2 for simplicity. That is,

$$E[\bar{G}] = G \tag{8.5a}$$

$$E[s^2] = \text{Var}[\hat{G}] = \sigma^2 \tag{8.5b}$$

From Eq. (8.3), the theoretical normalized variance ϵ^2 for the estimates is given by

$$\epsilon^2 = \frac{\sigma^2}{G^2} \tag{8.6}$$

From the experimental data gathered, an estimate for the normalized variance is given by

$$\hat{\epsilon}^2 = \frac{s^2}{(\bar{G})^2} \tag{8.7}$$

8.1.1 Distribution for Sample Values

It is first necessary to define a sampling distribution for the estimates $\hat{\epsilon}^2$. An exact sampling distribution for $\hat{\epsilon}^2$ could perhaps be determined from basic statistical sampling theory, but such an exact determination would, at best, be quite difficult. By imposing minor restrictions on the experimental procedures, simplifying assumptions can be made which will yield an approximate sampling distribution for $\hat{\epsilon}^2$.

From Eq. (8.7), it is seen that $\hat{\epsilon}^2$ is a function of a sample variance s^2 and a sample mean $\bar{G}$. A variance for $\hat{\epsilon}^2$ in terms of s^2 and $\bar{G}$ can be established by expanding $\hat{\epsilon}^2$ into a Taylor series about the point $\epsilon^2 = \sigma^2/G^2$ as follows.

$$\hat{\epsilon}^2 = \frac{s^2}{(\bar{G})^2} = \frac{\sigma^2}{G^2} + (s^2 - \sigma^2)\frac{\partial \hat{\epsilon}^2}{\partial s^2}\bigg|_{\sigma^2, G} + (\bar{G} - G)\frac{\partial \hat{\epsilon}^2}{\partial G}\bigg|_{\sigma^2, G}$$
$$+ \text{ higher-order terms}$$

$$= \frac{\sigma^2}{G^2} + (s^2 - \sigma^2)\left(\frac{1}{G^2}\right) + (\bar{G} - G)\left(\frac{-2\sigma^2}{G^3}\right) + \text{ higher-order terms}$$

(8.8)

Neglecting higher-order terms and assuming that the random variables s^2 and $\bar{G}$ are independently distributed with expected values of σ^2 and G, respectively, the variance of $\hat{\epsilon}^2$ becomes

$$\text{Var}[\hat{\epsilon}^2] \approx \frac{1}{G^4}\text{Var}[s^2] + \frac{4\sigma^4}{G^6}\text{Var}[\bar{G}] \tag{8.9}$$

Consider first the variance for s^2. If it is assumed that the estimates $\hat{G}_i$ are normally distributed (the validity of this assumption is discussed later), then, from Section 4.3.2, s^2 will have a distribution associated with chi square as follows.

$$\frac{s^2}{\sigma^2} = \frac{\chi_n^2}{n} \qquad n = N - 1 \tag{8.10}$$

Noting that the variance for a chi-square distribution is $2n$, it follows that

$$\text{Var}[s^2] = \text{Var}\left[\frac{\sigma^2 \chi_n^2}{n}\right] = \frac{\sigma^4(2n)}{n^2} = \frac{2\sigma^4}{n} \tag{8.11}$$

Now consider the variance for $\bar{G}$. The sample mean $\bar{G}$ is the average of N number of repeated power spectral density measurements $\hat{G}_i$, each of which has a theoretical variance of σ^2. Hence the variance for $\bar{G}$ becomes

$$\text{Var}[\bar{G}] = \text{Var}\left[\frac{1}{N}\sum_{i=1}^{N}\hat{G}_i\right] = \frac{\sum_{i=1}^{N}\text{Var}[G_i]}{N^2} = \frac{\sigma^2}{N} \qquad (8.12)$$

Substituting Eqs. (8.11) and (8.12) into Eq. (8.9), and noting that $\epsilon = \sigma/G$,

$$\text{Var}[\hat{\epsilon}^2] \approx \frac{2\epsilon^4}{n} + \frac{4\epsilon^6}{N} \approx \frac{2\epsilon^4}{n}(1 + 2\epsilon^2) \qquad \text{for } N \gg 1 \qquad (8.13)$$

From Eq. (8.11), it is seen that the term $2\epsilon^4/n$ in Eq. (8.13) represents the normalized portion of the variance due to s^2, and the term $4\epsilon^6/n$ represents the normalized portion of the variance contributed by $\bar{G}$. As ϵ^2 becomes small, the contribution of the variance of $\bar{G}$ to the variance of $\hat{\epsilon}^2$ clearly becomes negligible. For such cases, the sampling distribution for $\hat{\epsilon}^2$ may be assumed to be equal to the sampling distribution for s^2/σ^2 as given in Eq. (8.10).

Referring back to Eq. (8.9), the assumption that the sample variance and mean, s^2 and $\bar{G}$, are independently distributed is theoretically valid if the sample values $\hat{G}_i$ are normally distributed. This same requirement applies to the assumption in Eq. (8.10) that the sample variance s^2 is distributed as chi square. However, the values of $\hat{G}_i$ are power spectral density measurements which are effectively mean square value estimates. Assuming the sampled random signal is Gaussian, the values $\hat{G}_i$ would be distributed as chi-square rather than normally. Nevertheless, the normality assumption should be acceptable here as long as the normalized variance for the measurements ϵ^2 is small. This is true because a chi-square distribution approaches a normal distribution as the number of degrees of freedom becomes large. A small value for ϵ^2 is equivalent to a large number of degrees of freedom ($n = 2/\epsilon^2$).

8.1.2 Basic Statistical Hypothesis Test

The ultimate goal of the experiment is to establish that the normalized variance of RC averaged power spectral density measurements is equal to the theoretical value given by Eq. (8.3). This equality, or lack of equality, may be established using a hypothesis test as discussed in Section 4.5.

Specifically, let it be hypothesized that the true normalized variance ϵ^2 is equal to $1/2B_eK$, as given by Eq. (8.3). That is,

$$\epsilon^2 = \frac{1}{2B_eK} \qquad (8.14)$$

The hypothesis is tested by comparing the observed difference between $\hat{\epsilon}^2$ and $1/2B_eK$ with the difference that would be expected due to statistical variability in $\hat{\epsilon}^2$. As already noted, the sampling distribution for $\hat{\epsilon}^2$ may be approximated (with certain restrictions) as follows

$$\frac{\hat{\epsilon}^2}{\epsilon^2} \sim \frac{\chi_n^2}{n} \qquad n = N - 1 \tag{8.15}$$

From Eq. (8.15), the acceptance region for the hypothesis test at any desired level of significance α is given by

$$\frac{\chi_{n;1-\alpha/2}^2}{n} < 2B_eK\hat{\epsilon}^2 \le \frac{\chi_{n;\alpha/2}^2}{n} \tag{8.16}$$

8.1.3 Selection of Sample Size

Assume one is prepared to accept a 100α per cent risk of incurring a Type I Error and a 100β per cent risk of incurring a Type II Error for detecting a ratio of d^2 between the true value and hypothesized value (the difference to be detected is expressed as a ratio because χ^2/n is the distribution for a ratio). The true normalized variance for a power spectral density measurement to be detected with a probability of β may be either higher or lower than $1/2B_eK$. The value to be detected on the high side is $d^2/2B_eK$ and the value to be detected on the low side is $1/2B_eKd^2$, as illustrated in Figure 8.1. Given the information in the figure, the following relationships apply:

$$\text{upper limit} = \frac{\chi_{n;\alpha/2}^2}{2B_eKn} = \frac{d^2\chi_{n;1-\beta/2}^2}{2B_eKn} \tag{8.17a}$$

$$\text{lower limit} = \frac{\chi_{n;1-\alpha/2}^2}{2B_eKn} = \frac{\chi_{n;\beta/2}^2}{2B_eKnd^2} \tag{8.17b}$$

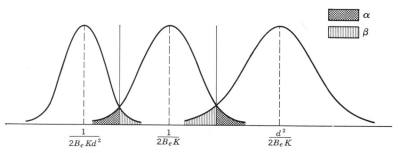

Figure 8.1 Type I and type II error regions.

From Eqs. (8.17), it follows that

$$\chi^2_{n;\alpha/2} = d^2\chi^2_{n;1-\beta/2}$$
$$d^2\chi^2_{n;1-\alpha/2} = \chi^2_{n;\beta/2}$$

(8.18)

By selecting an equal risk of making a Type I or a Type II Error ($\alpha = \beta$), Eq. (8.18) reduces to

$$d^2 = \frac{\chi^2_{n;\alpha/2}}{\chi^2_{n;1-\alpha/2}}$$

(8.19)

Hence, for any desired level of significance α and probability $\beta = \alpha$ of a Type II Error in detecting a given ratio d^2, the number of samples required for the hypothesis is that value of $N = n + 1$ which satisfies the chi-square ratio in Eq. (8.19).

The first step required to apply Eq. (8.19) is to decide upon the difference from the hypothesized variance which is to be detected with a probability of β. In some specific situations, one might have suspicions about the theory being tested and hence might anticipate some particular value other than the hypothesized value. In other situations, the difference to be detected with probability β is arrived at somewhat arbitrarily. In any case, however, the selected difference should be relatively large compared to possible bias errors anticipated in the measured values to be used for the hypothesis test.

For example, if the measurements used to compute $\hat{\epsilon}^2$ were 5 per cent too high because of a calibration error, this would result in an estimate with an expected value of $(1.05)^2\epsilon^2$. If the selected ratio to be detected with high probability were $d^2 = (1.05)^2$, it is clear that the resulting hypothesis test would almost certainly result in a Type I Error. For the experiment at hand, a ratio of standard deviations of 1.2 ($d^2 = 1.44$) should be adequate to minimize the effect of bias errors in the power spectral density measurements while still providing for a rigorous hypothesis test.

The next step required to apply Eq. (8.19) is to decide upon an acceptable value for α and β to be used in the test. To make this decision, the difficulty and expense of collecting sampled data must be weighed against the consequences of incurring a Type I or Type II error. For those cases where a dollar value can be associated with both the collection of data and the consequences of an error, an optimum value for α and β can be selected by quantitative techniques of statistical decision theory. However, in most practical cases, the decision is made in a more qualitative manner. Generally speaking, if data are very difficult to obtain and the prospect of an error is not catastrophic, a value of $\alpha = \beta = 0.05$ or greater might be used for a hypothesis test. On the other hand, if data are relatively easy to obtain, and/or if an error would involve serious consequences, a value of $\alpha = \beta = 0.01$ or less should be used. For the experiment at hand, data are relatively easy to obtain. Hence a Type I and Type II error risk of $\alpha = \beta = 0.01$ will be selected for the hypothesis test.

With the preceding information substituted in Eq. (8.19), it follows that the sample size for the experiment must satisfy the following equation.

$$\frac{\chi^2_{n;0.005}}{\chi^2_{n;0.995}} = 1.44 \tag{8.20}$$

From the normal approximation for $\chi^2_{n;\alpha}$ given in Table 4.8, this relationship is satisfied for $n \approx 400$. Hence the required sample size here is $N \approx 400$.

8.2 Experimental Procedures and Instruments

From Eq. (8.16), for $n \approx 400$ and $\alpha = \beta = 0.01$, the region of acceptance for the test is

$$[0.83 \leq 2B_e K \hat{\epsilon}^2 \leq 1.19] \tag{8.21}$$

If the computed quantity $2B_e K \hat{\epsilon}^2$ falls outside the noted interval, the hypothesis will be rejected at the 1 per cent level of significance. Otherwise, the hypothesis will be accepted.

To properly verify the functional relationships indicated by Eq. (8.14), the experiment should be performed with several different bandwidths, averaging time constants, and center frequencies. This may be accomplished by dividing the required $N \approx 400$ measurements into several groups, each having a different set of values for B_e, K, and f_c. A sample mean and variance can be computed for each group of measurements using Eq. (8.4). The values of $2B_e K \hat{\epsilon}^2$ computed for each group should be equivalent. Their average will yield the value needed to test the hypothesis of Eq. (8.14).

A final problem is to select a proper range of values for ϵ^2 to be tested. The important requirement here is that ϵ^2 should be sufficiently large so that bias errors in the measurements will be insignificant compared to the estimates $\hat{\epsilon}^2$. However, because of assumptions in the experimental design procedures discussed in Section 8.1.1, ϵ^2 should also be sufficiently small to make the noted assumptions reasonable. For the experiment at hand, a range for ϵ^2 between 0.01 to 0.10 appears appropriate, particularly since this range covers the values for ϵ^2 which are most commonly found in practice.

8.2.1 Grouping of Experiments

The $N \approx 400$ required power spectral density measurements will be divided into seven groups, each representing a combination of values for B_e, K, and f_c as outlined in Table 8.1. Hence, 57 measurements will be required for each group, for a total of 399 samples.

Table 8.1 **Measurement Parameters for Experiment**

Group	B_e (cps)	K (seconds)	f_c (cps)	ϵ^2
1	56	0.84	1,000	0.011
2	56	0.40	1,000	0.022
3	56	0.13	1,000	0.068
4	56	0.84	100	0.011
5	56	0.84	10,000	0.011
6	28	0.84	1,000	0.023
7	14	0.84	1,000	0.043

From Table 8.1, it is seen that three different filter bandwidths (14, 28, 56 cps), three different averaging time constants (0.13, 0.40, 0.84 seconds) and three different center frequencies (100, 1000, 10,000 cps) are chosen for the experiment. These values represent a practical range of available selections for the parameters of the commercial PSD analyzer used for the experiment. Observe, however, that each combination of parameters is selected to result in a value for ϵ^2 between 0.01 and 0.10.

8.2.2 Test Set-Up

A block diagram of the test set-up is illustrated in Figure 8.2. The random noise generator (item A) is used as the source of a stationary random signal which has an approximately Gaussian probability density function and a reasonably uniform power spectral density function over the frequency range of interest. The actual measured probability density function for the noise generator is shown in Figure 8.3, and the actual measured power spectrum from 100 to 10,000 cps is shown in Figure 8.4.

The voltmeter (item B) is used to measure the output of the noise generator for reference purposes. The PSD analyzer (item C) is used to obtain the required power spectral density estimates at various center frequencies and with various bandwidths and averaging times, as discussed in Section 6.4. The instrument employs the heterodyne principle to transpose the applied signal in frequency past a highly selective narrow-band crystal filter. The instrument performs the final averaging operation by smoothing with an equivalent low-pass RC filter. The strip chart recorder (item D) is used to record power spectral density time history samples.

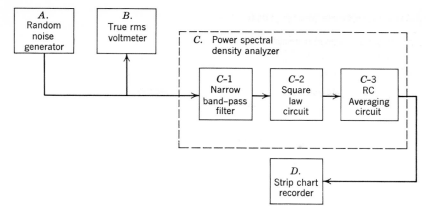

Figure 8.2 Block diagram of test set-up.

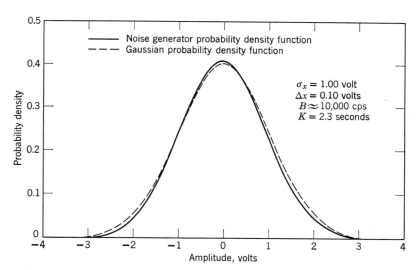

Figure 8.3 Measured probability density function for random noise generator.

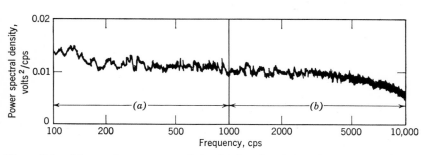

Figure 8.4 Measured power spectral density function for random noise generator.
(a) $B_e = 14$ cps. $K = 15$ seconds. (b) $B_e = 56$ cps. $K = 4$ seconds.

Table 8.2 Experimental Power Spectral Density Estimates $\hat{G}$ for Different Filter Bandwidths, Center Frequencies and Averaging Time Constants

Estimate No.	$B_e = 56$ cps $f_c = 1000$ cps			$K = 0.84$ sec $B_e = 56$ cps		$f_c = 1000$ cps $K = 0.84$ sec	
	$K = 0.84$	$K = 0.40$	$K = 0.13$	$f_c = 100$	$f_c = 10,000$	$B_e = 28$	$B_e = 14$
1	5.10	4.60	4.75	4.55	5.53	4.80	3.20
2	4.20	4.74	2.71	5.34	4.80	2.85	4.42
3	5.13	4.28	4.06	5.13	5.08	3.13	4.98
4	4.33	4.19	3.50	4.29	4.73	3.96	4.40
5	4.79	5.00	4.00	4.93	4.41	4.02	4.61
6	4.58	5.95	3.71	4.52	5.22	3.69	4.69
7	4.83	4.02	4.41	5.04	5.13	4.16	5.10
8	4.44	4.40	3.16	4.36	5.12	3.28	4.62
9	4.00	4.72	5.00	4.40	4.84	3.83	4.16
10	5.01	4.30	2.75	5.30	4.51	3.34	5.00
11	3.78	4.24	5.60	4.43	4.72	4.56	3.45
12	3.95	5.00	5.39	4.79	4.95	3.13	5.10
13	4.51	4.55	3.46	3.92	4.60	3.70	3.99
14	5.03	4.97	5.70	4.47	4.84	4.67	6.08
15	4.52	5.09	3.10	4.12	3.98	4.20	5.81
16	5.64	5.40	2.92	5.15	4.92	3.79	4.82
17	4.30	4.75	3.45	5.03	5.79	4.14	4.70
18	3.94	5.12	4.71	4.84	4.79	4.22	5.02
19	4.46	4.99	2.98	4.60	4.60	3.99	4.60
20	4.90	3.97	3.15	4.28	4.99	3.90	4.93
21	4.65	4.78	5.95	3.88	3.83	3.78	5.88
22	4.42	6.12	2.54	4.71	6.22	4.32	4.67
23	4.96	5.62	2.69	4.19	4.40	3.60	6.40
24	5.07	5.23	3.61	4.80	4.92	5.01	4.32
25	4.15	6.35	4.52	3.92	5.03	4.81	4.06
26	4.20	5.28	2.90	5.25	4.65	3.32	6.02
27	4.62	6.12	2.26	4.08	4.30	4.93	5.30
28	4.54	4.30	3.97	4.83	5.16	3.42	5.62
29	4.45	5.60	3.44	4.81	4.80	3.17	4.10
30	4.28	5.48	5.12	4.82	4.78	3.15	3.01
31	5.24	5.02	3.50	4.08	5.46	3.23	4.85
32	4.57	4.36	4.58	4.93	6.19	3.60	5.53
33	4.10	5.79	4.25	4.90	5.35	2.89	4.60
34	5.25	5.36	4.27	4.75	5.58	3.42	4.41
35	4.58	5.39	3.00	4.10	4.60	3.54	3.95
36	5.05	6.88	5.95	5.02	5.21	4.50	3.53
37	5.28	4.92	1.92	4.25	4.77	3.50	4.08
38	4.60	4.65	5.31	4.66	4.59	4.40	3.22
39	5.53	6.22	1.71	4.23	4.61	3.52	4.80
40	4.04	4.20	3.70	4.12	4.50	3.48	4.19
41	4.52	4.62	3.40	4.75	5.05	5.39	5.76
42	4.88	4.34	4.50	4.11	5.02	3.70	3.42
43	4.83	5.32	2.01	4.30	4.11	3.01	4.55
44	4.70	4.24	4.38	5.70	4.55	4.08	4.90
45	4.61	4.43	4.39	4.13	4.35	3.61	5.50
46	4.42	4.48	3.59	4.68	4.68	3.75	4.30
47	3.95	5.27	3.72	5.16	5.01	4.34	3.59
48	5.16	5.58	3.71	4.45	4.90	4.52	4.63
49	5.43	4.99	4.32	4.60	4.55	3.13	5.48
50	4.78	5.27	4.53	3.74	4.49	4.02	3.97
51	4.40	5.76	4.01	4.92	5.30	4.18	3.41
52	4.52	3.65	3.22	3.73	4.08	4.80	6.55
53	4.45	4.61	1.80	4.52	3.78	3.75	5.90
54	4.08	4.42	3.50	4.45	5.42	4.89	5.68
55	5.27	3.80	2.30	4.89	4.00	4.00	4.94
56	4.40	4.02	3.60	5.22	4.29	4.32	4.52
57	4.08	4.21	2.44	5.11	4.40	3.10	4.75

8.3   Results of Experiment

The 57 power spectral density estimates gathered for each of the seven combinations of B_e, K, and f_c are presented in Table 8.2. A picture of some typical test data for power spectral density estimates obtained by continuous RC averaging is shown in Figure 8.5. Each spectral density measurement in Table 8.2 was obtained by reading the value of the continuous spectral density time history plot at equally spaced intervals of time. A time interval of at least four time constants ($4K$) was allowed to make sure that the resulting set of estimates would be statistically independent.

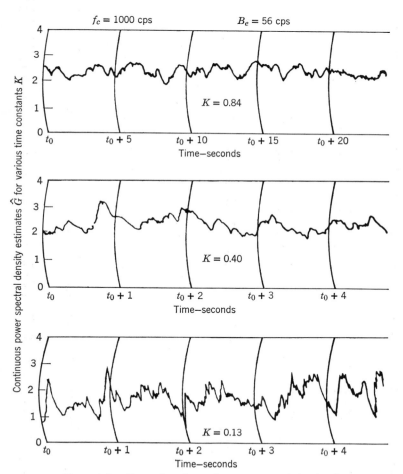

Figure 8.5   Examples of actual power spectral density data.

Table 8.3   Sample Variance for Power Spectral Density Estimates

Group	$\bar{G}$ [Eq. (8.4a)]	s^2 [Eq. (8.4b)]	$\hat{\epsilon}^2$ [Eq. (8.7)]	$2B_eK$	$2B_eK\hat{\epsilon}^2$
1	4.623	0.195	0.0091	94	0.86
2	4.929	0.484	0.020	45	0.90
3	3.739	1.10	0.079	15	1.2
4	4.619	0.186	0.0087	94	0.82
5	4.815	0.264	0.011	94	1.0
6	3.887	0.364	0.024	47	1.1
7	4.703	0.693	0.031	24	0.74
					Sum = 6.6

Average value for $2\,B_eK\hat{\epsilon}^2$ based on 399 samples $= 0.94$.

The various computations needed to arrive at the value for $2B_eK\hat{\epsilon}^2$ are summarized in Table 8.3. It should be noted that no effort was made to use the same power spectral density for the different experiments, which is why the values for $\bar{G}$ vary. From Table 8.3, the result of the experiment is that $2B_eK\hat{\epsilon}^2 = 0.94$. Referring to Eq. (8.21), the hypothesis that $\epsilon^2 = 1/2B_eK$ is *accepted*. Hence there is no reason to question the practical validity of Eq. (8.3).

9

ANALYSIS OF
NONSTATIONARY DATA

The material in previous chapters has been restricted largely to the measurement and analysis of stationary data. The theoretical ideas, the processing techniques, and the statistical error formulas do not, for the most part, apply when the data are nonstationary. Special considerations and procedures are required for analyzing nonstationary data which will be discussed in this chapter.

Nonstationary data represent any class of data whose statistical properties change with time. Consequently, the vast majority of physical data actually falls in this area. It is only for reasons of approximation and simplicity that many data are arbitrarily assumed to be stationary. Nonstationary data are obtained, for example, during transient operating conditions when an environment changes suddenly, or during long-range operating periods when system properties change so that a given input will produce a variable output.

A totally adequate methodology does not exist as yet for the analysis of all types of nonstationary data. This is partly due to the fact that a nonstationary conclusion is generally a negative statement specifying the lack of stationary properties, rather than defining the precise nature of the nonstationarity. On the other hand, when a process is deemed stationary, certain positive results are known which apply to all stationary data. Special techniques must be developed for nonstationary data which apply only to limited classes of these data. Examples of different types of nonstationary data are shown in Figure 9.1.

The characterization of nonstationary data should begin by studying various types of nonstationarity. Three basic and important types which can represent certain physically occurring nonstationary data are: (1) A time-varying mean value, Figure 9.1(a). (2) A time-varying mean square value, Figure 9.1(b). (3) A combination of the above, Figure 9.1(c).

333

For joint statistical properties between values of a single nonstationary process at different times, the process can be described further in terms of its: (1) nonstationary probability density function, (2) nonstationary autocorrelation function, (3) nonstationary power spectral density func-

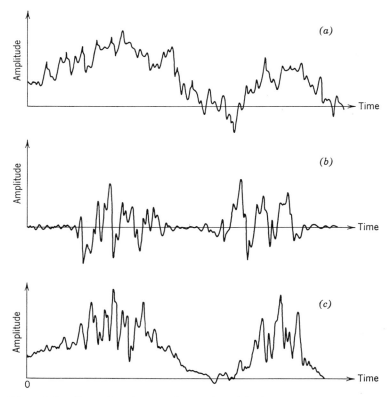

Figure 9.1 Examples of nonstationary data. (*a*) Time-varying mean value. (*b*) Time-varying mean square value. (*c*) Time-varying mean and mean square value.

tion. Interpretations of these functions, assuming they are measured properly, is a critical issue.

For pairs of nonstationary processes, one should investigate (1) joint nonstationary probability density functions, (2) nonstationary cross-correlation functions, and (3) nonstationary cross-spectral density functions. It is important to determine input-output relations for passage of nonstationary data through physical systems.

9.1 Probability Structure of Nonstationary Data

For a nonstationary random process $\{x(t)\}$, as discussed in Chapters 1 and 3, statistical properties over the ensemble at any time t are not invariant with respect to translations in t. Hence, at any value of $t = t_1$, the probability structure of the random variable $x(t_1)$ would be a function of t_1. To be precise, the *first-order nonstationary probability density function* $p(x, t_1)$ for $\{x(t_1)\}$ is defined by

$$p(x, t_1) = \lim_{\Delta x \to 0} \frac{\text{Prob} \left[x < x(t_1) \leq x + \Delta x \right]}{\Delta x} \tag{9.1}$$

and has the following basic properties for any t.

$$1 = \int_{-\infty}^{\infty} p(x, t) \, dx$$

$$\mu_x(t) = E[x(t)] = \int_{-\infty}^{\infty} x \, p(x, t) \, dx$$

$$\Psi_x^2(t) = E[x^2(t)] = \int_{-\infty}^{\infty} x^2 \, p(x, t) \, dx \tag{9.2}$$

$$\sigma_x^2(t) = E[\{x(t) - \mu_x(t)\}^2] = \Psi_x^2(t) - \mu_x^2(t)$$

These formulas also apply to stationary cases where $p(x, t) = p(x)$, independent of t. The measurement of nonstationary mean values $\mu_x(t)$ and nonstationary mean square values $\Psi_x^2(t)$ is discussed in Sections 9.2 and 9.3.

The *first-order nonstationary probability distribution function* $P(x, t_1)$ is defined by

$$P(x, t_1) = \text{Prob} \left[-\infty < x(t_1) \leq x \right] \tag{9.3}$$

and clearly is a simpler quantity than $p(x, t_1)$. Similar relationships exist for $P(x, t_1)$ as for the stationary probability distribution function $P(x)$ discussed in Chapter 3.

If the nonstationary random process $\{x(t)\}$ is *Gaussian* at $t = t_1$, then $p(x, t_1)$ takes the special form

$$p(x, t_1) = [\sigma_x(t_1)\sqrt{2\pi}]^{-1} \exp \left\{ \frac{-[x - \mu_x(t_1)]^2}{2\sigma_x^2(t_1)} \right\} \tag{9.4}$$

which is completely determined by the nonstationary mean and mean square values of $x(t)$ at $t = t_1$. This result indicates that the measurement of these two quantities may be quite significant in many nonstationary applications just as in previous stationary applications.

For a pair of times t_1 and t_2, the *second-order nonstationary probability density function* for $x(t_1)$ and $x(t_2)$ is defined by

$$p(x_1, t_1; x_2, t_2)$$
$$= \lim_{\substack{\Delta x_1 \to 0 \\ \Delta x_2 \to 0}} \frac{\text{Prob}\,[x_1 < x(t_1) \leq x_1 + \Delta x_1 \text{ and } x_2 < x(t_2) \leq x_2 + \Delta x_2]}{(\Delta x_1)(\Delta x_2)}$$

$$(9.5)$$

and has the following basic properties for any t_1, t_2.

$$1 = \iint\limits_{-\infty}^{\infty} p(x_1, t_1; x_2, t_2)\, dx_1\, dx_2$$

$$p(x_1, t_1) = \int_{-\infty}^{\infty} p(x_1, t_1; x_2, t_2)\, dx_2$$

$$(9.6)$$

$$p(x_2, t_2) = \int_{-\infty}^{\infty} p(x_1, t_1; x_2, t_2)\, dx_1$$

$$R_x(t_1, t_2) = E[x(t_1)\, x(t_2)] = \iint\limits_{-\infty}^{\infty} x_1 x_2\, p(x_1, t_1; x_2, t_2)\, dx_1\, dx_2$$

For stationary cases, $p(x_1, t_1; x_2, t_2) = p(x_1, 0; x_2, t_2 - t_1)$. The measurement of nonstationary autocorrelation functions $R_x(t_1, t_2)$ is discussed in Section 9.4.

Second-order nonstationary probability distribution functions may be defined analogous to Eq. (9.3) by the simpler quantity

$$P(x_1, t_1; x_2, t_2) = \text{Prob}\,[-\infty < x(t_1) \leq x_1 \text{ and } -\infty < x(t_2) \leq x_2] \quad (9.7)$$

Continuing in this way, higher-order nonstationary probability distribution and density functions may be defined which describe the nonstationary random process $\{x(t)\}$ in greater and greater detail. This procedure supplies a rigorous characterization for the nonstationary random process $\{x(t)\}$, and similarly for stationary random processes where these probability functions are invariant with respect to translations in t.

The measurement of even the first-order nonstationary probability density function is, in general, a tremendous task. As Eq. (9.1) shows, all possible combinations of x and t_1 must be considered, and the probability in question will only be meaningful if there is a large number of records available. For a nonstationary Gaussian process, Eq. (9.4) reduces the problem of measuring $p(x, t_1)$ to measuring $\mu_x(t_1)$ and $\sigma_x^2(t_1)$, or equivalently $\mu_x(t_1)$ and $\Psi_x^2(t_1)$, which is a much simpler undertaking.

Consider next two different nonstationary random processes $\{x(t)\}$ and $\{y(t)\}$. For $x(t_1)$ and $y(t_2)$, the *joint (second-order) nonstationary probability density function* is defined by

$$p(x, t_1; y, t_2)$$
$$= \lim_{\substack{\Delta x \to 0 \\ \Delta y \to 0}} \frac{\text{Prob } [x < x(t_1) \le x + \Delta x \text{ and } y < y(t_2) \le y + \Delta y]}{(\Delta x)(\Delta y)} \quad (9.8)$$

and has similar basic properties as Eq. (9.6). In particular, the nonstationary cross-correlation function, which is discussed in Section 9.4, satisfies the relation

$$R_{xy}(t_1, t_2) = E[x(t_1)\, y(t_2)] = \int\!\!\!\int_{-\infty}^{\infty} xy\, p(x, t_1; y, t_2)\, dx\, dy \quad (9.9)$$

For stationary cases, $p(x, t_1; y, t_2) = p(x, 0; y, t_2 - t_1)$.

9.2 Mean Value Measurements of Nonstationary Data

For nonstationary data, a basic statistical problem is to determine how the nonstationary mean values change with time. Mean values can be estimated by using a special-purpose instrument or a computer that performs the following operation to calculate a sample mean value from a sample of size N. Specifically, for N sample functions $x_i(t)$; $0 \le t \le T$; $i = 1, 2, \ldots, N$, from a nonstationary process $\{x(t)\}$, fix t and compute the ensemble average estimate

$$\hat{\mu}_x(t) = \frac{1}{N} \sum_{i=1}^{N} x_i(t) \quad (9.10)$$

The estimate $\hat{\mu}_x(t)$ will differ over different choices of the N samples $\{x_i(t)\}$. Consequently, one must investigate for every t how closely an arbitrary estimate will approximate the true mean value. The expected value of $\hat{\mu}_x(t)$ is given by

$$E[\hat{\mu}_x(t)] = \frac{1}{N} \sum_{i=1}^{N} E[x_i(t)] = \mu_x(t) \quad (9.11)$$

where

$$\mu_x(t) = E[x_i(t)] \quad (9.12)$$

is the true mean value of the nonstationary process at time t. Hence $\hat{\mu}_x(t)$ is an *unbiased* estimate of $\mu_x(t)$ for all t, independent of N.

Two main steps are involved in the measurement of $\hat{\mu}_x(t)$. The first step is to obtain and store each record $x_i(t)$ as a function of t. This may be done continuously for all t in the range $0 \le t \le T$, or discretely by some digitizing procedure. After this has been done for N records, the next step is to perform an ensemble averaging by adding the records together and dividing by N. If each $x_i(t)$ is digitized in, say, M steps, then the total number of stored values would by MN. This ensemble averaging procedure for measuring nonstationary mean values is illustrated in Figure 9.2, and should be compared with the procedure discussed in Section 6.1.

Although this technique is easy to mechanize, it suffers from the fact that large sample sizes are required to reduce the estimation error to an acceptable level. For some applications, such as in space experiments, the cost may prohibit more than a few tests and a specialized procedure must be developed. Two special procedures are short-time averaging and orthogonal function approximation, Ref. 30. For other applications, such as in biomedical experiments, large numbers of tests may be feasible.

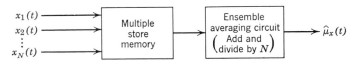

Figure 9.2   Nonstationary mean value measurement.

A measure of the error involved in estimating $\mu_x(t)$ by $\hat{\mu}_x(t)$ is the variance of $\hat{\mu}_x(t)$ given by

$$\text{Var}\,[\hat{\mu}_x(t)] = E[\{\hat{\mu}_x(t) - \mu_x(t)\}^2] \qquad (9.13)$$

9.2.1   Independent Samples

In most practical applications, the N sample functions used to compute $\hat{\mu}_x(t)$ will be statistically independent. Hence independence will be assumed here. Upon expanding Eq. (9.13), as in the derivation of Eq. (4.33), it is seen that the sample variance at time t,

$$\text{Var}\,[\hat{\mu}_x(t)] = \frac{\sigma_x^2(t)}{N} \qquad (9.14)$$

where $\sigma_x^2(t)$ is the variance associated with the underlying nonstationary process $\{x(t)\}$. Thus the sample variance approaches zero as N approaches infinity so that $\hat{\mu}_x(t)$ is a *consistent* estimate of $\mu_x(t)$ for all t.

A knowledge of the mean value and standard deviation for the sample estimate $\hat{\mu}_x(t)$ at any time t enables one to predict the range of the results at any time t without knowing the exact probability distribution function for $\hat{\mu}_x(t)$. This follows from the Tchebycheff inequality of Eq. (3.15), which states that for any constant $c > 0$, there exists a probability $P(c)$ such that

$$P(c) = \text{Prob}\,[|\hat{\mu}_x(t) - \mu_x(t)| \geq c(\text{s.d.}\,[\hat{\mu}_x(t)])] \leq \frac{1}{c^2} \qquad (9.15)$$

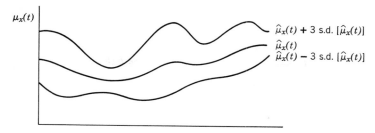

Figure 9.3 Eighty-nine per cent confidence limits for arbitrary distribution based upon Tchebycheff inequality.

where s.d. $[\hat{\mu}_x(t)] = \sqrt{\mathrm{Var}\ [\hat{\mu}_x(t)]}$. For example, for $c = 3$, this probability is at most $\frac{1}{9}$, giving 89 per cent confidence limits, as illustrated in Figure 9.3. An equivalent expression for Eq. (9.15) is

$$1 - P(c) = \mathrm{Prob}\ [|\hat{\mu}_x(t) - \mu_x(t)| \le c(\mathrm{s.d.}\ [\hat{\mu}_x(t)])] \ge 1 - \frac{1}{c^2} \quad (9.16)$$

The equality sign in Eq. (9.16) yields the two limiting range values within which $\mu_x(t)$ lies with probability $1 - P(c)$. That is,

$$\mu_x(t) = \hat{\mu}_x(t) \pm c(\mathrm{s.d.}\ [\hat{\mu}_x(t)]) \quad (9.17)$$

Substitution of Eq. (9.14) into Eq. (9.17) shows

$$\mu_x(t) = \hat{\mu}_x(t) \pm c\ \frac{\sigma_x(t)}{\sqrt{N}} \quad (9.18)$$

The solution for $\mu_x(t)/\hat{\mu}_x(t)$ in terms of $\sigma_x(t)/\mu_x(t)$ is

$$\frac{\mu_x(t)}{\hat{\mu}_x(t)} = \left(1 \mp c\left[\frac{\sigma_x(t)}{\sqrt{N}\ \mu_x(t)}\right]\right)^{-1} \quad (9.19)$$

The probability $P(c)$, defined in Eq. (9.15), takes on different values if one can assume that $x(t)$ follows a particular distribution, for example, a Gaussian distribution at any time t. To be specific, the value $c = 3$ yields a 99 per cent Gaussian confidence interval instead of an 89 per cent Tchebycheff confidence interval. Thus, for a given value of c, one has greater confidence that the resulting interval includes the true mean value in a Gaussian case than in a Tchebycheff case.

From Eq. (9.18), it follows that by increasing N one may guarantee that $\hat{\mu}_x(t)$ will fall close to $\mu_x(t)$ regardless of the magnitude of $\sigma_x(t)$ and the underlying distribution. Equation (9.19) indicates how the ratio $\mu_x(t)/\hat{\mu}_x(t)$ varies as a function of the parameter c, the input ratio $\mu_x(t)/\sigma_x(t)$ and the

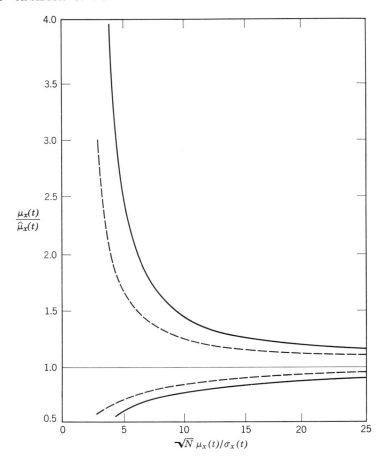

Figure 9.4 Confidence limits for nonstationary mean value measurements.

Case 1: 89 per cent confidence interval for arbitrary distribution ———
Case 2: 95 per cent confidence interval for Gaussian distribution – – – –

number of samples N. Figure 9.4 is a plot of Eq. (9.19) for two cases: Case 1 applies to arbitrary distributions and sets $c = 3$, corresponding to an 89 per cent confidence interval as given by the Tchebycheff inequality. Case 2 applies to a Gaussian distribution and sets $c = 2$, corresponding to a 95 per cent Gaussian confidence interval. The lower and upper limits for Figure 9.4 are shown in Table 9.1.

The change in sample size N required to study unknown distributions as opposed to Gaussian distributions may be inferred from Eq. (9.19). To illustrate this point, for an arbitrary input ratio $\mu_x(t)/\sigma_x(t)$, and for an unknown distribution, the parameter $c_1 = 3$ corresponds to an 89 per cent Tchebycheff confidence interval. For the same input ratio and the same 89 per cent confidence interval, a Gaussian distribution has associated with

Table 9.1   Data for Figure 9.4

$\dfrac{\sqrt{N}\,\mu_x(t)}{\sigma_x(t)}$	Case 1		Case 2	
	Lower Limit	Upper Limit	Lower Limit	Upper Limit
2	—	—	0.50	∞
3	0.50	∞	0.60	3.00
4	0.57	4.00	0.67	2.00
5	0.63	2.50	0.71	1.67
6	0.67	2.00	0.75	1.50
8	0.73	1.60	0.80	1.33
10	0.77	1.43	0.83	1.25
12	0.80	1.33	0.86	1.20
15	0.83	1.25	0.88	1.15
18	0.86	1.20	0.90	1.12
20	0.87	1.18	0.91	1.11
25	0.89	1.14	0.93	1.09

it the parameter $c_2 = 1.6$. From Eq. (9.19), the corresponding sample sizes must then satisfy

$$\frac{c}{\sqrt{N}} = \frac{3}{\sqrt{N_1}} = \frac{1.6}{\sqrt{N_2}} \qquad \text{hence } N_1 = 3.5 N_2$$

Thus, for this situation, an acceptable sample size of N_2 for an 89 per cent confidence interval with a Gaussian distribution would need to be increased 3.5 times for an unknown distribution in order to obtain the same 89 per cent confidence interval. For example, $N_2 = 30$ changes to $N_1 = 105$.

Consider a different case where $c_1 = 2$, corresponding to a 75 per cent Tchebycheff confidence interval. The associated Gaussian parameter value is $c_2 = 1.15$. This leads to

$$\frac{2}{\sqrt{N_1}} = \frac{1.15}{\sqrt{N_2}} \qquad \text{hence } N_1 = 3 N_2$$

Here, for example, $N_2 = 30$ would need to be increased to $N_1 = 90$ to obtain the same 75 per cent confidence interval. Related sample sizes of N_1 and N_2 as a function of confidence interval are summarized in Table 9.2.

9.2.2   Correlated Samples

Consider a general situation where sample functions $x_i(t)$; $0 \le t \le T$, $i = 1, 2, 3, \ldots, N$, from a nonstationary random process are correlated such that for every t,

$$E[x_i(t) x_j(t)] = R_x(k, t) \qquad \text{where } k = j - i \qquad (9.20)$$

The quantity $R_x(k, t)$ is called a *nonstationary spatial cross-correlation function* at time t between all pairs of records $x_i(t)$ and $x_j(t)$ satisfying

Table 9.2 Related Sample Sizes for Unknown versus Gaussian Distribution

Confidence Interval	N_1/N_2
75%	3.0
89%	3.5
92%	4.1
95%	5.2
98%	9.2
99%	15.0

N_1 = sample size required for unknown distribution. N_2 = sample size required for Gaussian distribution.

$k = j - i$. It follows from the preceding definition of Eq. (9.20) by interchanging i and j that

$$R_x(-k, t) = R_x(k, t) \qquad (9.21)$$

When the sample functions $x_i(t)$ and $x_j(t)$ are independent, for $i \neq j$ corresponding to $k \neq 0$,

$$R_x(k, t) = E[x_i(t) x_j(t)] = E[x_i(t)] E[x_j(t)] = \mu_x^2(t) \qquad \text{for } k \neq 0 \quad (9.22)$$

At $k = 0$, Eq. (9.20) becomes

$$R_x(0, t) = E[x_i^2(t)] = \sigma_x^2(t) + \mu_x^2(t) \qquad (9.23)$$

These relations yield the independent sample case in the preceding section. For correlated samples, Eq. (9.14) now takes the general form

$$\text{Var}\,[\hat{\mu}_x(t)] = \frac{\sigma_x^2(t)}{N} + \frac{1}{N^2} \sum_{\substack{i,j=1 \\ i \neq j}}^{N} E\{[x_i(t) - \mu_x(t)][x_j(t) - \mu_x(t)]\}$$

$$= \frac{\sigma_x^2(t)}{N} + \frac{1}{N^2} \sum_{\substack{i,j=1 \\ i \neq j}}^{N} [R_x(j - i, t) - \mu_x^2(t)] \qquad (9.24)$$

The next problem is to simplify the double sum appearing in Eq. (9.24). The index $k = j - i$ takes on values $k = 1, 2, \ldots, N - 1$. Altogether, there are $N^2 - N$ terms. Since $R_x(-k, t) = R_x(k, t)$, the $N^2 - N$ terms in this double sum can be arranged so that there are two terms where $k = N - 1$ of form $R_x(N - 1, t)$, four terms where $k = N - 2$ of form $R_x(N - 2, t), \ldots$, and $2(N - 1)$ terms where $k = 1$ of form $R_x(1, t)$. Thus one derives the simplified expression

$$\sum_{\substack{i,j=1 \\ i \neq j}}^{N} R_x(j - i, t) = 2\sum_{k=1}^{N}(N - k) R_x(k, t) \qquad (9.25)$$

As a check, note that the sum

$$2\sum_{k=1}^{N-1}(N - k) = N^2 - N \qquad (9.26)$$

Substitution of Eq. (9.25) into Eq. (9.24) yields

$$\text{Var}\,[\hat{\mu}_x(t)] = \frac{\sigma_x^2(t)}{N} + \frac{2}{N^2}\sum_{k=1}^{N-1}(N - k)[R_x(k, t) - \mu_x^2(t)] \qquad (9.27)$$

Equation (9.22) shows that Eq. (9.27) reduces to Eq. (9.13) when the records are independent, providing another check on the validity of Eq. (9.27). The result of Eq. (9.27) is an important extension of Eq. (9.13) and should be used in place of Eq. (9.13) for correlated samples.

A special situation of *complete dependence* between all samples is worthy of mention. For this case,

$$R_x(k, t) = R_x(0, t) = \sigma_x^2(t) + \mu_x^2(t) \qquad \text{for all } k \qquad (9.28)$$

Equation (9.27) now becomes

$$\text{Var}\,[\hat{\mu}_x(t)] = \frac{\sigma_x^2(t)}{N} + \frac{1}{N^2}(N^2 - N)\,\sigma_x^2(t) = \sigma_x^2(t) \qquad (9.29)$$

Thus no reduction in variance occurs when the samples are completely dependent.

For physical situations where a partial correlation may exist between the different samples, the following example may be helpful in giving quantitative results.

Example **9.1. Variance of Mean Value Estimates for Exponential Correlation between Samples.** An exponential form for the nonstationary cross-correlation function $R_x(k, t)$ will now be assumed so as to obtain some quantitative results to characterize different degrees of correlation. This particular form may fit some physical situations and it is therefore deemed appropriate for consideration here. To be specific, assume that

$$R_x(k, t) = \mu_x^2(t) + \sigma_x^2(t)e^{-kc} \qquad (9.30)$$

where k and c are positive constants. Determine the corresponding sample variance for nonstationary mean value estimates.

From Eq. (9.27), this sample variance is given by

$$\text{Var}\,[\hat{\mu}_x(t)] = \frac{\sigma_x^2(t)}{N} + \frac{2\sigma_x^2(t)}{N^2} \sum_{k=1}^{N-1} (N - k)\, e^{-kc} \tag{9.31}$$

To evaluate the sum above, let

$$f(c) = \sum_{k=1}^{N-1} e^{-kc} = \frac{1 - e^{-(N-1)c}}{e^c - 1} \tag{9.32}$$

Then

$$f'(c) = -\sum_{k=1}^{N-1} k\, e^{-kc} = \frac{N\, e^{-(N-2)c} - (N - 1)\, e^{-(N-1)c} - e^c}{(e^c - 1)^2} \tag{9.33}$$

Now

$$F(c) = \sum_{k=1}^{N-1} (N - k)\, e^{-kc} = N f(c) + f'(c) = \frac{(N - 1)\, e^c - N + e^{-(N-1)c}}{(e^c - 1)^2} \tag{9.34}$$

Substitution into Eq. (9.31) gives

$$\text{Var}\,[\hat{\mu}_x(t)] = \frac{\sigma_x^2(t)}{N} + \frac{2\sigma_x^2(t)}{N^2}\left[\frac{(N - 1)\, e^c - N + e^{-(N-1)c}}{(e^c - 1)^2}\right] \tag{9.35}$$

Equation (9.35) can be used to generate a set of curves for different values of $\sigma_x^2(t)$, N, and c. Experimental results would enable one to estimate the constant c for application of these curves.

9.3   Mean Square Value Measurements of Nonstationary Data

A similar analysis to the one given in Section 9.2 will now be carried out to determine how the nonstationary mean square values change with time. This can be estimated by using a special purpose instrument or a computer that performs the following operation to calculate a sample mean square value from a sample of size N. Specifically, for N samples functions $x_i(t)$; $0 \le t \le T$; $i = 1, 2, 3, \ldots, N$, from a nonstationary process $\{x(t)\}$, fix t and compute the ensemble average estimate

$$\hat{\Psi}_x^2(t) = \frac{1}{N} \sum_{i=1}^{N} x_i^2(t) \tag{9.36}$$

Independent of N, the quantity $\hat{\Psi}_x^2(t)$ is an *unbiased* estimate of the true mean square value of the nonstationary process $\{x(t)\}$ at any time t since the expected value

$$E[\hat{\Psi}_x^{\,2}(t)] = \frac{1}{N}\sum_{i=1}^{N} E[x_i^{\,2}(t)] = \Psi_x^{\,2}(t) \tag{9.37}$$

The quantity

$$\Psi_x^{\,2}(t) = E[x_i^{\,2}(t)] = \mu_x^{\,2}(t) + \sigma_x^{\,2}(t) \tag{9.38}$$

is the true mean square value of the nonstationary process at time t. Figure 9.2 indicates how to measure $\hat{\Psi}_x^{\,2}(t)$ by merely replacing $x_i(t)$ by $x_i^{\,2}(t)$.

9.3.1   Independent Samples

It will now be assumed that the N sample functions $x_i(t)$ are independent so that for all i and j,

$$E[x_i(t)\,x_j(t)] = E[x_i(t)]\,E[x_j(t)] = \mu_x^{\,2}(t) \tag{9.39}$$

The sample variance associated with the estimates $\hat{\Psi}_x^{\,2}(t)$ will be calculated. By definition,

$$\text{Var }[\hat{\Psi}_x^{\,2}(t)] = E[\{\hat{\Psi}_x^{\,2}(t) - \Psi_x^{\,2}(t)\}^2] = E[\{\hat{\Psi}_x^{\,2}(t)\}^2] - \Psi_x^{\,4}(t) \tag{9.40}$$

where $\Psi_x^{\,2}(t)$ is given by Eq. (9.38) and where

$$\begin{aligned}
E[\{\hat{\Psi}_x^{\,2}(t)\}^2] &= \frac{1}{N^2}\sum_{i,j=1}^{N} E[x_i^{\,2}(t)\,x_j^{\,2}(t)] \\
&= \frac{1}{N^2}\left[\sum_{i=1}^{N} E[x_i^{\,4}(t)] + \sum_{\substack{i,j=1 \\ i \neq j}}^{N} E[x_i^{\,2}(t)\,x_j^{\,2}(t)]\right]
\end{aligned} \tag{9.41}$$

Thus the problem reduces to evaluation of the expected values appearing in Eq. (9.41).

In order to obtain reasonable closed-form answers, it will be assumed now that the random process $\{x_i(t)\}$ at any time t follows a Gaussian distribution with mean value $\mu_x(t)$ and variance $\sigma_x^{\,2}(t)$. One can then derive

$$E[x_i^{\,4}(t)] = 3\Psi_x^{\,4}(t) - 2\mu_x^{\,4}(t) \tag{9.42}$$

$$E[x_i^{\,2}(t)\,x_j^{\,2}(t)] = \Psi_x^{\,4}(t) \qquad \text{for } i \neq j \tag{9.43}$$

The derivation of Eqs. (9.42) and (9.43) is based upon a nonstationary form for the fourth-order Gaussian relation of Eq. (3.112), namely,

$$\begin{aligned}
E[x_i(t)\,x_j(t)\,x_m(t)\,x_n(t)] &= E[x_i(t)\,x_j(t)]\,E[x_m(t)\,x_n(t)] \\
&\quad + E[x_i(t)\,x_m(t)]\,E[x_j(t)\,x_n(t)] \\
&\quad + E[x_i(t)\,x_n(t)]\,E[x_j(t)\,x_m(t)] - 2\mu_x^{\,4}(t)
\end{aligned} \tag{9.44}$$

Substitution into Eqs. (9.40) and (9.41) yields the result

$$\text{Var}\,[\hat{\Psi}_x^2(t)] = \frac{2}{N}\,[\Psi_x^4(t) - \mu_x^4(t)] \tag{9.45}$$

Thus the sample variance approaches zero as N approaches infinity so that $\hat{\Psi}_x^2(t)$ is a *consistent* estimate of $\Psi_x^2(t)$ for all t.

Confidence limits similar to those obtained in Section 9.2 may be obtained from the Tchebycheff inequality. For any positive constant c,

$$1 - P(c) = \text{Prob}\,[|\hat{\Psi}_x^2(t) - \Psi_x^2(t)| \le c(\text{s.d.}\,[\hat{\Psi}_x^2(t)])] \ge 1 - \frac{1}{c^2} \tag{9.46}$$

The end limits within which $\Psi_x^2(t)$ will lie with probability $1 - P(c)$ satisfies an equation similar to Eq. (9.17), as given by

$$\Psi_x^2(t) = \hat{\Psi}_x^2(t) \pm c(\text{s.d.}[\hat{\Psi}_x^2(t)]) \tag{9.47}$$

One may now proceed exactly as before to determine how $\Psi_x^2(t)/\hat{\Psi}_x^2(t)$ varies as a function of the basic parameters. The result is

$$\frac{\Psi_x^2(t)}{\hat{\Psi}_x^2(t)} = \left[1 \mp c\sqrt{2/N}\sqrt{1 - [\mu_x(t)/\Psi_x(t)]^4}\right]^{-1} \tag{9.48}$$

If $\mu_x(t) = 0$, Eq. (9.48) takes a similar form

$$\frac{\Psi_x^2(t)}{\hat{\Psi}_x^2(t)} = \left[1 \mp c\sqrt{2/N}\right]^{-1} \tag{9.49}$$

To illustrate Eq. (9.49), suppose $c = 3.0$ and $N = 50$. Then there is 89 per cent confidence that $\Psi_x^2(t)$ lies in the range bounded by

$$\Psi_x^2(t) = \frac{\hat{\Psi}_x^2(t)}{1 \mp 0.60} = [0.625\hat{\Psi}_x^2(t) \text{ to } 2.5\hat{\Psi}_x^2(t)]$$

9.3.2 Correlated Samples

For situations of correlated samples, it will be assumed as in Section 9.2.2 that the sample functions satisfy the relation

$$E[x_i(t)\,x_j(t)] = R_x(k, t) \qquad \text{where } k = j - i \tag{9.50}$$

Equation (9.43) where $i \ne j$ is now replaced by

$$E[x_i^2(t)\,x_j^2(t)] = \Psi_x^4(t) + 2[R_x^2(k, t) - \mu_x^2(t)] \tag{9.51}$$

where $k = j - i \ne 0$. When $i = j$, Eq. (9.50) becomes

$$E[x_i^2(t)] = R_x(0, t) = \Psi_x^2(t) \tag{9.52}$$

Proper steps for including $R_x(k, t)$ in the analysis are developed in the previous section. A similar procedure here yields the result

$$\text{Var } [\hat{\Psi}_x{}^2(t)] = \frac{2}{N} [\Psi_x{}^4(t) - \mu_x{}^4(t)] + \frac{4}{N^2} \sum_{k=1}^{N-1} (N - k)[R_x{}^2(k, t) - \mu_x{}^4(t)]$$
(9.53)

which is a useful and important generalization of Eq. (9.45).

Example 9.2. **Variance of Mean Square Value Estimates for Exponential Correlation between Samples.** In order to obtain some quantitative expressions corresponding to Eq. (9.53) which will characterize different degrees of correlation, assume that $R_x(k, t)$ has the exponential form

$$R_x(k, t) = \mu_x{}^2(t) + \sigma_x{}^2(t) e^{-kc}$$
(9.54)

where k and c are positive constants. Determine the corresponding sample variance for mean square value estimates.

This sample variance is given by Eq. (9.53). To carry out this evaluation, let $f(c)$ and $F(c)$ be defined as in Eqs. (9.32) and (9.34). Then from Eq. (9.54), the term

$$R_x{}^2(k, t) - \mu_x{}^4(t) = \sigma_x{}^2(t)[2\mu_x{}^2(t) e^{-kc} + \sigma_x{}^2(t) e^{-2kc}]$$
(9.55)

Hence the second term in Eq. (9.53) is

$$\frac{4\sigma_x{}^2(t)}{N^2} \sum_{k=1}^{N-1} (N - k)[2\mu_x{}^2(t) e^{-kc} + \sigma_x{}^2(t) e^{-2kc}]$$

$$= \frac{4\sigma_x{}^2(t)}{N^2} [2\mu_x{}^2(t) F(c) + \sigma_x{}^2(t) F(2c)] \quad (9.56)$$

The desired variance is now given by Eq. (9.56) and the first term in Eq. (9.53).

Example 9.3. **Nonstationary Data with Time-Varying Mean and Mean Square Values.** Suppose an ensemble of N independent nonstationary records $x_i(t); i = 1, 2, \ldots, N$, appears to have both a time-varying mean and mean square value, similar to Figure 9.1(c). How might one represent an underlying (possibly stationary) ensemble of records?

The first step is to compute the mean value estimate $\hat{\mu}_x(t)$ by the ensemble averaging procedure of Eq. (9.10). The next step is to compute the mean square value estimate $\hat{\Psi}_x{}^2(t)$ by the ensemble averaging procedure of Eq. (9.36). The desired underlying (possibly stationary) ensemble $\{y_i(t)\}$ of N records may now be represented by

$$y_i(t) = \frac{x_i(t) - \hat{\mu}_x(t)}{\sqrt{\hat{\Psi}_x{}^2(t) - \hat{\mu}_x{}^2(t)}} \qquad i = 1, 2, \ldots, N$$

and has the properties

$$\hat{\mu}_y(t) = \frac{1}{N} \sum_{i=1}^{N} y_i(t) = 0$$

$$\hat{\Psi}_y^2(t) = \frac{1}{N} \sum_{i=1}^{N} y_i^2(t) = 1$$

Further analysis of $\{y_i(t)\}$ is now required to determine its stationary properties, perhaps by the procedure of Section 5.6.1. Observe that the original ensemble $\{x_i(t)\}$ is represented here by the model

$$x_i(t) = \left[\sqrt{\hat{\Psi}_x^2(t) - \hat{\mu}_x^2(t)} \right] y_i(t) + \hat{\mu}_x(t)$$

9.4 Correlation Structure of Nonstationary Data

For nonstationary random processes $\{x(t)\}$ and $\{y(t)\}$, as in Section 3.2, the *mean values* at arbitrary fixed values of time t are defined by the expected values (ensemble averages)

$$\mu_x(t) = E[x(t)]$$
$$\mu_y(t) = E[y(t)]$$
(9.57)

The *covariance functions* at arbitrary fixed values of t_1 and t_2 are defined by the expected values (ensemble averages)

$$C_x(t_1, t_2) = E\{[x(t_1) - \mu_x(t_1)][x(t_2) - \mu_x(t_2)]\}$$
$$C_x(t_1, t_2) = E\{[y(t_1) - \mu_y(t_1)][y(t_2) - \mu_y(t_2)]\}$$
(9.58)

$$C_{xy}(t_1, t_2) = E\{[x(t_1) - \mu_x(t_1)][y(t_2) - \mu_y(t_2)]\}$$
(9.59)

For stationary random processes, these results would be a function of the time difference $t_1 - t_2$ or $t_2 - t_1$ rather than t_1 and t_2. In general, however, for nonstationary processes, these quantities will vary with both t_1 and t_2

The *correlation functions* for nonstationary processes are defined by the expected values (ensemble averages)

$$R_x(t_1, t_2) = E[x(t_1)x(t_2)]$$
$$R_y(t_1, t_2) = E[y(t_1)y(t_2)]$$
(9.60)

$$R_{xy}(t_1, t_2) = E[x(t_1)y(t_2)]$$
(9.61)

The quantities $R_x(t_1, t_2)$ and $R_y(t_1, t_2)$ are called *nonstationary autocorrelation* functions, whereas $R_{xy}(t_1, t_2)$ is called a *nonstationary cross-correlation* function.

For arbitrary values of $\mu_x(t)$ and $\mu_y(t)$, the covariance functions and correlation functions are related by

$$C_x(t_1, t_2) = R_x(t_1, t_2) - \mu_x(t_1)\,\mu_x(t_2)$$
$$C_y(t_1, t_2) = R_y(t_1, t_2) - \mu_y(t_1)\,\mu_y(t_2) \qquad (9.62)$$
$$C_{xy}(t_1, t_2) = R_{xy}(t_1, t_2) - \mu_x(t_1)\,\mu_y(t_2)$$

By a similar derivation as Eq. (3.50), an upper bound for the nonstationary cross-correlation (or cross-covariance) function is given by the inequality

$$|R_{xy}(t_1, t_2)|^2 \leq R_x(t_1, t_1)\,R_y(t_2, t_2) \qquad (9.63)$$

From the original definitions, one sees that the following symmetry properties are satisfied:

$$R_x(t_2, t_1) = R_x(t_1, t_2)$$
$$R_y(t_2, t_1) = R_y(t_1, t_2) \qquad (9.64)$$
$$R_{xy}(t_2, t_1) = R_{yx}(t_1, t_2)$$

Thus the correlation structure of nonstationary random processes $\{x(t)\}$ and $\{y(t)\}$ may be described by the four functions $R_x(t_1, t_2)$, $R_y(t_1, t_2)$, $R_{xy}(t_1, t_2)$, and $R_{yx}(t_1, t_2)$. These need be calculated only for values of $t_1 \leq t_2$ since the symmetry properties of Eq. (9.64) yield results for $t_2 < t_1$.

Consider the problem of measuring $R_x(t_1, t_2)$ using a set of N sample functions $x_i(t)$; $i = 1, 2, \ldots, N$, from the nonstationary random process. In place of Eq. (9.61), one should compute the ensemble average estimate

$$\hat{R}_x(t_1, t_2) = \frac{1}{N}\sum_{i=1}^{N} x_i(t_1)\,x_i(t_2) \qquad (9.65)$$

A recommended procedure is to hold t_1 fixed and to vary t_2. Let $t_1 = t$ and let $t_2 = t - \tau$ where τ is a fixed time delay value. This yields

$$\hat{R}_x(t, t - \tau) = \frac{1}{N}\sum_{i=1}^{N} x_i(t)\,x_i(t - \tau) \qquad (9.66)$$

which for stationary processes would be a function of τ only, but for nonstationary processes would be a function of both t and τ. For each fixed delay value τ and each record $x_i(t)$, calculate and store the product $x_i(t)\,x_i(t - \tau)$. Repeat for all N records and then perform an ensemble average to yield the estimate of Eq. (9.66). This whole operation must be repeated for every different τ of concern. Figure 9.5 illustrates this procedure for measuring nonstationary autocorrelation functions. A similar procedure may be followed for nonstationary cross-correlation function measurements. It is instructive to compare Figure 9.5 with the procedure that one would follow for stationary data, as shown in Figure 6.3. Note also that Figure 9.2 indicates how to measure $\hat{R}_x(t, t - \tau)$ by merely replacing $x_i(t)$ by $x_i(t)\, x_i(t - \tau)$.

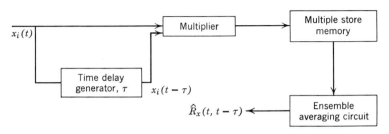

Figure 9.5   Nonstationary autocorrelation measurement.

From the three preceding sections, it is seen that the estimation of any parameter of the nonstationary random process $\{x(t)\}$ may be related to the estimation of the *mean value* of a second random process $\{y(t)\}$, which is derived from the first process. To be specific, observe the following:

1. Mean value

Let $$y(t) = x(t)$$

Then $$E[y(t)] = \mu_x(t)$$

2. Mean square value

Let $$y(t) = x^2(t)$$

Then $$E[y(t)] = \Psi_x^2(t)$$

3. Autocorrelation function

Let $$y(t) = x(t)\, x(t - \tau)$$

Then $$E[y(t)] = R_x(t, t - \tau)$$

This summary shows the importance of detailed consideration of mean values. Of course, the appropriate error analysis in each case depends upon the particular transformation of $x(t)$ into $y(t)$.

9.5   Spectral Structure of Nonstationary Data

Four different methods for describing nonstationary spectra will now be discussed. Each has very special features and properties. These methods are: (1) double frequency (generalized) spectra, (2) time-varying power spectra, (3) time-averaged power spectra, (4) instantaneous (frequency-time) spectra. Methods 1 and 4 are considered to be the significant theoretical ways to analyze nonstationary spectra. The time-varying and time-averaged power spectra of Methods 2 and 3 are measurable experimentally by direct filtering procedures.

9.5.1   Double Frequency Spectra

As in Section 3.2.2, the spectral decomposition for a pair of nonstationary random processes, $\{x(t)\}$ and $\{y(t)\}$, may be developed heuristically by assuming that each sample function of either random process has a complex Fourier transform

$$X(f) = \int_{-\infty}^{\infty} x(t)\, e^{-j2\pi ft}\, dt$$
$$Y(f) = \int_{-\infty}^{\infty} y(t)\, e^{-j2\pi ft}\, dt \tag{9.67}$$

Inverse Fourier transforms yield

$$x(t) = \int_{-\infty}^{\infty} X(f)\, e^{j2\pi ft}\, df$$
$$y(t) = \int_{-\infty}^{\infty} Y(f)\, e^{j2\pi ft}\, df \tag{9.68}$$

Thus, as before, an original pair of real-valued nonstationary random processes, $\{x(t)\}$ and $\{y(t)\}$, may be described in terms of two new complex-valued random processes, $\{X(f)\}$ and $\{Y(f)\}$.

When $x(t)$ is real-valued, it follows that the complex conjugate $X^*(f)$ is given by

$$X^*(f) = \int_{-\infty}^{\infty} x(t)\, e^{j2\pi ft}\, dt = X(-f) \tag{9.69}$$

Also, since $x(t)$ is real-valued,

$$x(t) = \int_{-\infty}^{\infty} X^*(f)\, e^{-j2\pi ft}\, df \tag{9.70}$$

Consider now the nonstationary autocorrelation function $R_x(t_1, t_2)$. From Eqs. (9.68) and (9.70), one finds that the product

$$x(t_1)\, x(t_2) = \int_{-\infty}^{\infty} X^*(f_1)\, e^{-j2\pi f_1 t_1}\, df_1 \int_{-\infty}^{\infty} X(f_2)\, e^{j2\pi f_2 t_2}\, df_2$$

The expected value yields

$$R_x(t_1, t_2) = E[x(t_1)\, x(t_2)] = \int\!\!\int_{-\infty}^{\infty} S_x(f_1, f_2)\, e^{-j2\pi(f_1 t_1 - f_2 t_2)}\, df_1\, df_2 \tag{9.71}$$

where

$$S_x(f_1, f_2) = E[X^*(f_1) X(f_2)] \tag{9.72}$$

A special case of Eq. (9.71) yields the variance $R_x(t, t)$. Note that by definition $S_x(f_1, f_2)$ is a complex covariance function. Also, note that $R_x(t_1, t_2)$ is the double Fourier transform of $S_x(f_1, f_2)$. By inversion,

$$S_x(f_1, f_2) = \int\limits_{-\infty}^{\infty}\!\!\int R_x(t_1, t_2) \, e^{j2\pi(f_1t_1 - f_2t_2)} \, dt_1 \, dt_2 \tag{9.73}$$

The quantity $S_x(f_1, f_2)$ is called the *generalized (nonstationary) spectral density function* of the random process $\{x(t)\}$, and is the double Fourier transform of $R_x(t_1, t_2)$. It is defined for both positive and negative f_1 and f_2.

The similarity of Eqs. (9.60) and (9.72) is quite striking. Equation (9.60) is a standard definition of the correlation function of a real-valued random process, whereas Eq. (9.72) is a standard definition for the correlation function of a complex-valued random process. The quantity $X(f)$ may, in general, be written as

$$X(f) = X_1(f) + j \, X_2(f) \tag{9.74}$$

where $X_1(f)$ and $X_2(f)$ are real-valued random processes with the frequency parameter f.

Expanding Eq. (9.72) in terms of $X_1(f)$ and $X_2(f)$ yields

$$\begin{aligned}
S_x(f_1, f_2) &= E\{[X_1(f_1) - j \, X_2(f_1)][X_1(f_2) + j \, X_2(f_2)]\} \\
&= E[X_1(f_1) \, X_1(f_2)] + E[X_2(f_1) \, X_2(f_2)] \\
&\quad + j\{E[X_1(f_1) \, X_2(f_2)] - E[X_2(f_1) \, X_1(f_2)]\} \\
&= S_{11}(f_1, f_2) + S_{22}(f_1, f_2) + j[S_{12}(f_1, f_2) - S_{21}(f_1, f_2)] \tag{9.75}
\end{aligned}$$

where

$$S_{ab}(f_1, f_2) = E[X_a(f_1) \, X_b(f_2)] \qquad a, b = 1, 2 \tag{9.76}$$

The real part of $S_x(f_1, f_2)$ is the sum of the individual autocorrelation functions of $X_1(f)$ and $X_2(f)$, whereas the imaginary part is the difference of the cross-correlation functions between $X_1(f)$ and $X_2(f)$. Along the line $f = f_1 = f_2$, the quantity $S_x(f, f)$ is real and gives the mean square value of $X(f)$ at the frequency f. The double frequency spectrum $S_x(f_1, f_2)$, defined by Eq. (9.72), is thus seen to be a measure of the correlation between frequencies f_1 and f_2 of the nonstationary random process, and is a generalization of Eq. (3.64).

Similarly, one derives the double Fourier transform relations

$$R_{xy}(t_1, t_2) = \int\limits_{-\infty}^{\infty}\!\!\int S_{xy}(f_1, f_2) \, e^{-j2\pi(f_1t_1 - f_2t_2)} \, df_1 \, df_2 \tag{9.77}$$

and

$$S_{xy}(f_1,f_2) = \int\!\!\int_{-\infty}^{\infty} R_{xy}(t_1, t_2)\, e^{j2\pi(f_1 t_1 - f_2 t_2)}\, dt_1\, dt_2 \qquad (9.78)$$

where

$$S_{xy}(f_1,f_2) = E[X^*(f_1)\, Y(f_2)] \qquad (9.79)$$

The quantity $S_{xy}(f_1, f_2)$ is called the *generalized (nonstationary) cross-spectral density function* between the pair of processes $\{x(t)\}$ and $\{y(t)\}$. One should note the basic symmetry between $R_{xy}(t_1, t_2)$ and $S_{xy}(f_1, f_2)$ as exhibited by Eqs. (9.61) and (9.79).

It is verified that

$$S_x(f_1, f_2) = S_x(f_2, f_1) = S_x(-f_1, -f_2) \qquad (9.80)$$

$$S_{xy}(f_1, f_2) = S_{yx}(f_2, f_1) = S_{xy}(-f_1, -f_2) \qquad (9.81)$$

For the special point $t = t_1 = t_2$, Eq. (9.77) becomes

$$R_{xy}(t, t) = E[x(t)\, y(t)] = \int\!\!\int_{-\infty}^{\infty} S_{xy}(f_1, f_2)\, e^{j2\pi(f_2 - f_1)t}\, df_1\, df_2 \qquad (9.82)$$

Note that for nonstationary random processes, the dependence on t is shown in the exponent in Eq. (9.82).

A major limitation to the usefulness of the double frequency spectra $S_x(f_1, f_2)$ or $S_{xy}(f_1, f_2)$ in engineering applications is that these quantities are not subject to direct measurement since $X(f)$ and $Y(f)$ are not observable quantities. Instead, the associated nonstationary correlation functions $R_x(t_1, t_2)$ or $R_{xy}(t_1, t_2)$ must be computed for all possible time pairs, and then a double Fourier transform must be computed for the various frequency pairs of interest, according to Eq. (9.73) or (9.78). This is a proper rigorous way to define these double frequency spectra, and assumes only that related nonstationary correlation functions exist and that they have double Fourier transforms. These conditions apply to a wider class of problems than those where each sample function is assumed to have a Fourier transform. In spite of this limitation, however, significant theoretical studies can be carried out which depend on this representation. This is illustrated by the examples in Sections 9.5.5 and 9.7, where the double frequency spectra are permitted to include delta functions.

Special Case of Stationary Processes. For stationary processes, Eq. (9.82) would be independent of t. That is,

$$R_{xy}(t, t) = R_{xy}(0, 0) = \int\!\!\int_{-\infty}^{\infty} S_{xy}(f_1, f_2)\, df_1\, df_2 \qquad (9.83)$$

It follows that, for stationary processes,

$$R_{xy}(0, 0) = \int_{-\infty}^{\infty} S_{xy}(f_2) \, df_2 \qquad (9.84a)$$

where

$$S_{xy}(f_2) = \int_{-\infty}^{\infty} S_{xy}(f_1, f_2) \, df_1 \qquad (9.84b)$$

is the two-sided theoretical cross-spectral density function. Hence, for stationary processes,

$$S_{xy}(f_1, f_2) = S_{xy}(f_1) \, \delta(f_2 - f_1) \qquad (9.85)$$

where $\delta(f_2 - f_1)$ is the usual delta function at $f_2 = f_1$. In geometrical terms, $S_{xy}(f_1, f_2)$ is concentrated only on the line $f_2 = f_1$ in the (f_1, f_2) plane. Note also that $S_{xy}(f_1, f_2) = 0$ for $f_2 \neq f_1$. Equation (9.85) is the same result as Eq. (3.64).

Conversely, suppose that a generalized cross-spectral density function has the form of Eq. (9.85). One can then derive from Eq. (9.77), letting $\tau = t_2 - t_1$,

$$R_{xy}(t_1, t_2) = R_{xy}(t_2 - t_1) = R_{xy}(\tau) = \int_{-\infty}^{\infty} S_{xy}(f) \, e^{j2\pi f\tau} \, df$$

where

$$S_{xy}(f) = \int_{-\infty}^{\infty} R_{xy}(\tau) \, e^{-j2\pi f\tau} \, d\tau$$

Thus the cross-correlation function $R_{xy}(t_1, t_2)$ corresponding to Eq. (9.85) is stationary.

General Case of Nonstationary Processes. Return now to the consideration of general nonstationary processes. Let

$$\tau = t_2 - t_1 \qquad t = \frac{t_1 + t_2}{2}$$

$$\qquad\qquad\qquad\qquad\qquad\qquad\qquad (9.86)$$

$$t_1 = t - \frac{\tau}{2} \qquad t_2 = t + \frac{\tau}{2}$$

Then, through the above change of variables,

$$E[x(t_1) \, y(t_2)] = R_{xy}(t_1, t_2) = R_{xy}\left(t - \frac{\tau}{2}, t + \frac{\tau}{2}\right)$$

$$= \mathcal{R}_{xy}(\tau, t) = E\left[x\left(t - \frac{\tau}{2}\right) y\left(t + \frac{\tau}{2}\right)\right] \qquad (9.87)$$

Note that the definition for $\mathcal{R}_{xy}(\tau, t)$ is quite different from $R_{xy}(\tau, t)$. The quantity $\mathcal{R}_{xy}(\tau, t)$ is not a conventional correlation function. The reason for introducing this transformation from the (t_1, t_2) plane to the (τ, t) plane is to separate, if possible, the nonstationary from the stationary portion of the process. For stationary processes, there would be no dependence upon t. The special value $R_{xy}(t, t) = \mathcal{R}_{xy}(0, t)$; the notation $\mathcal{R}_{xx}(\tau, t) = \mathcal{R}_{xx}(\tau, t)$.

From Eq. (9.87), one obtains

$$\mathcal{R}_x(-\tau, t) = \mathcal{R}_x(\tau, t)$$
$$\mathcal{R}_{xy}(-\tau, t) = \mathcal{R}_{yx}(\tau, t)$$

(9.88)

Thus $\mathcal{R}_x(\tau, t)$ is an even function of τ for all t. Substitution of Eqs. (9.86) and (9.87) into Eq. (9.78) yields

$$S_{xy}(f_1, f_2) = \int_{-\infty}^{\infty} \int_{-\infty}^{\infty} \mathcal{R}_{xy}(\tau, t) \exp \left\{ -j2\pi \left[\left(\frac{f_1 + f_2}{2} \right)\tau + (f_2 - f_1)t \right] \right\} d\tau \, dt$$

$$= S_{xy} \left[\left(\frac{f_1 + f_2}{2} \right), (f_2 - f_1) \right]$$

(9.89)

Through a change in variables, where

$$f = \frac{f_1 + f_2}{2} \qquad g = f_2 - f_1$$

$$f_1 = f - \frac{g}{2} \qquad f_2 = f + \frac{g}{2}$$

(9.90)

Equation (9.89) becomes

$$S_{xy}(f, g) = S_{xy} \left(f - \frac{g}{2}, f + \frac{g}{2} \right) = E \left[X^* \left(f - \frac{g}{2} \right) Y \left(f + \frac{g}{2} \right) \right] \quad (9.91)$$

Thus $S_{xy}(f_1, f_2)$ in the (f_1, f_2) plane is transformed to $S_{xy}(f, g)$ in the (f, g) plane, and

$$S_{xy}(f, g) = \iint_{-\infty}^{\infty} \mathcal{R}_{xy}(\tau, t) \, e^{-j2\pi(f\tau + gt)} \, d\tau \, dt$$

(9.92)

By inversion,

$$\mathcal{R}_{xy}(\tau, t) = \iint_{-\infty}^{\infty} S_{xy}(f, g) \, e^{j2\pi(f\tau + gt)} \, df \, dg$$

(9.93)

This transformation to $S_{xy}(f, g)$ is required in order to bring out intrinsic frequency properties of the transformed nonstationary correlation function $\mathcal{R}_{xy}(\tau, t)$. For a stationary random process, $S_{xy}(f, g)$ must be zero everywhere in the (f, g) plane except along the line $g = 0$.

Special cases of Eq. (9.93) are

$$\mathcal{R}_x(0, t) = E[x^2(t)] = \iint_{-\infty}^{\infty} \mathcal{S}_x(f, g)\, e^{j2\pi gt}\, df\, dg$$

and

$$\mathcal{R}_x(\tau, 0) = E\left[x\left(-\frac{\tau}{2}\right)x\left(\frac{\tau}{2}\right)\right] = \iint_{-\infty}^{\infty} \mathcal{S}_x(f, g)\, e^{j2\pi f\tau}\, df\, dg$$

Separable Case. Assume that the nonstationary correlation function $\mathcal{R}(\tau, t)$ can be separated into the products

$$\mathcal{R}(\tau, t) = R_1(t)\, R_2(\tau) = R_1\left(\frac{t_1 + t_2}{2}\right) R_2(t_2 - t_1) \qquad (9.94)$$

where $R_2(\tau) = R_2(t_2 - t_1)$ is a stationary correlation function, and $R_1(t) = R_1[(t_1 + t_2)/2]$ is a variable scale factor defined at the midpoint (average) of the points t_1 and t_2. For stationary random processes, $R_1(t)$ is a constant.

The process is said to be *locally stationary* if $R_1(t)$ is a non-negative function of t. Although, in general, $R_1(t)$ is an arbitrary function of t, it may be possible to break up a random process into a number of smaller samples such that these smaller samples are stationary or locally stationary. For example, a physical process (such as turbulence phenomena) may be considered locally stationary in some cases if its average instantaneous mean square value is varying slowly with respect to its correlation interval $t_2 - t_1$. See Ref. 27.

Substitution of Eq. (9.94) into Eq. (9.92) yields

$$S(f, g) = \iint_{-\infty}^{\infty} R_1(t)\, R_2(\tau)\, e^{-j2\pi(f\tau + gt)}\, d\tau\, dt = S_1(g)\, S_2(f) \qquad (9.95)$$

where

$$S_1(g) = \int_{-\infty}^{\infty} R_1(t)\, e^{-j2\pi gt}\, dt \qquad g = f_2 - f_1$$

$$S_2(f) = \int_{-\infty}^{\infty} R_2(\tau)\, e^{-j2\pi f\tau}\, d\tau \qquad f = \frac{f_1 + f_2}{2} \qquad (9.96)$$

By inversion

$$R_1(t) = \int_{-\infty}^{\infty} S_1(g)\, e^{j2\pi gt}\, dg$$

$$R_2(\tau) = \int_{-\infty}^{\infty} S_2(f)\, e^{j2\pi f\tau}\, df \qquad (9.97)$$

For a stationary random process where $R_1(t)$ is a constant, say $R_1(t) = 1$, the corresponding $S_1(g)$ is a delta function given by $S_1(g) = \delta(g)$. Thus, for a stationary process, Eqs. (9.94) and (9.95) become

$$\mathcal{R}(\tau, t) = R_2(\tau)$$

with

$$S(f, g) = \delta(g) \, S_2(f)$$

(9.98)

In words, when $R(\tau, t)$ has no dependence on t and is a function only of the time difference $\tau = t_2 - t_1$, the spectral density function $S(f, g)$ is concentrated on the line $g = 0$ in the (f, g) plane, and has the shape of $S_2(f)$.

For the special case of nonstationary white noise where $R_2(\tau) = \delta(\tau)$, a delta function, the corresponding $S_2(f) = 1$, a constant. Now, Eqs. (9.94) and (9.95) become

$$\mathcal{R}(\tau, t) = R_1(t) \, \delta(\tau)$$

with

$$S(f, g) = S_1(g)$$

(9.99)

Thus, for this case, the spectral density function $S(f, g)$ has the shape of $S_1(g)$ for all f in the (f, g) plane.

9.5.2 Time-Varying Power Spectra

Let $x_i(t)$ be a sample function of a zero mean, nonstationary process $\{x(t)\}$ which is operated upon as shown below.

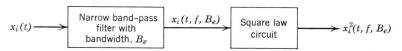

Assume that the filter is an ideal rectangular filter with a frequency response function given by

$$H(\nu) = 1, \qquad f - \frac{B_e}{2} < |\nu| < f + \frac{B_e}{2}$$
$$= 0, \qquad \text{elsewhere}$$

(9.100)

where B_e is the filter bandwidth and f is the center frequency. Although the ideal filter is not physically realizable, it is a good approximation to many narrow-band filters.

The corresponding weighting function is simply the Fourier transform of $H(\nu)$ so that

$$h(\tau) = \int_{-\infty}^{\infty} H(\nu) \, e^{j2\pi\nu\tau} \, d\nu$$
$$= \frac{2 \sin(\pi B_e \tau)}{\pi\tau} \cos(2\pi f\tau)$$

(9.101)

The filter output is given by

$$x_i(t, f, B_e) = \int_{-\infty}^{\infty} h(\xi) \, x_i(t - \xi) \, d\xi \qquad (9.102)$$

and is the instantaneous value of that part of $x_i(t)$ which lies within the bandwidth B_e centered at the frequency f. The output of the squaring device is

$$x_i^2(t, f, B_e) = \left(\int_{-\infty}^{\infty} h(\xi) \, x_i(t - \xi) \, d\xi \right)^2$$

$$= \iint_{-\infty}^{\infty} h(\xi) \, h(\eta) \, x_i(t - \xi) \, x_i(t - \eta) \, d\xi \, d\eta \qquad (9.103)$$

It should be noted that the right side of Eq. (9.103) is always non-negative since it represents the square of a real function of time. Moreover, f and B_e are contained in $h(\xi)$ and $h(\eta)$, and $f \geq 0$ for actual narrow-band filters. This requirement on f will be assumed henceforth so as to derive a one-sided spectrum.

By recording $x_i^2(t, f, B_e)$ as a function of time, repeating the filter-square-record operation N times, and ensemble averaging, an estimate of the average value of $x^2(t, f, B_e)$ is obtained. Letting N become arbitrarily large will cause the estimate to converge to the true average value. Thus

$$E[x^2(t, f, B_e)] = \lim_{N \to \infty} \frac{1}{N} \sum_{i=1}^{N} x_i^2(t, f, B_e) \qquad (9.104)$$

Dividing by the bandwidth B_e now yields a nonstationary time-varying power spectrum

$$G_x(t, f) = \frac{E[x^2(t, f, B_e)]}{B_e} = \lim_{N \to \infty} \frac{1}{B_e N} \sum_{i=1}^{N} x_i^2(t, f, B_e) \qquad (9.105)$$

where the one-sided power spectral notation $G_x(t, f)$ states the fact that $f \geq 0$. If it is desired for mathematical reasons to include negative f, then $G_x(t, f)$ would be replaced in the usual way by the two-sided power spectrum $S_x(t, f)$, where half the power is distributed in the negative frequency range. Observe that $G_x(t, f)$ or $S_x(t, f)$ will be non-negative for all t and f, in agreement with physical requirements for a meaningful spectrum. In terms of $G_x(t, f)$, the mean square value $E[x^2(t)]$ can be calculated by carrying out the summation

$$E[x^2(t)] = \sum_{f \geq 0} G_x(t, f) \, B_e \qquad (9.106)$$

The mean square value portion in any positive frequency range (f_1, f_2) can be found by summing over that frequency range.

The concept of the time-varying power spectrum involves one serious restriction. This concerns the specification of the bandwidth B_e in Eq. (9.105). On the one hand, B_e should be very narrow so that $G_x(t,f)$ will present properly resolved spectral information for all values of f. On the other hand, B_e should be sufficiently wide to permit proper response to nonstationary time trends in the data. That is, if B_e is too narrow, time trends in the data will be smoothed out since the narrow bandpass filtering operation is equivalent to taking a weighted time average. In more practical terms, if $G_x(t,f)$ is properly to describe the time trends in the nonstationary data, the narrow bandpass filter must have a rise time

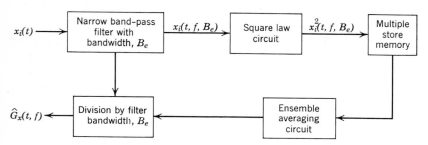

Figure 9.6   Time-varying power spectrum measurement.

which is very short compared to such time trends. The rise time for an ideal rectangular bandpass filter with a bandwidth of B_e cps is approximated by $\tau_r \approx 1/B_e$. Hence, if F_t represents the highest frequency of a nonstationary time trend in the data, $1/F_t$ should be less than τ_r, or $B_e > F_t$. If this requirement is not complied with, the spectrum that will be measured is actually a time-averaged power spectrum, as discussed in the next section.

For finite B_e, an estimate of $G_x(t,f)$ from a set of N records is given clearly by

$$\hat{G}_x(t,f) = \frac{1}{B_e N} \sum_{i=1}^{N} x_i^2(t, f, B_e) \qquad (9.107)$$

This estimate will always be non-negative for all t and f, and may be measured as illustrated in Figure 9.6. Equation (9.105) shows that this estimate approximates the true value only if $N \to \infty$. The nonstationary procedure of Figure 9.6 should be compared with the stationary procedure of Figure 6.4.

To measure $\hat{G}_x(t,f)$ accurately, one would need a large collection of records to perform an ensemble averaging. This may be a major problem for some applications. Another limitation to the usefulness of $\hat{G}_x(t,f)$ is that it must be determined for each frequency of interest. At each frequency, there are two types of errors analogous to estimating power spectra for stationary data. The use of the finite bandwidth B_e introduces a bias error, and the use of a finite number N of records introduces a variability error. The entire sequence of filtering, squaring, and averaging must be performed at some initial frequency f_1, and then repeated at all other frequencies of interest. The result of this processing is the generation of a family of one-dimensional functions, $G_x(t, f_j)$, $j = 1, \ldots, M$, which approximates the two-dimensional function $G_x(t, f)$.

To compute $E[x^2(t, f, B_e)]$ mathematically, take the expected value of Eq. (9.103). This yields

$$E[x^2(t, f, B_e)] = \iint\limits_{-\infty}^{\infty} h(\xi)\, h(\eta)\, R_x(t - \xi, t - \eta)\, d\xi\, d\eta \qquad (9.108)$$

where $R_x(t_1, t_2)$ is the nonstationary autocorrelation function of $\{x(t)\}$. Equation (9.108) may be expressed in terms of the double-frequency spectrum by using the relation of Eq. (9.71) as follows.

$$R_x(t_1, t_2) = \iint\limits_{-\infty}^{\infty} S_x(f_1, f_2)\, e^{-j2\pi[f_1 t_1 - f_2 t_2]}\, df_1\, df_2 \qquad (9.109)$$

Substitution of Eq. (9.109) into Eq. (9.108) gives

$$E[x^2(t, f, B_e)] = \iint\limits_{-\infty}^{\infty} h(\xi)\, h(\eta) \iint\limits_{-\infty}^{\infty} S_x(f_1, f_2)\, e^{-j2\pi[f_1(t-\xi)-f_2(t-\eta)]}\, df_1\, df_2\, d\xi\, d\eta$$

$$= \iint\limits_{-\infty}^{\infty} \left(\int_{-\infty}^{\infty} h(\xi)\, e^{j2\pi f_1 \xi}\, d\xi \right)\left(\int_{-\infty}^{\infty} h(\eta)\, e^{-j2\pi f_2 \eta}\, d\eta \right)$$

$$\times\, S_x(f_1, f_2)\, e^{-j2\pi(f_1-f_2)t}\, df_1\, df_2$$

$$= \iint\limits_{-\infty}^{\infty} H^*(f_1)\, H(f_2)\, S_x(f_1, f_2)\, e^{-j2\pi t(f_1-f_2)}\, df_1\, df_2 \qquad (9.110)$$

From Eqs. (9.105) and (9.110), the time-varying power spectrum may be expressed as

$$G_x(t, f) = \frac{1}{B_e} \iint\limits_{-\infty}^{\infty} H^*(f_1)\, H(f_2)\, S_x(f_1, f_2)\, e^{-j2\pi t(f_1-f_2)}\, df_1\, df_2 \qquad (9.111)$$

From Eq. (9.108)

$$G_x(t, f) = \frac{1}{B_e} \int\!\!\int_{-\infty}^{\infty} h(\xi)\, h(\eta)\, R_x(t - \xi, t - \eta)\, d\xi\, d\eta \qquad (9.112)$$

9.5.3 Time-Averaged Power Spectra

A function related to the time-varying power spectrum $G_x(t, f)$, and which may have important applications in the characterization of non-stationary processes, is the *time-averaged power spectrum* defined for $f \geq 0$ by

$$\bar{G}_x(f, T) = \frac{1}{T} \int_T G_x(t, f)\, dt \qquad (9.113)$$

where T is the interval of interest. The value of T could be the entire duration of the nonstationary process, in which case a limiting operation on T may be involved, or some smaller interval, such as a tape loop length, in which the spectral structure of the process is of particular interest. Clearly, $\bar{G}_x(f, T)$ is non-negative for all f and T.

When T approaches infinity, $\bar{G}_x(f, T)$ will be replaced by $\bar{G}_x(f)$ where

$$\bar{G}_x(f) = \lim_{T \to \infty} \bar{G}_x(f, T) = \lim_{T \to \infty} \frac{1}{T} \int_T G_x(t, f)\, dt \qquad (9.114)$$

If the two-sided spectrum $S_x(t, f)$ is used in place of $G_x(t, f)$, then $\bar{G}_x(f, T)$ should be replaced by $\bar{S}_x(f, T)$. This, in turn, becomes $\bar{S}_x(f)$ as T approaches infinity.

For a sample function $x(t)$ of length T from a nonstationary process, an estimate of $\bar{G}_x(f, T)$ is given by

$$\hat{\bar{G}}_x(f, T) = \frac{1}{B_e T} \int_T x^2(t, f, B_e)\, dt \qquad (9.115)$$

Equations (9.105) and (9.115) show

$$\bar{G}_x(f, T) = E[\hat{\bar{G}}_x(f, T)] \qquad (9.116)$$

A procedure for measuring $\bar{G}_x(f, T)$ is illustrated in Figure 9.7. This is precisely the same procedure as one would follow for stationary data, as shown in Figure 6.4.

Time-averaged power spectra estimates will involve a bias error due to the finite bandwidth B_e and a variability error due to the finite averaging time T, just as for power spectra estimates of stationary data. The time-averaging operation on nonstationary data, however, introduces a third

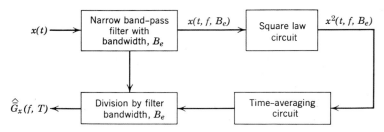

Figure 9.7   Time-averaged power spectrum measurement.

source of error called the time interval bias error. This error reflects the smoothing of nonstationary time trends in the data caused by the averaging operation, and is clearly a function of the averaging time T as well as the magnitude of the nonstationary time trends. For a fixed averaging time T, the time interval bias error becomes small as the data becomes more stationary. For a given time trend in the data, the time interval bias error becomes small as T becomes small. Note that in all cases the analyzer filter bandwidth must be greater than the reciprocal of the averaging time, that is, $B_e > 1/T$. Otherwise, the analyzer filter may control the averaging operation and produce a longer averaging time than indicated by T. This restriction fixes the minimum value for B_e which can be used for short time-averaged power spectra estimates.

The time-averaged power spectrum can be a valuable tool for describing the time varying spectral characteristics of an important special class of nonstationary random processes which possess the following characteristics.

1. The lack of stationarity is due to deterministic time trends which are represented in every sample function.
2. The time trends are very slow relative to the instantaneous fluctuations of the data.

Locally stationary data defined in Eq. (9.94) are examples of nonstationary random processes which meet these requirements. For such cases, the time-varying power spectrum computed from an ensemble of sample records, as discussed in Section 9.5.2, will be closely approximated by a short time-averaged power spectrum computed from a single sample record where T is just short enough not to introduce significant time interval bias errors, but long enough to average the instantaneous fluctuations of the data. The selection of a proper value for T must usually be based upon trial and error procedures. An example of the application of this technique for actual nonstationary data is presented in Reference 25.

To continue with the mathematical development, substitution of Eq.

(9.112) into Eq. (9.113) yields

$$\bar{G}_x(f, T) = \frac{1}{T} \int_T \left[\frac{1}{B_e} \int\!\!\!\int_{-\infty}^{\infty} h(\xi)\, h(\eta)\, R_x(t - \xi, t - \eta)\, d\xi\, d\eta \right] dt$$

$$= \frac{1}{B_e} \int\!\!\!\int_{-\infty}^{\infty} h(\xi)\, h(\eta) \left[\frac{1}{T} \int_0^T R_x(t - \xi, t - \eta)\, dt \right] d\xi\, d\eta \quad (9.117)$$

It will now be shown that the integration over t produces a function which depends only upon the difference $\xi - \eta$, and thus represents the auto-correlation function of a stationary process.

When the sample functions are of length T, the nonstationary auto-correlation function $R_x(t_1, t_2)$ is defined over a square in the t_1, t_2 plane and is zero outside the square. For convenience, denote the end points of the sample functions by 0 and T. Then the parameters $t - \xi$ and $t - \eta$ in Eq. (9.117) must satisfy the conditions

$$0 \le (t - \xi) \le T \quad \text{and} \quad 0 \le (t - \eta) \le T$$

Hence t itself must satisfy

$$\xi \le t \le T + \eta \quad \text{and} \quad \xi \le t \le T + \eta$$

For definiteness, assume that $\xi \ge \eta$. A similar proof holds when $\xi < \eta$. Then the single requirement on t is

$$\xi \le t \le T + \eta$$

The t integration in Eq. (9.117) now takes the form

$$\frac{1}{T} \int_0^T R_x(t - \xi, t - \eta)\, dt = \frac{1}{T} \int_\xi^{T+\eta} R_x(t - \xi, t - \eta)\, dt$$

$$= \frac{1}{T} \int_0^{T-\tau} R_x(r, r + \tau)\, dr = \bar{R}_x(\tau, T) \qquad \tau = \xi - \eta \quad (9.118)$$

where the last line results from changing the variable of integration to $r = t - \xi$, $dr = dt$, and setting $\tau = \xi - \eta$. The notation $\bar{R}_x(\tau, T)$ expresses the fact that the integral is a function only of τ and T. Separate direct proofs will verify that $\bar{R}_x(\tau, T)$ is an even function of τ with a maximum at $\tau = 0$. When T approaches infinity, $\bar{R}_x(\tau, T)$ becomes $\bar{R}_x(\tau)$ alone, where

$$\bar{R}_x(\tau) = \lim_{T \to \infty} \frac{1}{T} \int_T R_x(t - \xi, t - \eta)\, dt \qquad \tau = \xi - \eta \quad (9.119)$$

By substituting Eq. (9.118) into Eq. (9.117), one obtains

$$\bar{G}_x(f, T) = \frac{1}{B_e} \int\!\!\!\int_{-\infty}^{\infty} h(\xi)\, h(\eta)\, \bar{R}_x(\xi - \eta)\, d\xi\, d\eta \tag{9.120}$$

The quantity found in Eq. (9.118) is a function only of τ for fixed T and may be considered to be the autocorrelation function of a stationary process. Hence one is justified in employing results available for stationary processes in studying the time-averaged power spectrum. In particular, a very useful expression for the physically realizable power spectrum $\bar{G}_x(f, T)$ which is associated with $\bar{R}_x(\tau, T)$ is obtained by noting that, in the stationary case, such spectra and autocorrelation functions are related by a Fourier transformation. Hence

$$\bar{G}_x(f, T) = 4 \int_0^{\infty} \bar{R}_x(\tau, T) \cos 2\pi f\tau\, d\tau \tag{9.121}$$

Equations (9.118) and (9.121) provide practical ways to calculate $\bar{R}_x(\tau, T)$ and $\bar{G}_x(f, T)$, and will be applied in the example of Section 9.5.5.

9.5.4 Instantaneous (Frequency-Time) Spectra

Another approach may be considered which should not be confused with the physically meaningful time-varying power spectrum of Eq. (9.105). This approach begins with the nonstationary autocorrelation function $\mathfrak{R}_x(\tau, t)$ of Eq. (9.87). The Fourier transform of $\mathfrak{R}_x(\tau, t)$ with respect to τ is then defined by

$$s_x(f, t) = \int_{-\infty}^{\infty} \mathfrak{R}_x(\tau, t)\, e^{-j2\pi f\tau}\, d\tau \quad \text{where} \quad \mathfrak{R}_x(\tau, t) = E\left[x\left(t - \frac{\tau}{2}\right)x\left(t + \frac{\tau}{2}\right)\right] \tag{9.122}$$

The quantity $s_x(f, t)$ is called the *instantaneous spectrum*, Ref. 21, of the nonstationary random process described by $\mathfrak{R}_x(\tau, t)$. The inverse Fourier transform of Eq. (9.122) yields

$$\mathfrak{R}_x(\tau, t) = \int_{-\infty}^{\infty} s_x(f, t)\, e^{j2\pi f\tau}\, df \tag{9.123}$$

At the special point $\tau = 0$,

$$E[x^2(t)] = \mathfrak{R}_x(0, t) = \int_{-\infty}^{\infty} s_x(f, t)\, df \geq 0 \tag{9.124}$$

Thus $s_x(f, t)$ indicates how the mean square value $E[x^2(t)]$ is distributed in the (f, t) plane, providing a possible physical interpretation for the meaning of $s_x(f, t)$. Equation (9.124) shows that integrating $s_x(f, t)$ over all f gives the same result as integrating $S_x(t,f)$ from Eq. (9.106) over all f. It will be shown later in an example in Section 9.5.5 that, for particular values of f and t, the quantity $s_x(f, t)$ may be negative without violating this requirement on its integral.

The proper interpretation for $s_x(t,f)$ is that it is the Fourier transform of $\mathcal{R}_x(\tau, t)$ with respect to τ as carried out in Eq. (9.122). This quantity is not directly measurable in practice, but it may be useful in certain theoretical studies because of its following relationship to the two-sided, time-averaged power spectrum $\bar{S}_x(f)$.

$$\bar{S}_x(f) = \lim_{T \to \infty} \frac{1}{T} \int_T s_x(t,f)\, dt \tag{9.125}$$

A proof for Eq. (9.125) is as follows. Start with Eq. (9.119) and let $\xi = \tau/2$, $\eta = -\tau/2$. Then

$$\bar{R}_x(\tau) = \lim_{T \to \infty} \frac{1}{T} \int_T R_x\left(t - \frac{\tau}{2}, t + \frac{\tau}{2}\right) dt$$

From Eq. (9.87), the integrand

$$R_x\left(t - \frac{\tau}{2}, t + \frac{\tau}{2}\right) = E\left[x\left(t - \frac{\tau}{2}\right) x\left(t + \frac{\tau}{2}\right)\right] = \mathcal{R}_x(\tau, t)$$

Hence

$$\bar{R}_x(\tau) = \lim_{T \to \infty} \frac{1}{T} \int_T \mathcal{R}_x(\tau, t)\, dt \tag{9.126a}$$

and

$$\bar{S}_x(f) = \int_{-\infty}^{\infty} \bar{R}_x(\tau)\, e^{-j2\pi f\tau}\, d\tau = \lim_{T \to \infty} \frac{1}{T} \int_T s_x(t,f)\, dt \tag{9.126b}$$

assuming that the limiting operations may be interchanged.

An example of an instantaneous (frequency-time) spectrum is illustrated in Figure 9.8 in Section 9.5.5.

9.5.5   Spectra for Separable and Periodic Nonstationary Processes

Let $\{y(t)\}$ be a nonstationary random process composed of the product of a zero mean stationary random process $\{x(t)\}$ multiplied by a periodic function $\cos 2\pi Ft$ where $F = \text{constant}$. This leads to sample functions of the form

$$y(t) = x(t) \cos 2\pi Ft \tag{9.127}$$

The double-frequency spectrum, the instantaneous (frequency-time) spectrum, and the time-averaged spectrum of $\{y(t)\}$ will be computed to illustrate some of the previously discussed material in this section. Derivation of the time-varying spectrum is more difficult and is developed in the Section 9.7.

This example is a special case of the class of separable nonstationary random processes described by sample functions of the form

$$y(t) = A(t) x(t) \tag{9.128}$$

where $A(t)$ is an integrable function and $\{x(t)\}$ is an arbitrary random process. The nonstationary autocorrelation function for $\{y(t)\}$ is

$$R_y(t_1, t_2) = E[y(t_1) y(t_2)] = A(t_1) A(t_2) R_x(t_1, t_2)$$

where
$$R_x(t_1, t_2) = E[x(t_1) x(t_2)]$$

may be stationary or nonstationary depending upon the nature of $\{x(t)\}$. Even if $R_x(t_1, t_2)$ is stationary, the quantity $R_y(t_1, t_2)$ will be nonstationary unless $A(t)$ is such that the product $A(t_1)A(t_2)$ is an even function of the parameter $(t_2 - t_1)$. Thus, in general, $\{y(t)\}$ will be a nonstationary process when $\{x(t)\}$ is a stationary process. Moreover, in general, if $\{x(t)\}$ is a stationary Gaussian process with probability density function $p(x)$, independent of t, the process $\{y(t)\}$ will be a nonstationary Gaussian process with probability density function $p(y, t)$, a function of both y and t. If the fluctuations of $A(t)$ are very slow compared to the fluctuations of $\{x(t)\}$, then the time varying spectral characteristics of $\{y(t)\}$ can be approximated by

$$G_y(t, f) \approx A^2(t) G_x(f) \tag{9.129}$$

This time varying power spectrum applies to locally stationary data with separable correlation functions of the form $\Re(\tau, t) \approx A^2(t) R_x(\tau)$, as defined in Eq. (9.94). Note that for this special case the time-averaged power spectrum is given by

$$\bar{G}_y(f, T) = \frac{1}{T} \int_T A^2(t) G_x(f) \, dt = A_0^2 G_x(f) \tag{9.130}$$

where

$$A_0^2 = \frac{1}{T} \int_T A^2(t) \, dt$$

Hence, the time-averaged power spectrum will be the same (except for a gain factor) as the time varying power spectrum, independent of the averaging time. This result can be applied to improve the quality of nonstationary spectral measurements for locally stationary data since time varying power spectra can be measured by two simple steps. The first is to measure a short time-averaged mean square value which estimates $A^2(t)$. The second is to measure a long time-averaged power spectrum with unit area which estimates $G_x(f)$. Because the total bandwidth of the data is used in the first step and the total record length is used in the second step, the resulting spectrum will have a smaller random error than would be present in a short time-averaged power spectrum.

Returning now to the periodic nonstationary process in Eq. (9.127), the nonstationary autocorrelation function for $\{y(t)\}$ is

$$R_y(t_1, t_2) = E[x(t_1)\, x(t_2)]\cos 2\pi F t_1 \cos 2\pi F t_2$$

$$= \tfrac{1}{2}R_x(t_2 - t_1)[\cos 2\pi F(t_2 - t_1) + \cos 2\pi F(t_1 + t_2)]$$

where $R_x(t_2 - t_1)$ is the stationary autocorrelation function for $\{x(t)\}$. Through the change in variables of Eq. (9.86),

$$\tau = t_2 - t_1 \qquad t = \frac{t_1 + t_2}{2}$$

the function $R_y(t_1, t_2)$ becomes $\mathcal{R}_y(\tau, t)$ where

$$\mathcal{R}_y(\tau, t) = \tfrac{1}{2}R_x(\tau)[\cos 2\pi F\tau + \cos 4\pi Ft] \tag{9.131}$$

Note that $\mathcal{R}_y(\tau, t)$ is the sum of two separable parts, and at $\tau = 0$,

$$\mathcal{R}_y(0, t) = E[y^2(t)] = \tfrac{1}{2}\mathcal{R}_x(0)[1 + \cos 4\pi Ft] \geq 0$$

In general, however, for $\tau \neq 0$, $\mathcal{R}_y(\tau, t)$ may be positive or negative.

From Eq. (9.95), the double-frequency spectrum corresponding to Eq. (9.128) is now given by

$$S_y(f, g) = \tfrac{1}{4}\delta(g)[S_x(f - F) + S_x(f + F)]$$
$$+ \tfrac{1}{4}[\delta(g - 2F) + \delta(g + 2F)]\, S_x(f) \tag{9.132}$$

where $S_x(f)$ is the two-sided spectrum for $x(t)$, and where $\delta(g)$ is the usual delta function. Through the change in variables of Eq. (9.90),

$$g = f_2 - f_1 \qquad f = \frac{f_1 + f_2}{2}$$

the function $S_y(f, g)$ becomes $S_y(f_1, f_2)$, where

$$S_y(f_1, f_2) = \tfrac{1}{4}\delta(f_2 - f_1)\left[S_x\!\left(\frac{f_1 + f_2}{2} - F\right) + S_x\!\left(\frac{f_1 + f_2}{2} + F\right)\right]$$

$$+ \tfrac{1}{4}[\delta(f_2 - f_1 - 2F) + \delta(f_2 - f_1 + 2F)]\, S_x\!\left(\frac{f_1 + f_2}{2}\right) \tag{9.133}$$

Examination of Eqs. (9.132) and (9.133) shows that the function $S_y(f, g)$ exists only along the lines $g = 0$ and $g = \pm 2F$ in the (f, g) plane, and that the function $S_y(f_1, f_2)$ exists only along the lines $f_2 = f_1$ and $f_2 = f_1 \pm 2F$ in the (f_1, f_2) plane. These are equivalent representations for the double-frequency spectrum.

The instantaneous (frequency-time) spectrum $s_y(f, t)$ may be calculated by taking the Fourier transform of $\mathcal{R}_y(\tau, t)$ of Eq. (9.131) with respect to τ.

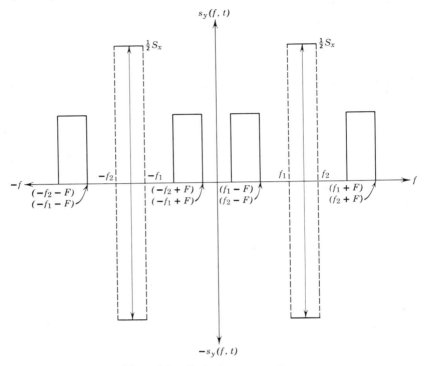

Figure 9.8   Instantaneous spectrum.

This gives the result

$$s_y(f, t) = \tfrac{1}{4}[S_x(f - F) + S_x(f + F)] + \frac{\cos 4\pi F t}{2} S_x(f) \quad (9.134)$$

indicating how this particular nonstationary spectrum varies with frequency and time. For special $S_x(f)$, and for certain particular values of f and t, the quantity $s_y(f, t)$ may be *negative* in this example. A special case of Eq. (9.134) to show this fact follows.

Consider $\{x(t)\}$ with a narrow bandwidth spectrum given by

$$S_x(f) = \begin{cases} S_x & f_1 < |f| < f_2 \\ 0 & \text{otherwise} \end{cases}$$

The instantaneous (frequency-time) spectrum would be as given in Figure 9.8, where the peak between f_1 and f_2 is varying harmonically between $\frac{1}{2}S_x$ and $-\frac{1}{2}S_x$.

The physically realizable time-averaged spectrum may be obtained from Eqs. (9.118) and (9.121). For simplicity, assume that the record length is infinite. Then Eq. (9.118) may be replaced by Eq. (9.126). Substitution of Eq. (9.131) into Eq. (9.126) yields

$$\bar{R}_y(\tau) = \tfrac{1}{2} R_x(\tau) \cos 2\pi Ft \tag{9.135}$$

When T approaches infinity, $\bar{G}_y(f, T)$ becomes $\bar{G}_y(f)$. Substitution of Eq. (9.135) into Eq. (9.121) now gives the desired result

$$\bar{G}_y(f) = \tfrac{1}{4}[G_x(f - F) + G_x(f + F)] \tag{9.136}$$

where $G_x(f)$ is the one-sided physically realizable spectrum for $x(t)$. The interpretation of $\bar{G}_y(f)$ is that a single-peaked spectrum for $G_x(f)$ centered at $f = f_0$ is changed into a double-peaked spectrum for $\bar{G}_y(f)$ centered at $f = f_0 \pm F$.

Observe that the long-time average of the instantaneous (frequency-time) spectrum of Eq. (9.134) leads to the same result as Eq. (9.136), in agreement with Eq. (9.125). This provides a useful check on these formulas.

9.6   Input-Output Relations for Nonstationary Data

Consider sample functions from a nonstationary random process $\{x(t)\}$ acting as input to a time-varying linear system with weighting function $h(\alpha, t)$ and frequency response function $H(f, t)$. For an arbitrary input $x(t)$ belonging to $\{x(t)\}$, the output $y(t)$ belonging to $\{y(t)\}$ is

$$y(t) = \int_{-\infty}^{\infty} h(\tau, t)\, x(t - \tau)\, d\tau \tag{9.137}$$

If the system is physically realizable, then $h(\tau, t) = 0$ for $\tau < 0$. For constant parameter linear systems, $h(\tau, t) = h(\tau)$, independent of t, and $H(f, t) = H(f)$. It is clear that, in general, $\{y(t)\}$ will be a nonstationary random process since its statistical properties will be a function of t. For a pair of times t_1, t_2, the product $y(t_1)\, y(t_2)$ is given by

$$y(t_1)\, y(t_2) = \iint_{-\infty}^{\infty} h(\tau, t_1)\, h(\xi, t_2)\, x(t_1 - \tau)\, x(t_2 - \xi)\, d\tau\, d\xi \tag{9.138}$$

Upon taking expected values, one obtains

$$R_y(t_1, t_2) = E[y(t_1)\, y(t_2)] = \int\!\!\int_{-\infty}^{\infty} h(\tau, t_1)\, h(\xi, t_2)\, R_x(t_1 - \tau, t_2 - \xi)\, d\tau\, d\xi \tag{9.139}$$

This general result shows how an output nonstationary autocorrelation function may be determined from the input nonstationary autocorrelation function and the system weighting function. The operations in Eq. (9.139) all take place in a real-valued time domain.

By transforming to a complex-valued frequency domain, one can derive the equivalent relation

$$S_y(f_3, f_4) = \int\!\!\int_{-\infty}^{\infty} S_x(f_1, f_2)\, J^*(f_1, f_1 - f_3)\, J(f_2, f_2 - f_4)\, df_1\, df_2 \tag{9.140}$$

where

$$J(f_1, f_0) = \int_{-\infty}^{\infty} H(f_1, t)\, e^{j2\pi f_0 t}\, dt \tag{9.141}$$

The quantity $J^*(f_1, f_0)$ is the complex conjugate of $J(f_1, f_0)$. The reason for using the frequencies (f_3, f_4) instead of (f_1, f_2) in $S_y(f_3, f_4)$ is to reserve (f_1, f_2) for $S_x(f_1, f_2)$.

Equations (9.139) and (9.140) are double Fourier transforms of one another, namely,

$$S_y(f_3, f_4) = \int\!\!\int_{-\infty}^{\infty} R_y(t_1, t_2)\, e^{j2\pi(f_3 t_1 - f_4 t_2)}\, dt_1\, dt_2 \tag{9.142}$$

$$R_y(t_1, t_2) = \int\!\!\int_{-\infty}^{\infty} S_y(f_3, f_4)\, e^{-j2\pi(f_3 t_1 - f_4 t_2)}\, df_3\, df_4 \tag{9.143}$$

For $t_1 = t_2 = t$, one obtains from Eq. (9.139) the nonstationary output variance

$$R_y(t, t) = \int\!\!\int_{-\infty}^{\infty} h(\tau, t)\, h(\xi, t)\, R_x(t - \tau, t - \xi)\, d\tau\, d\xi \tag{9.144}$$

From Eq. (9.143), one obtains the equivalent result

$$R_y(t, t) = \int\!\!\int_{-\infty}^{\infty} S_y(f_3, f_4)\, e^{-j2\pi t(f_3 - f_4)}\, df_3\, df_4 \tag{9.145}$$

If $S_x(f_1, f_2) = S_x(f_1)\, \delta(f_2 - f_1)$, a stationary process, then Eq. (9.140) becomes

$$S_y(f_3, f_4) = \int_{-\infty}^{\infty} S_x(f_2)\, J^*(f_2, f_2 - f_3)\, J(f_2, f_2 - f_3)\, df_2 \qquad (9.146)$$

When the system is a constant parameter linear system, where $h(\tau, t) = h(\tau)$ and $H(f_1, t) = H(f_1)$, Eq. (9.141) takes the form

$$J(f_1, f_0) = H(f_1) \int_{-\infty}^{\infty} e^{j2\pi f_0 t}\, dt = H(f_1)\, \delta(f_0) \qquad (9.147)$$

where $\delta(f_0)$ is the usual delta function. Now, Eq. (9.140) yields

$$S_y(f_3, f_4) = H^*(f_3)\, H(f_4)\, S_x(f_3, f_4) \qquad (9.148)$$

where

$$H(f) = \int_{-\infty}^{\infty} h(\tau)\, e^{-j2\pi f \tau}\, d\tau \qquad (9.149)$$

is the frequency response function of the constant parameter linear system.

For the special case of stationary random processes where $S_x(f_3, f_4)$ is nonzero only for $f = f_3 = f_4$, Eq. (9.148) reduces to the familiar result of Eq. (3.137),

$$S_y(f) = |H(f)|^2 S_x(f) \qquad (9.150)$$

The change in form exhibited by Eqs. (9.140), (9.146), (9.148), and (9.150) is worthy of note.

For the constant parameter linear system described by $H(f)$, substitution of Eq. (9.148) into Eq. (9.145) yields

$$R_y(t, t) = \iint_{-\infty}^{\infty} H^*(f_3)\, H(f_4)\, S_x(f_3, f_4)\, e^{-j2\pi t(f_3 - f_4)}\, df_3\, df_4 \qquad (9.151)$$

Equation (9.151) is the same as Eq. (9.110), which is used to derive physically meaningful time-varying power spectra when $S_x(f_3, f_4)$ is the double-frequency spectrum corresponding to the nonstationary autocorrelation function $R_x(t_1, t_2)$, and $H(f)$ is the frequency response function of the narrow-band filter.

Further interesting input-output relations can be found by examining the nonstationary cross-correlation function and the nonstationary cross-spectral density function between the input process $\{x(t)\}$ and the output process $\{y(t)\}$. From Eq. (9.137) the product of $x(t_1)$ by $y(t_2)$ is

$$x(t_1)y(t_2) = \int_{-\infty}^{\infty} h(\tau, t_2)\, x(t_1)\, x(t_2 - \tau)\, d\tau \qquad (9.152)$$

The taking of expected values now yields

$$R_{xy}(t_1, t_2) = E[x(t_1)\,y(t_2)] = \int_{-\infty}^{\infty} h(\tau, t_2)\,R_x(t_1, t_2 - \tau)\,d\tau \quad (9.153)$$

Equation (9.153) is a general result in the real-valued time domain between the nonstationary input autocorrelation function, the time-varying linear system weighting function, and the nonstationary input-output cross-correlation function.

When Eq. (9.153) is transformed to a complex-valued frequency domain, there results

$$S_{xy}(f_3, f_4) = \int_{-\infty}^{\infty} S_x(f_3, f_2)J(f_2, f_2 - f_4)\,df_2 \quad (9.154)$$

The quantity J is defined by Eq. (9.141). Observe that the form of Eq. (9.154) is simpler than that of Eq. (9.140).

If $S_x(f_3, f_2) = S_x(f_3)\,\delta(f_3 - f_2)$, a stationary process, then Eq. (9.154) becomes

$$S_{xy}(f_3, f_4) = S_x(f_3)\,J(f_3, f_3 - f_4) \quad (9.155)$$

For the important class of constant parameter linear systems, Eq. (9.154) becomes, with the aid of Eq. (9.147),

$$S_{xy}(f_3, f_4) = H(f_4)\,S_x(f_3, f_4) \quad (9.156)$$

Upon further reduction to the special case of stationary random processes, Eq. (9.156) gives the familiar result of Eq. (3.138),

$$S_{xy}(f) = H(f)\,S_x(f) \quad (9.157)$$

This result, like Eq. (9.150), provides a required check on these formulas.

9.7   Filtered Periodic Nonstationary Process

Assume that sample functions from the periodic nonstationary process discussed in Section 9.5.5, are passed through an ideal narrow band-pass filter so as to produce a nonstationary output process $\{u(t)\}$.

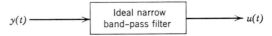

$y(t)$ → Ideal narrow band-pass filter → $u(t)$

An analysis will be conducted for two significant problems:

1. The nonstationary output variance $R_u(t, t)$ for arbitrary $S_x(f)$.
2. The physically meaningful time-varying power spectrum for $\{y(t)\}$ when $\{x(t)\}$ is bandwidth limited white noise.

This material illustrates the mathematical difficulties present in carrying out detailed computations for specific problems.

The frequency response function $H(f)$ for the ideal rectangular filter is defined by

$$H(f) = 1 \qquad f_L \leq |f| \leq f_H$$
$$= 0 \qquad \text{otherwise} \tag{9.158}$$

where f_L is the lower cutoff frequency of the filter, and f_H is the higher cutoff frequency of the filter. The filter bandwidth is given by $B_e = (f_H - f_L)$ and its center frequency $f_0 = (f_L + f_H)/2$. See Figure 9.9.

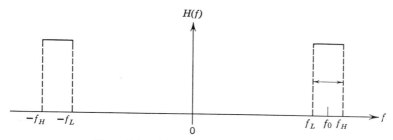

Figure 9.9   Ideal narrow band-pass filter.

By hypothesis, an input sample function $y(t)$ has the form

$$y(t) = x(t) \cos 2\pi F t \tag{9.159}$$

with a double-frequency spectrum $S_y(f_1, f_2)$ as derived in Eq. (9.133).

Consider now Eq. (9.145) with y replaced by u to correspond to the present output nonstationary process. Then, let the variables of integration be (f_1, f_2) instead of (f_3, f_4). Thus

$$R_u(t, t) = \int\!\!\!\int_{-\infty}^{\infty} S_u(f_1, f_2)\, e^{-j2\pi t(f_1 - f_2)}\, df_1\, df_2 \tag{9.160}$$

From Eq. (9.148), for the present problem where u replaces y, and y replaces x,

$$S_u(f_1, f_2) = H^*(f_1)\, H(f_2)\, S_y(f_1, f_2) \tag{9.161}$$

It follows from Eq. (9.133) that $S_u(f_1, f_2)$ exists only along the lines $f_2 = f_1$ and $f_2 = f_1 \pm 2F$ in the (f_1, f_2) plane.

From Eq. (9.158), the frequency response function $H(f)$ equals unity only for $f_L \leq f \leq f_H$ and is zero elsewhere. Hence the product $H^*(f_1) H(f_2)$ equals unity only within the four squares in the (f_1, f_2) plane bounded by $f_L \leq |f_1| \leq f_H, f_L \leq |f_2| \leq f_H$. See Figure 9.10.

Figure 9.10 and Eq. (9.161) now show that $S_u(f_1, f_2)$ is nonzero only along the portions of the lines $f_2 = f_1$ and $f_2 = f_1 \pm 2F$ which lie inside one of these four squares. In particular, $f_2 = f_1$ will always cross the two squares in the first and third quadrants, while $f_2 = f_1 \pm 2F$ will cross these same two squares if and only if $2F < f_H - f_L$. This condition must be assumed in order for the filter to respond to the nonstationary time trend.

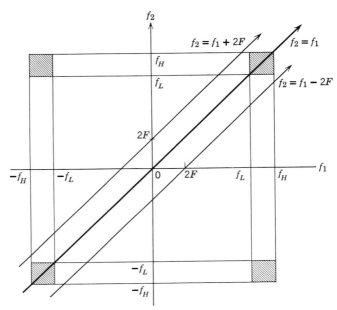

Figure 9.10 Domain for $H^*(f_1)\,H(f_2)$.

Equations (9.133) and (9.161) show that for the line $f_2 = f_1$,

$$S_u^{①}(f_1, f_2) = \tfrac{1}{4}\,\delta(f_2 - f_1)\left[S_x\!\left(\frac{f_1 + f_2}{2} - F\right) + S_x\!\left(\frac{f_1 + f_2}{2} + F\right) \right]$$

(9.162)

Equation (9.162) has the symmetry property

$$S_u^{①}(-f_1, -f_2) = S_u^{①}(f_1, f_2) \qquad (9.163)$$

Hence, from Eq. (9.160), it follows that

$$R_u^{①}(t, t) = 2\int_{f_L}^{f_H} \int_{f_L}^{f_H} S_u^{①}(f_1, f_2)\cos 2\pi t(f_1 - f_2)\,df_1\,df_2 \qquad (9.164)$$

Substituting Eq. (9.162) into (9.164) and carrying out the delta function integration yields the result

$$R_u^{①}(t, t) = \frac{1}{2}\int_{f_L}^{f_H} [S_x(f_2 - F) + S_x(f_2 + F)]\,df_2 \qquad (9.165)$$

Since the right-hand side of Eq. (9.165) is independent of t, this portion of the output variance is stationary. This is in agreement with the fact that only the line $f_2 = f_1$ has been involved in these considerations, and along this line the input process is stationary.

For the line $f_2 = f_1 + 2F$, one has

$$S_u^{(2)}(f_1, f_2) = \tfrac{1}{4}\,\delta(f_2 - f_1 - 2F)\,S_x\!\left(\frac{f_1 + f_2}{2}\right) \tag{9.166}$$

For the line $f_2 = f_1 - 2F$, one has

$$S_u^{(3)}(f_1, f_2) = \tfrac{1}{4}\,\delta(f_2 - f_1 + 2F)\,S_x\!\left(\frac{f_1 + f_2}{2}\right) \tag{9.167}$$

The corresponding contributions to $R_u(t, t)$ from Eq. (9.160) are

$$R_u^{(2)}(t, t) = \int_{f_L}^{f_H}\int_{-f_H}^{-f_L} S_u^{(2)}(f_1, f_2)e^{-j2\pi t(f_1 - f_2)}\,df_1\,df_2 \tag{9.168}$$

and

$$R_u^{(3)}(t, t) = \int_{-f_H}^{-f_L}\int_{f_L}^{f_H} S_u^{(3)}(f_1, f_2)e^{-j2\pi t(f_1 - f_2)}\,df_1\,df_2 \tag{9.169}$$

One may now verify that the sum reduces to

$$R_u^{(2)}(t, t) + R_u^{(3)}(t, t) = \frac{1}{2}\int_{f_L}^{f_H}\int_{-f_H}^{-f_L} \delta(f_2 - f_1 - 2F)\,S_x\!\left(\frac{f_1 + f_2}{2}\right)$$
$$\times \cos 2\pi t(f_1 - f_2)\,df_1\,df_2 \tag{9.170}$$

To simplify Eq. (9.170), let $v = f_2 - f_1$, $dv = -df_1$. Then Eq. (9.170) becomes

$$R_u^{(2)}(t, t) + R_u^{(3)}(t, t)$$
$$= \frac{1}{2}\int_{f_L}^{f_H}\int_{f_2+f_L}^{f_2+f_H} \delta(v - 2F)\,S_x\!\left(f_2 - \frac{v}{2}\right)\cos 2\pi vt\,dv\,df_2 \tag{9.171}$$

In order to properly interpret this expression, it is now necessary to change the order of integration between v and f_2. Figure 9.11 shows how to find the new limits, and shows that for this case one must break up the integration into two parts when the limits are reversed. This gives a pair of integrals

$$A_1(t) = \frac{1}{2}\int_{2f_L}^{f_L+f_H} \delta(v - 2F)\cos 2\pi vt\left[\int_{f_L}^{v-f_L} S_x\!\left(f_2 - \frac{v}{2}\right)df_2\right]dv$$
$$A_2(t) = \frac{1}{2}\int_{f_L+f_H}^{2f_H} \delta(v - 2F)\cos 2\pi vt\left[\int_{v-f_H}^{f_H} S_x\!\left(f_2 - \frac{v}{2}\right)df_2\right]dv \tag{9.172}$$

The sum

$$R_u^{(2)}(t, t) + R_u^{(3)}(t, t) = A_1(t) + A_2(t) \tag{9.173}$$

and is clearly a function of t. Equation (9.173) gives the nonstationary portion of the output variance.

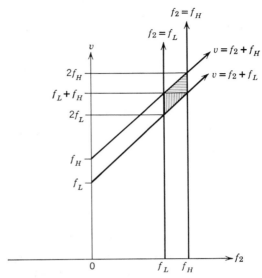

Figure 9.11   Reversal of limits.

The complete output variance for *arbitrary* $S_x(f)$ is the sum of Eqs. (9.165) and (9.173), namely,

$$\begin{aligned}
R_u(t, t) &= R_u^{(1)}(t, t) + R_u^{(2)}(t, t) + R_u^{(3)}(t, t) \\
&= R_u^{(1)}(t, t) + A_1(t) + A_2(t)
\end{aligned} \tag{9.174}$$

This answers the first problem.

To answer the second problem, recall that the quantity $R_u(t, t) = E[y^2(t, f, B_e)]$, as defined in Eq. (9.104). Hence the time-varying power spectrum $G_y(t, f)$ for arbitrary $S_x(f)$ is given by

$$G_y(t, f) = \frac{R_u(t, t)}{B_e} \tag{9.175}$$

To illustrate the application of these results, consider the special case when $\{x(t)\}$ is bandwidth limited white noise such that its power spectral density function is a constant over all the finite limits of integration in the above formulas. To be specific, suppose

$$S_x(f) = 1 \qquad \text{for all desired finite } f \tag{9.176}$$

Then Eq. (9.165) shows that the stationary portion of the output variance is

$$R_u^{\text{①}}(t, t) = \int_{f_L}^{f_H} df = f_H - f_L = B_e \qquad (9.177)$$

where B_e is the bandwidth of the filter. Equation (9.172) simplifies to

$$A_1(t) = \frac{1}{2} \int_{2f_L}^{f_L+f_H} \delta(v - 2F)(v - 2f_L) \cos 2\pi v t \, dv$$

$$A_2(t) = \frac{1}{2} \int_{f_L+f_H}^{2f_H} \delta(v - 2F)(2f_H - v) \cos 2\pi v t \, dv$$

whose sum is

$$A_1(t) + A_2(t) = B_e \cos 4\pi F t \qquad (9.178)$$

Hence the total output variance for this special case is given by

$$R_u(t, t) = R_u^{\text{①}}(t, t) + A_1(t) + A_2(t) = B_e + B_e \cos 4\pi F t \qquad (9.179)$$

The physically meaningful nonstationary power spectrum $G_y(t, f)$ for this nonstationary input process $y(t)$ is now derived easily. Substitution of Eq. (9.179) into Eq. (9.175) yields the answer

$$G_y(t, f) = 1 + \cos 4\pi F t \qquad (9.180)$$

Thus $G_y(t, f) \geq 0$ for all t and is independent of f in agreement with the condition that the output will be white noise when the input is white noise. This concludes the analysis.

9.8   Research Areas

There are many research areas in need of further study dealing with the theory and application of nonstationary data. Certain past work and results obtained assuming stationary data should be investigated again with more realistic models that can consider nonstationary aspects of the problems. Broad areas in need of future research are as follows:

1. Analytical representation of mathematical models.
2. Tests for specific types of nonstationarity.
3. Measurement techniques and error analysis.
4. Engineering usage of results.

These topics represent opportunities for theoretical and engineering contributions to extend this field. The proper measurement and analysis of random data for various physical applications can provide better answers for many old problems, as well as permit consideration and solution for many new problems.

REFERENCES

1. Bendat, J. S., *Principles and Applications of Random Noise Theory*, John Wiley and Sons, New York, 1958.
2. Bendat, J. S., "Interpretation and Application of Statistical Analysis for Random Physical Phenomena," *Trans. IRE, Bio-Med. Electron.*, **BME-9** January 1962.
3. Bendat, J. S., "Probability Functions for Random Responses: Prediction of Peaks, Fatigue Damage, and Catastrophic Failure," National Aeronautics and Space Administration, Washington, D.C., NASA CR-33 April 1964.
4. Bendat, J. S., L. D. Enochson, G. H. Klein, and A. G. Piersol, "The Application of Statistics to the Flight Vehicle Vibration Problem," ASD TR 61-123, Aeronautical Systems Division, AFSC, Wright-Patterson AFB, Ohio, December 1961. (AD 271 913).
5. Bendat, J. S., L. D. Enochson, G. H. Klein, and A. G. Piersol, "Advanced Concepts of Stochastic Processes and Statistics for Flight Vehicle Vibration Estimation and Measurement," ASD TDR 62-973, Aeronautical Systems Division, AFSC, Wright-Patterson AFB, Ohio, December 1962. (AD 297 031).
6. Blackman, R. B., and J. W. Tukey, *The Measurement of Power Spectra*, Dover Publications, New York, 1958.
7. Broch, J. T., *Bruel and Kjaer Tech. Rev. No. 3*, 1963.
8. Cramer, H., *Mathematical Methods of Statistics*, Princeton Univ. Press, Princeton, N.J., 1946.
9. Crandall, S. H., "Zero-Crossings, Peaks, and Other Statistical Measures of Random Responses," *Proc., Acoustical Society of America Meeting*, Seattle, Washington, 1962.
10. Davenport, W. B., and W. L. Root, *Random Signals and Noise*, McGraw-Hill Book Co., New York, 1958.
11. Doob, J. L., *Stochastic Processes*, John Wiley and Sons, New York, 1953.
12. Enochson, L. D., "Frequency Response Functions and Coherence Functions for Multiple Input Linear Systems," National Aeronautics and Space Administration, Washington, D.C., NASA CR-32, April 1964.

13. Enochson, L. D., and N. R. Goodman, "Gaussian Approximation to the Distribution of Sample Coherence," AFFDL TR 65–57, Research and Technology Division, AFSC, Wright-Patterson AFB, Ohio, February 1965.
14. Epstein, B., "Elements of the Theory of Extreme Values," *Tech. Rep. No.* 2, Department of Mathematics, Wayne State University, Detroit, Michigan, April 1959.
15. Forlifer, W. R., "The Effects of Filter Bandwidth in Spectrum Analysis of Random Vibration," *Shock, Vibration and Associated Environments Bull. No.* 33, Part II, Department of Defense, Washington, D.C., February 1964.
16. Goodman, N. R., "On the Joint Estimation of the Spectra, Co-Spectrum and Quadrature Spectrum of a Two-Dimensional Stationary Gaussian Process," *Scientific Paper No.* 10, Engineering Statistics Laboratory, New York Univ., New York, 1957.
17. Goodman, N. R., "Measurement of Matrix Frequency Response Functions and Multiple Coherence Functions," AFFDL TR 65–56, Research and Technology Division, AFSC, Wright-Patterson AFB, Ohio, February 1965.
18. Laning, J. H., Jr., and R. H. Battin, *Random Processes in Automatic Control,* McGraw-Hill Book Co., New York, 1956.
19. Levenbach, H., "The Zero-Crossing Problem," *Res. Rep. No.* 63–4, Electrical Engineering Department, Queens Univ., Kingston, September 1963.
20. Loeve, M., *Probability Theory,* second edition, G. Van Nostrand Co., Princeton, N.J., 1960.
21. Page, C. G., "Instantaneous Power Spectra," *J. Applied Physics,* **23**, No. 1, January 1952.
22. Parzen, E., "Mathematical Considerations in the Estimation of Spectra," *Tech. Rept. No.* 3, Applied Mathematics and Statistics Laboratories, Stanford Univ., Stanford, Calif., 1960.
23. Piersol, A. G., "Nonparametric Test for Equivalence of Vibration Data," *Paper* 748*c,* SAE National Aeronautic and Space Engineering Meeting, Los Angeles, Calif., September 1963.
24. Piersol, A. G., "The Measurement and Interpretation of Ordinary Power Spectra for Vibration Problems," National Aeronautics and Space Administration, Washington, D.C., NASA CR-90, September 1964.
25. Piersol, A. G., "Spectral Analysis of Nonstationary Spacecraft Vibration Data," National Aeronautics and Space Administration, Washington, D.C., NASA CR-341, December 1965.
26. Rice, S. O., "Mathematical Analysis of Random Noise," *Selected Papers on Noise and Stochastic Processes,* edited by N. Wax, Dover Publications, New York, 1954.
27. Silverman, R. A., "Locally Stationary Random Processes," *Trans. IRE, Inf. Theory,* **IT-3**, September 1957.
28. Thrall, G. P., "Extreme Values of Random Processes in Seakeeping Applications," MAC 307-03, prepared under contract Nonr-4305(00) for the David Taylor Model Basin(USN), August 1964.
29. Thrall, G. P., "An Analysis of Amplitude Probability Measurements," FDL-TDR-64-116, Research and Technology Division, AFSC, Wright-Patterson AFB, Ohio, January 1965.
30. Thrall, G. P., and J. S. Bendat, "Mean and Mean Square Measurements of Nonstationary Random Processes," National Aeronautics and Space Administration, Washington, D.C., NASA CR-226, May 1965.

31. Tick, L. J., "Conditional Spectra, Linear Systems, and Coherency," Chapter 13, *Time Series Analysis*, M. Rosenblatt (Ed.), John Wiley and Sons, New York, 1963.

32. Williams, C. A., Jr., "On the Choice of the Number and Width of Classes for Chi-Square Test of Goodness of Fit," *J. Am. Statistical Assoc.*, **45**, pp. 77–86, March 1950.

INDEX